Building Conversion and Rehabilitation

Building Conversion and Rehabilitation

Designing for Change in Building Use

Edited by

Thomas A. Markus, BA, MA, MArch(MIT), RIBA
Department of Architecture and Building Science
University of Strathclyde, Scotland

NEWNES—BUTTERWORTHS
LONDON—BOSTON
Sydney—Wellington—Durban—Toronto

THE BUTTERWORTH GROUP

UNITED KINGDOM
Butterworth & Co (Publishers) Ltd
London: 88 Kingsway, WC2B 6AB

AUSTRALIA
Butterworths Pty Ltd
Sydney: 586 Pacific Highway, NSW 2067
Also at Melbourne, Brisbane, Adelaide and Perth

CANADA
Butterworth & Co (Canada) Ltd
Toronto: 2265 Midland Avenue, Scarborough, Ontario, M1P 4S1

NEW ZEALAND
Butterworths of New Zealand Ltd
Wellington: 77—85 Customhouse Quay, Box CP 472

SOUTH AFRICA
Butterworth & Co (South Africa) (Pty) Ltd
Durban: 152—154 Gale Street

USA
Butterworth (Publishers) Inc
Boston: 19 Cummings Park, Woburn, Mass. 01801

First published 1979

© The several contributors as listed in the Contents, 1979

British Library Cataloguing in Publication Data

Building conversion and rehabilitation.
1. Buildings — Repair and reconstruction — Congresses
I. Markus, Thomas Andrew
690'.24   TH3401   78-40210

ISBN 0-408-00313-8

Typeset by Butterworths Litho Preparation Department

Printed in England by Cox & Wyman Ltd.,
London, Fakenham and Reading

Preface

There is no doubt that the conversion of existing building to new uses is a growing activity throughout the Western World. Some of the economic, social, architectural and psychological forces which have brought about this rapid shift from the post-World War II urban development ('destruction', in the eyes of some) are discussed in this book.

The book is the outcome of a Symposium held at the University of Strathclyde in May 1977, which took place during an exhibition of executed projects. There was a deliberate attempt to bring together ideas, theories and experimental techniques, with practice, executed projects and experience. In architecture this juxtaposition of theory and practice is all too rare and the bridges and continuities which exist in other disciplines are only just being built (or, re-built). As editor of these contributions, one of my aims is to encourage this building process.

Thomas A. Markus

Authors

Thomas A. Markus, BA, MA, MArch(MIT), RIBA.
Professor of Building Science, Department of Architecture and Building Science, University of Strathclyde.

Graeme M. Aylward, AADip(Hons), MCP(MIT), RIBA, MRTPI.
Lecturer, Department of Architecture and Building Science, University of Strathclyde.

Thomas W. Maver, BSc, PhD, MCIBS.
Professor and Director of ABACUS (Architecture and Building Aids Computer Unit Strathclyde), Department of Architecture and Building Science, Universiry of Strathclyde.

Hildebrand W. Frey, Dipl-Ing.Arch.
Lecturer, Department of Architecture and Building Science, University of Strathclyde.

James H. Johnson, Dip Arch, RIBA, ARIAS.
Senior Lecturer and Director of ASSIST (Community Design Unit), Department of Architecture and Building Science, University of Strathclyde.

Terry Farrell, OBE, MCP, MArch, MRTPI, RIBA.
Partner, Farrell/Grimshaw Partnership, Architects, Engineers and Town Planners, London.

Julian Bicknell, MA, DipArch, RIBA.
Director Project Office, Department of Environmental Design, Royal College of Art, London.

Richard Frewer, MA, AA Dip, RIBA.
and
Derek Sugden, MICE, MIStructE.
Partners. Arup Associates, Architects, Engineers, Quantity Surveyors, London.

N. Keith Scott, MA BArch(Hons), Dip CD (L'pool), MArch (MIT), MRTPI, RIBA.
Partner, BDP, Building Design Partnership, Preson.

John Warren, M.Litt, FRTPI, RIBA.
Partner, The Architectural and Planning Partnership, Horsham, Sussex.

John Worthington, MArch, AA Dip(Hons).
and
Peter Eley, MArch, MCP, AA Dip(Hons), RIBA.
Partners, DEGW, Duffy, Eley, Giffone, Worthington. Space Planners and Architects, London.

David Rock, BArch (Dunelm), RIBA, MSIA.
Partner, Rock Townsend, Architects, Planners, Designers. London.

Robert J. Greenslade, Dip Arch (Manc), RIBA.
and
Richard G. Saxon, BArch(Hons)(L'pool), RIBA.
Partner, BDP, Building Design Partnership, Manchester.

Contents

Acknowledgements

General

The editor wishes to acknowledge the following people who assisted in the preparation of this book and in the Symposium and concurrent Exhibition that preceded it.

Peter Nelson, Director of Continuing Education, University of Strathclyde — for help in organising and running the Symposium 'Old into New' in May 1977. Michael and Brenda Munday — for their substantial help with literary editing, and Mary Markus — for similar help with the graphic and layout work. Graeme Aylward, Neil Maxwell and Ken Taylor — for assistance in collecting and mounting the material for the Exhibition. Margaret Ling — for assistance with the considerable administrative and clerical tasks both for the Exhibition and Symposium, and the preparation of the manuscript. The individual authors of the chapters, not only for their collaboration in the production of this book, but also for lending a substantial amount of material for the Exhibition.

Chapter Four

Jim Johnson was assisted in the preparation of this chapter by his colleagues in ASSIST. Their stimulus, advice and co-operation in carrying out the rehabilitation work on which it is based is also acknowledged.

Chapter Five

Terry Farrell was assisted in the preparation of this chapter by John Chatwin RIBA of the Farrell/Grimshaw Partnership.

Case Study One: *Client* — The International Students Club Ltd. *Architects* — The Farrell Grimshaw Partnership. *Quantity Surveyors* — The Hanscombe Partnership. *Structural Engineers* — Ove Arup and Partners. *General Contractors* — A. Bell and Son Ltd. *Trolley Frame Unit* — D. Sebel and Co. Ltd.

Case Study Two: *Client* — Comyn Ching. *Architects* — The Farrell Grimshaw Partnership. *Quantity Surveyors* — Michael Edwards. *Structural Engineers* — W. E. Budgen and Partners. *Consultant Surveyors and Valuers* — Sweby Cowan and Partners.

Case Study Three: *Client* — Samual Properties Ltd. *Architects* — The Farrell Grimshaw Partnership. *Quantity Surveyors* — Monk and Dunstone Associates. *Structural Engineers* — Pel Frischman. *General Contractors* — Wates Ltd.

The illustrations in this chapter are by the Farrell Grimshaw Partnership, except for Figures 5.29 and 5.31, which are by G. Hana Ltd., London.

Chapter Six

Case Study: *Royal College of Art Student Projects* by — James Blair, Edward Hutchison, David Lyall, Koorosh Mehri, Tim Miles, John Redmond, Dick Swain, Keith Webber, and John Whyatt. *Architect in charge* — Julian Bicknell, with Dennis Hirst, and Guillermo Gil, Andrij Melnyk, Gaby Moore, Richard Scott and John Whyatt. *Student Assistants* — Des Ager, Peter Bonser, John Dowson, Nigel Haselden, Grenville Horner, John Hughes, Roger Huntley, Barrie Legg, David Nelson, Karen Nicol, Barbara O'Callaghan, Andrew Packham, Dennis Robson, Chris Watkins. *Quantity Surveyors* — Brian Davis and Associates. *Structural Engineers* — Stephen Revess Associates. *Services Engineers* — John Bradley Associates. *Landscaping & Planting* — Margaret Maxwell and Jenny Cox. *General Contractors* — Amey Roadstone Construction Ltd. *Services Sub-contractor* — Fred G. Alden (Heating) Ltd. *Clerk of the Works* for Vale of White Horse District Council — John Jordan.

The illustrations in this chapter are by the Architects except for Figures 6.6 to 6.11 inclusive which are by Thomas Photos, Oxford.

Chapter Seven

Richard Frewer and Derek Sugden were assisted in the preparation of this chapter by John S. Braithwaite of Arup Associates.

Case Study One: *Client* — Southwark Rehearsal Hall Trust Ltd. *Architects, Engineers, Quantity Surveyors, Acoustic Consultants* — Arup Associates.

Case Study Two: *Client* — Scottish Opera Theatre Royal Ltd. *Architects, Engineers, Quantity Surveyors, Acoustic Consultants* — Arup Associates. *Theatre Consultants* — John Wyckham Associates.

The illustrations in this chapter are by Arup Associates, London.

Chapter Eight

Case Study: *Client* — Lancashire County Council. *Architects, Quantity Surveyors, Structural, Mechanical and Electrical Engineers* — Building Design Partnership with partner in charge — Keith Scott, Architect — John Angell, Quantity Surveyor — John Adams, Structural Engineer — Reg Goodfellow, Mechanical Engineer — Boyd McPhail, Electrical Engineer — David Taylor. *General Contractor* — John Laing Construction Ltd.

The illustrations in this Chapter are by Roger Park, photographer with Building Design Partnership.

Chapter Nine

R. T. Mason FSI — archaeologist to the Landmark Trust. Gunolt Greiner — independent Master Craftsman in Carpentry.

Case Study One: *Architects* — The Architectural and Planning Partnership. *General Contractors* — Wm. C. Reade. Aldeburgh.

Case Study Two: *Architects* — The Architectural and Planning Partnership. *General Contractors* — Clement Theobold and Son Ltd, Sudbury.

Chapter Ten

Case Study One: *Client* — Camden Industrial Action Group and West Hampstead Community Action Group. *Architects* — Duffy, Eley, Giffone, Worthington. Project Architect — Peter Eley. *General Contractors* — Direct Labour.

Case Study Two: *Client* — Industrial Building Preservation Trust (IBPT). *Architects* — Duffy, Eley, Giffone, Worthington. Project Architect — Colin Cave. *Structural and Service Engineers* — Ove Arup and Partners. *IBPT project co-ordinator* — Richard Waddington. *General Contractors* — Home Office Building Project and Direct Labour.

Case Study Three: *Client* — Urban and Economic Development Group (URBED). Report prepared by John Worthington, partner in charge, Duffy, Eley, Giffone and Worthington,

Space Planners and Architects supported by Martin Symes and John Simpson, and with valuation advice from Christopher Howes, and economic advice from Bernard Williams Associates.

Chapter Eleven

Case Study One: *Client* — IPC: *Architects* — Rock Townsend, with John Townsend, partner in charge and Alistair Hay. *Quantity Surveyors* — Townsend and Renaudon with John Renaudon, partner. *Members' space layouts* by Trickett Associates. *General Contractors* Phase I — direct works organised by architects, Phase 2 — H. Clifford & Co Ltd. *Nominated subcontractors: Electrical* — Electration Ltd. *Heating* — Geo S. Hall Ltd. *Screening* — NKR Environment Ltd.

Case Study Two: *Client* — Barley Mow Workspace Ltd: *Architects* — Rock Townsend with John Townsend, partner in charge and associate Alistair Hay, with Paul Burrows. *Quantity Surveyors* — Townsend and Renaudon with Richard Dobson. *General Contractors* — H. H. Darvill & Co. Ltd. *Nominated subcontractors: Electrical* — Electration Ltd. *Heating* — Geo S. Hall Ltd. *Screening* — Linden-Pride Ltd.

The illustrations in this chapter are all by Rock Townsend, except for Figures 11.7 and 11.9 which are by Colin Maher, London, and Figures 11.1 and 11.4 which are by the late Crispin Eurich, London.

Chapter Twelve

Case Study: *Client* — Liverpool City Council, W. A. Home, Dip. Arch., RIBA, City Architect. *Design Team* — Building Design Partnership, Manchester. Architects — Robert J. Greenslade, partner in charge, Richard G. Saxon, partner, Frank Williams, Project Architect, Ken Moth, Duncan Templeton. Nicholas Terry. Civil and Structural Engineers — Robert B. Leyland, partner, Harry Halsall, associate, Mike Fordyce, associate. Mechanical, Electrical and Public Health Engineers — John R. J. Ellis, partner, Robert Hargreaves (M) associate, Terry Wilson (E) associate, Mike Hargreaves (PH) associate, Darryl Eckersley (M), Geoffrey Depledge (E). Quantity Surveyors — David Allen, Partner, Peter Snape, associate, Trevor Martin. Industrial Designer — David Cowler. Programmer — John Jeff. Graphic Designer — Doreen Caulfield.

The illustrations in this chapter are all by Building Design Partnership except Figures 12.13, 12.15 and 12.17 by Elsam, Mann and Cooper Ltd., Liverpool, and Figures 12.2, 12.4, 12.5 and 12.11 by Anthony Price, Lostock Hall, Preston, and Figures 12.1, 12.3 and 12.6 by John Mills Photography Ltd., Liverpool.

Introduction

This book is concerned with problems associated with the continuous re-use of the existing stock of buildings. In particular it focuses on those instances where a building constructed for one purpose is to be used for another: putting a new activity into an existing set of spaces. The whole question of the re-use of buildings has created widespread interest in the architecture profession over recent years. Historically there have been a number of different approaches, each embodying a different activity and conceptual emphasis. These have included 'restoration', 'conservation', 'repair', 'rehabilitation', 'conversion', 'refurbishment' and 'alteration'. As the authors in this book show, the situation is, increasingly, that although the labels vary, the unifying concept is the same. The only approach excluded from the discussion is that where repair or restoration is limited to the building fabric, often with emphasis on historical veracity, and no change of use is involved.

The theme of the re-use of buildings was the subject of a symposium* at which the authors of this book explored the forces which have given rise to this type of activity. These forces can perhaps be drawn together and summarised in the following way.

First, already mentioned, is the age-old business of repairing buildings which are deteriorating due both to the forces of nature acting on materials and to the stresses which human use places upon the fabric. This type of activity is a normal everyday process, and always has been, but it takes on a special importance in buildings of historical significance the more so where parts of the fabric or decorative detail have deteriorated to such an extent that there is a choice to be made between careful reproduction of the original or some simplification of it which maintains, or perhaps even emphasises, the original character.

Repair and restoration of this kind carried out at the modest level of dwellings and small-scale communal buildings is, of course, as ancient as building and architecture itself. It has been part of the vernacular process of design, building and

re-building which can still be seen in many parts of the world and which the recent 'do-it-yourself' movement in the West and the self-build process in squatter settlements around the edges of cities in many developing countries have re-emphasised.

Another force which has become evident much more recently is a 'perceived resource' crisis in which, as a result of shortages of all kinds — energy, skilled labour, materials, building land and cash — society and individuals have become aware of the need to make better use of existing building stock and to re-use it effectively for as long as possible. As yet, little research has been done in which genuine comparative resource costs between alternative solutions based on either new construction or conversion have been clearly presented. Many people have a hunch that this kind of activity, when all the factors are taken into account, actually conserves resources but, whereas this is doubtless true in some instances, it remains to be shown that this is a universal law. If it turns out not to be the case, then the resource implications of a conversion proposal have to be clearly established at an early stage. In such cases, comparative cost-prediction techniques are essential, and the system described by Hildebrand Frey is typical of the work required to develop them.

Certainly another influence has been nostalgia for the earlier solutions. But deeper than nostalgia may be a growing sense of revolt against the rapid and often meaningless changes in environment of the last thirty years or so, especially those caused by large-scale developments in cities resulting from commercial activities, urban motorway construction and wholesale housing renewal.

The desire to retain old structures is not only a desire for the physical form of these structures but, evidently, a desire for a certain stability in the mental images or maps which people have of their environment. These images become established over time and the instability resulting from their rapid destruction may well be at the root of many social reactions which are now being witnessed in the form of vandalism, public complaints, the feeling of malaise. A common, though less obviously critical, example can be seen in personal experiences of revisiting a city after a few years and experi-

* 'Old into New' Building Conversion Symposium. University of Strathclyde, Department of Architecture and Building Science, Glasgow. May 1977

encing disorientation and a sense of loss from the destruction that has taken place.

Then again, a certain historicism or archaeological interest in the old has inspired many conservation projects. This awareness which used to be limited to rather narrow academic quarters, has now become more popularised as a result of a considerably wider interest in history, especially of the industrial revolution and after, generated by television and other media. Public attitudes have also perhaps been influenced by the notion of 'pleasing decay', a debate that surrounds not only issues of building preservation but also those of the restoration of paintings and other objects of art.

The market for buildings itself has changed significantly in the light of some of the above considerations. The result is that older buildings, even of no great historical or architectural significance, which some years ago would have been considered ready only for demolition and site redevelopment, are now given planning permission for change of use, fetching surprising prices.

Finally, there is a new appreciation that the natural rate of development is in fact often composed of smaller increments than has recently been the case. Change at the reduced scale certainly seems easier to monitor, allows for greater flexibility and is also less destructive of physical and psychological structures.

The change from a vernacular building process to that where design is professionalised and building activity itself carried out by specialists, has the same kind of effect on building conversion as on the design of new buildings. In other words, the designer somehow has to 'get inside' the minds and values of individuals and groups in society for whom he is designing — a bridging problem which is equally important in either type of design activity. In the case of building conversion, however, a framework already exists which makes the dangers of professionalisation less than in new work where the gap can remain unbridged as a result of the apparent 'freedom' enjoyed by the designer.

The focussing of attention on the conversion of buildings to new uses has given both education and practice a new area of interest. In practice, those who are engaged on this kind of work have developed, as we can see in their case studies, many valuable practical methods and techniques but as yet few systematised or general theories of design analogous to those which they use in the planning and design of new buildings. Those in education, in their turn, are to some extent also looking for practical techniques in design, construction, servicing and costing that can be passed on to students for application in practice.

There might appear to be some common ground here but without an underlying theoretical base the links are but superficial. No systematised or general theories of conversion design analogous to those used in the planning and design of new buildings have yet emerged. Educationalists are looking for such concepts and seek theoretical material which is capable of being formulated into an educationally worthwhile core from which systematic techniques of application can be derived.

This book contains contributions from both educationalists and practitioners and is a serious attempt to bring together the theoretical and the applied experience. Perhaps the most useful purpose of this is to highlight how wide the gap is between the two, particularly if the outcome is to encourage teachers and research workers on the one hand, and design practitioners on the other, to seek ways of bridging it.

As has already been hinted, the notion of conversion, as opposed to that of new design, depends entirely on the viewpoint which one adopts. To the city planner the pulling down of a city block and the construction of a new one to replace it is a 'conversion' of the city, whereas to the architect it is a new project. To the interior designer the gutting and refurbishing of a single space in the building is a new job, whereas to the architect it may be seen as part of the conversion of that building to another use. To the locksmith the design and manufacture of a special piece of door furniture for an existing door is seen as a new job whereas to the interior designer it is a minor part of a conversion. Thus, boundaries of interest and activities distinguish between one approach and another and perhaps one lesson to be learnt, which most of the authors in this book underline, is that for many political and economic reasons the boundaries have recently all shifted several steps too high.

A more ecological approach would ensure a closer analogy to, for instance, the growth, decay and rebirth of a forest. The scale of this kind of development is that of equating a building with an individual tree — if the whole forest were to die simultaneously, the scale would be too large and, on the other hand, if different leaves on a single tree were to die at different seasons of the year, the scale would be too small and uneconomical from the point of view of the tree's energy system. So the right scale, which is neither too large nor too small, depends on the energy content of the system and this is something which Graeme Aylward emphasises.

Some of the case studies described in this book, such as those of Abingdon Gaol, the Glasgow Opera House and the Southwark Church, London, are rather unique examples and the lessons to be learnt from them are not of detail but rather of a general approach which could equally well be applied in similar instances. A similar 'instance' would include buildings with a very marked architectural character, buildings which are often rare examples of a small class, and buildings with outstanding historical and architectural interest.

The mediaeval buildings discussed by John Warren are perhaps extreme cases of this type and he rightly emphasises the strict archaeological approach to his work. Most designers would not readily concede a similar approach in more mundane and less valuable buildings. But perhaps one of the more significant of Warren's conclusions is that adherence to sound archaeological principles may be important for future generations in many of the buildings which, today, we do not regard as coming within this framework. Moreover, this approach lends itself readily to resolving dilemmas about demolition, copying, replacement and updating of original structure or details.

The buildings in Blackburn and London, described by Keith Scott and David Rock respectively, are typical of many other examples which have no historical value. Here, there are not only general approaches but also demonstrations of practical techniques that could be of value in a large number of similar cases. In the London examples it is particularly interesting to see that a single mind and a single organisation was behind the imaginative concept both of designing a new organisation, and consequent activity patterns, and of designing a new physical environment to house those activities. This type of comprehensive, entrepreneurial, activity may become an important one for designers and requires new skills and perhaps new professional rules.

Tom Maver specifically highlights the fact that the matching of activities with spaces is a technique necessary and possible for new buildings and existing buildings alike. In the case of new buildings, even when the initial matching has been carried out, there is a continuous requirement for adapting the activities and the building so as to give the best interface over the whole life of the organisation.

In secondary schools, for instance, the revision of curricula and the construction of appropriate timetables is activity design and the alteration of the division of spaces, furniture, layout or equipment is the continuous building design activity. Unfortunately, whilst the initial matching of activities and spaces may be carried out by a single 'design' team, the continuous matching of the two against each other rarely involves anyone with design expertise. This division between the two activities is even more marked in the conversion of existing buildings, that is unless the job is tackled from the unifying approach outlined by Rock.

Aylward fits these ideas into a general model which has certain analogies with the physical world. In the range of activities discussed in the case studies it is interesting to note that the designers concerned seem to find a lot in common between the assumptions they have worked on and this general model and it would seem that considerable opportunities for developing the theory-practice links exist in this approach.

A similar approach, but in this case illustrated with practical examples, is that demonstrated by Terry Farrell. Here again, it is the total view that prevails and the designers have not been afraid to think both in physical and in organisational terms.

However, opinions differ as to the possibility of deriving a reasonably accurate design tool which would enable the capital cost of conversion to be predicted without the full design and approximate estimate exercise being undertaken. This kind of prediction exists, of course, and has long been successfully used for predicting the cost of new buildings. To extend it to the conversion of existing buildings implies a much more general language of space. The character of an existing space can be unambiguously described — in terms of its volume, load-bearing capacity, environmental conditions, service facilities and finishes — and the character of spaces suitable for a desired set of new activities can be described in the same language.

The development of a language of this kind (a kind of space algebra) and the process of matching the descriptive terms with the prescriptive terms is a technique inherent in some of the space programs described by Maver. The extent to which this can be extended to cost prediction remains to be seen. The research effort as described by Frey is large but the pay-offs would be significant, particularly if the re-use of existing buildings forms a higher percentage of the total of space provision than hitherto.

One observed effect that is clear from the descriptions in this book is that once architects become involved with user communities, whether in housing or otherwise, at a detailed scale in the design and continuous redesign of their existing environment, then many current professional structures begin to break down. These structures have certain underlying assumptions which were reasonable enough in the eighteenth or nineteenth centuries when they were developed. Firstly, they assume a client who is articulate and who, socially, if not in an elite group, at least is not in a deprived class. Architects have always worked for ultimate users who are in some sense deprived, e.g. prisoners, inmates of workhouses, users of wash-houses, tenement housing for the 'working man' whether in employment or not, but their ostensible client has invariably been an intermediate private or public body — e.g. the Charity Commissioners, the Peabody Trust or the Prison Commissioners. A second assumption is that basically architects are employed on new buildings and that it is a once-and-for-all design involvement — once the building is complete and handed over to the client the architect's involvement and his income from it ceases. A third assumption is that the user does not participate in the design or the construction of the final work.

In many of the situations described in this book, and in particular in the housing rehabilitation work from which Jim Johnson draws his experience, and in the examples which Rock describes, none of these assumptions hold. So far, it is only in a relatively small part of the architect's work that these assumptions are being broken down and hence relatively few of them are as yet having to make re-adjustments to this new pattern of work. It is clear, however, that this breakdown will accelerate as the proportion of small scale conversion work increases; the acceleration will not be only for social reasons but could be explained quite simply in terms of commercial pressures and efficiency. The new type of entrepreneurial architect respresented by Rock may soon find his way into many building types including community building, theatres, clubs, schools and factories.

The reader will be struck by the great variety of approaches in practice and the great variety of avenues being explored in theory in this field of architectural activity. Not only is the variety within each of these two sets large, but the gap in thinking between them is substantial indeed. The polarities of this gap might be labelled along such dimensions as: 'theory-practice', 'pragmatic-analytic', 'predictive-open-ended', and 'generalist-unique'.

These dimensions, however, are also those which describe the difference between current architectural theory and current architectural practice in new buildings and urban design on a larger scale. For instance, searching for theoretical explanations in the new application of mathematics, psychology, anthropology, spatial geography or history, reveals architectural theories that bear little or no relationship to the practical ways of solving these problems. This is not a criticism either of the theory or the practice, for after all it is the job of practitioners to do things well and not necessarily to be able to explain either to themselves or to others how their solutions are successful, and it is the job of theoreticians precisely to be able to explain the general principles which seem to differentiate between good and bad solutions.

So we should not be surprised that in this rapidly growing and somewhat passion-ridden field of building conversion — an activity which is in fact as ancient as the hills — we see reflected in microcosm the same kind of divisions as exist in architectural thought and practice in general. The encouraging thing, however, is that a bridging of this gap at this level may turn out to have significance on the macro scale of architectural activity also. If the pragmatic influence of an existing building can sufficiently temper the intellectual arrogance of the theoretician and the design arrogance of the practitioner, then enough common ground around which to close the gap might emerge.

CHAPTER ONE

Conversion and Rehabilitation

The subjective nature of change and stability:
a model and design strategies

Graeme Aylward

Fundamental to our perception of the environment should be the realisation that it is not just a physical/spatial world but one comprising people and the organisation of people. When we see a decrepit area it is not just physical decay we are observing but a manifestation of organisational lethargy, disinterest and financial withdrawal, and of individual despair and lack of motivation. These grim qualities are self-reinforcing and together make any change towards improvement a very difficult task.

A change in one set of problems, for example physical improvement, is not enough on its own. It is the total system that requires attention. This is the essential theme of this chapter; the problem of re-orientating the direction of change towards improvement is a massive one. It is reinforced not only by those suffering the substandard environment but by the external perceptions of society as a whole on the 'outside'. The flight to decay occurs at an exponential rate; conversely, to reverse this tide becomes increasingly difficult as the level of decay increases. A simplified model of this process will be presented.

Naturally when we think of rehabilitation it is normally in terms of some historical building or place, or a derelict housing area. The problem is of course broader than this. The quality of the working environment, particularly in industry, is often overlooked. The upgrading of our environment to some desired standard or the maintenance of the environment at its current standard are identical types of investment when viewed as ways of overcoming undesirable obsolescence and decay. The working environment receives little attention, either because the emphasis is on equipment, or, more simply, because it is not considered to be important: obsolescence and decay are accepted — discounted economic facts with little or no qualitative component.

The context within which buildings, people and organisations are placed is constantly changing. But change has several parameters that affect this trio of the building/activity system in a multitude of ways. Not everything changes at the same rate or is affected by a context change in the same way. Neither the frequency, magnitude nor duration of change have constant dimensions across different situations.

Since change is something we all observe, being filtered through our assessment of what the world is like, it is largely a subjective notion — at least our perception of whether it is a large or small change, a good or bad change. The world is in a constant state of flux. We can measure objectively against linear time the changes of states in matter, but our judgment of the order of change is subjective. We are aware of change in a variety of ways. Some is almost subliminal, such as growing old, some is imperceptible, for example the movement of atoms, while yet other change is supraliminal, for example an explosion. Most of what we regard as change is in the substantial 'middle range' of our experience, the dynamics of personal relationships, the opening and closing of shops and our movement through space.

Not everyone rejects and accepts the same information from the environment, though many of the common cues about what is happening are held by nearly all people within a particular culture. This common redundancy of information accounts for the fact that people of differing subjective perceptive abilities can discern the 'same' qualities in the same object or circumstance. In all our day-to-day experience, change is observed as the mismatch between the current state of things, people and places, and our memory of the former state: the subjective perception of difference.

The role of previous experience is vital to perceived change levels, examples of which are commonplace: the trained architectural eye discerns subtle differences between buildings where the untrained eye sees only similarity; to some many cars may look alike, for others a small change in motif is readily identified — they live in different perceptual worlds, linked only by the redundance of information intrinsic to our perception of objects. Consequently, differences have to be gross, expressed over relatively short periods of time, before perception of change can occur for a significant proportion of people and organisations.

Where the individual fits into this picture is a function of the 'optimum perceptual rate' that he has constructed for himself (Rapoport and Kantor, 1967)[12]. Rates of change below this subjective optimum promote boredom, and above this, stress, both of which are uncomfortable. This introduces the

1

important concept of stability. It is the constant change rate that each individual or group finds the most comfortable — a personal 'steady state'. We all desire change, it is only the degree to which we experience it outside of our desired rate of change that causes problems. Identifiable, significant and discontinuous change is a break in the normally discerned constant rate of change. Stability is preferred.

Stability, identity, imageity and structure in the environment transform otherwise evanescent actions into predictable repetitions, enabling learnt behaviour patterns to be confidently applied. In fact, much adult behaviour is probably an attempt to maintain the stability of a subjective world by continuous adaptation (Canter, 1970)[5]. Bachelard, in describing the act of dwelling as a central identity says — 'A house consists of a body of images that give mankind proofs or illusions of stability' (Bachelard, 1964)[3]. Part of this stability is a sense of continuity with the past. Many intervening changes may have occurred but a prevailing sense of history embodied in a building or place gives roots to this sense of stability and security — 'A proportion of the past has been saved as being good, and this promises that the future will so save the present' (Lynch, 1972)[10]. Thus continuity is maintained, or thought to be maintained, into the future.

As the rate of change in society increases, so generally does the value we place on the old. Sometimes it is facile, as when 'Georgian style' bay windows are built into speculative new housing, but in many instances certain old buildings and places are invested with great cultural value that accrues with interest through time. Such buildings are likely to be with us for a very long time since, even if considerable sums of money are involved to repair them, it will be small beside the intangible cultural investment. It is true that this applies to very few buildings: the Guildhall in London, Royal Crescent in Bath, or the Louvre in Paris. However, in stating an extreme case one can interpolate from it to the more mundane village street, discerning cultural value and the sense of continuity it holds.

Conventionally, buildings are considered to be narrowly adapted to a perceived stable rate of change, hence their misfit when the rate of change alters, as it must eventually since it is subjectively determined. Therefore, the stable rate of change to which the building was adapted upon construction will impose a constraint upon the rate of change of the activities that are subsequently contained within it at some future date. Indeed, without such constraints the subjective world would be chaotic. The environment must remain demonstrably stable whilst undergoing change so that its users can experience stability and security, and the feeling of living in the present rather than in the future — 'A town is, if the natural relationships are active, an organism which is never quite finished but which renews itself continually so that matter gains some of the mobility of life, and life receives some of the permanence of matter' (Habraken, 1972)[7].

Perhaps a building is sometimes endowed with constraining

qualities by the activities it houses. This may not just be a question of the activities, but one in which the activity finds some imagined comfort in the stability of the place in which it is housed. This could be manifested in the reluctance of an organisation to recast itself in its environment or indeed to change that environment. Such attitudes could be so institutionalised and established that only a crisis or a major shift in leadership will effect a new look at the 'stabilising', now constricting role of the building and organisational fabric.

Implications of perceived stability

Hypotheses and observations on decay and rehabilitation/ conversion can tentatively be stated with respect to the ideas on how people relate to change and stability:

1. Although some fairly objective measures of decay can be made, a substantial, and unknown, proportion is a subjective judgement of the state of a place or building. This judgement is made by the inhabitants and by the outside world. For inhabitants, the intermediate state of decay is hard to perceive from within and in fact they may forget much in the way of condition in favour of the 'stability' of the environment. In states of more rapid decay, towards the end of the effective life of the property, the conditions are more readily perceived because the rate of decline exceeds the expected stability or perceived rate of change. For those outside the system with different notions of stability, perhaps coming from environments that have quite different change rates, the rate of change and perceived decay is recognised at intermediate as well as final stages. But this does not make these perceptions.

2. Since the perception of 'decay' is substantially a relative matter, the onset of it in a small area within a larger one can have a far greater effect than is warranted. This decay can be more readily accepted and included within the perceptions of inhabitants of the area since their comparative judgements are less easily made. The cancer of this decline is likely to seem to grow at a faster rate for those outside the area than those inside because the insiders are part of an evolving situation whereas the outsiders' view is discontinuous; they are more able to compare different states.

3. New environments, that is, newly constructed, are not necessarily more stable than old ones, the high rate of change experienced by those moving being aggravated further by living in a place that provides little continuity. The buildings may be more stable in the sense of decay rate, but not necessarily stable for the inhabitants. Some may adopt and adapt to the new; others, though, may remain 'outside' the new place. It is perhaps neither like the place that has been left behind nor like some model environment to which they might aspire.

The implications of this lack of involvement will have severe consequences for the rate of change of that inhabited environment.

4. As the rate of change increases, the pressures to maintain continuity with the past, and hence stability, also increases. Naturally, much of the past is lost, and as a proportion of the total environment the old recedes in quantity. The more ancient, the more the implied continuity, and the greater is the resistance to its being lost.

5. Those external to an activity/space system are more likely to view only the hardware; those involved set higher priority on the activity systems. It is in the social fabric that stability mostly resides; it is only when this starts to dissolve that the physical environment is critically examined. Thus in new development, where social networks do not exist, the physical aspects are the focus of attention. The blinkers of social involvement are not present to mask the setting.

Aspects of this sense of continuity are developed by Lynch. 'Change and recurrence are the sense of being alive — things gone by, death to come, and present awareness. The world around us, so much of it our own creation, shifts continually and often bewilders us. We reach out of that world to preserve or to change it and so to make visible our desire. The arguments of planning all come down to the management of change.' (Lynch, 1972)[11].

A model for the changing environment

Before developing any strategic or tactical solutions for coping with stability and change, it is necessary to explain, in simple terms, a model of the change process. It is of course an analogue of what actually happens, one a designer can manipulate to relate different influences. It is to some extent a predictive tool, an essential quality when coping with change.

Energy is the common denominator of our world and, following well known physical laws, it is always conserved; for example, water is raised by the energy from the sun, deposited on high ground and runs to low ground; intervening dams and hydro-electric plant can extract this energy of downward flow; it is, indirectly, sun energy. And so it is for any system; energy that goes into a system can all be accounted for as growth in the system, offset to varying degrees by losses. Energy is not always obtained with equal facility from all sources in the system; some is easily usable, as in the case of electricity, and some is less easily obtained, for example, from a thick stone wall.

The sources of energy for the systems that describe the world of buildings and people are very diverse, but an essential point is that people, money, bricks and mortar, all individually have an energy to give, and a source from which it can be released. Some energy is so hard to release from mass that it may be regarded as entrapped and lost, i.e. entropic (but this is not to be confused with the notion of entropy that implies randomness). In the realm of building and organisational design it is the 'energy' of people's ideas that realises the potential any system has to offer. In the strict terms of physics it is the energy and mass of the physical world that is being capitalised upon. However, there is the analogous mass and energy of organisations and the people they contain. Thus it is not unreasonable to view ideas as having the potential to release and to re-allocate the energy of the system.

The 'idea' as an abstract concept does not have energy but we commonly give the implied energy of an idea to the idea itself. An innovator is regarded as 'full of energy' not simply in his ability to expend ergs and kilowatts but because he has many energy releasing ideas.

Such principles are employed here through the notions of mass/energy balances in a system. A discarded building has a great deal of mass, as does an over-staffed and declining organisation. A building with many potential uses and future alternatives harbours much potential energy, as does a burgeoning young firm with a good product to sell.

Not only the physical fabric of the world but also the people that inhabit it are considered. The three categories used will be:

1. physical/spatial,
2. operational/organisational, and
3. behavioural/cultural.

More generally the categories of 'activity' and 'space' are used.

There are many terms used freely when the question of change is discussed: these include adaptability, obsolescence, loose fit, etc. Any model should incorporate these notions in a related way. We perceive the cycles of seasons, of life and death, of growth and decay, of rise and fall, and of fluctuations of demand as continuing cycles of change which return to some subjective starting point. As a convention this change can be depicted as a representative point describing a circular orbit at a constant velocity or change rate (*Figure 1.1*).

The 'change rate' (CR) in the daily life of some activity/space system may itself change. The realisation that the CR is different is very likely to be subjective. If apparent continuity from one state to another is preserved during this time, the change is *incremental* (*Figure 1.2*); where the difference in states is beyond some tolerable limit the change in CR is *disjoint* (*Figure 1.3*). In both instances of incremental and disjoint change there can be growth, acceleration, *nascence* from a slow to fast 'change rate' (*Figure 1.4*) or, decay, deceleration, obsolescence from fast to slow (*Figure 1.5*). This latter negative adaptation can also be described as a decline

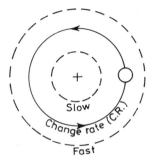

Figure 1.1 Change Rate (CR) orbits: 1 revolution = 1 unit of time

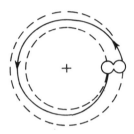

Figure 1.2 Change in CR: gradual/incremental

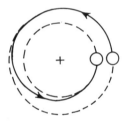

Figure 1.3 Change in CR: sudden/disjointed

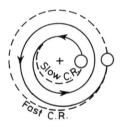

Figure 1.4 Change in CR slow → fast = growth/nascence
(i.e. nascence = positive change in CR)

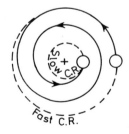

Figure 1.5 Change in CR fast → slow = decay/obsolescence
(i.e. obsolescence = negative change in CR)

in specific growth rates (le Gros Clark, 1945)[8]. The rate at which CR changes is dealt with later.

An entity under pressure to adapt to a new CR orbit, or desirous of attaining a higher CR in response to subjectively structured goals, will perceive a mismatch between the current CR and that of the new orbit. This will generate stress which will only be expiated by adapting the existing to the new perceived CR orbit. Where orbits are set higher, the comparison with the existing expresses *perceived obsolescence*. It is a comparative relationship between two orbits; the higher one is subjectively labelled 'good' and implies obsolescence for the entity at a slow CR, while the lower orbit is labelled 'bad' and implies the perceived nascence of the fast CR entity over the slow. For example, a new model of car will relatively depress the values of the superseded model, even though the locomotive ability of the old car remains the same. Similarly, an old building may be regarded as finished though overnight a new use may be found for it, suddenly relieving it of much of its obsolescence.

The subjective nature of most obsolescence is a vital concept. It does not deny the absolute obsolescence caused by decay and wear but emphasises the usually forgotten characteristics of a place that embody the artifically enhanced or depressed qualities that give it value. Most planning is concerned with the avoidance of perceived obsolescence and the determination of forces that bring about a negative change on CR to slower orbits. It strives for optimum CRs that will attain some goal orbit and re-establish equilibrium. Goal orbits are frequently set too high, either in response to some Utopian ideas, or through fear of the unknown, causing the perceived stress to be exaggerated (Becker, 1971)[4].

Recent essays into modelling change have tended toward a form which examines 'states' (as in static) of a system limited by steps in linear time. The probabilities of a given state give rise to a consequent state, usually expressed in terms of Markov chains, as with the Lowry model of urban land use (Lowry, 1960)[9].

Briefly, the parameters of change are:

1. Rate — change in change rate (orbital Velocity V) —positive for a faster rate, negative for a slower one;
2. Duration — time taken to move from one change rate to another;
3. Magnitude — the size of the difference between existing and new change rates;
4. Continuity — the constancy of rate of change in change rate.

These parameters are included to indicate that there are many qualities of change considered.

Thus far the model has expressed the orbit of an entity with no mass. Omitting many refinements not required to understand

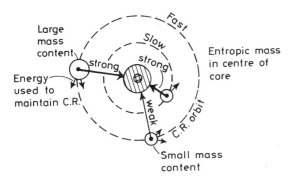

Figure 1.6 'Planetary' model (CR + mass and energy): pull of central mass = forces of decay and obsolescence. ○ = building/activity system

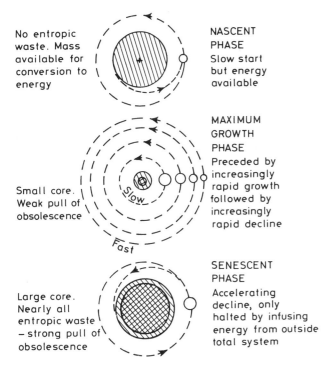

Figure 1.7 Growth/decline cycle of model. ○ = building/activity system

change rate. The larger the mass the more energy is required to hold an orbit, since two particles of matter attract one another with a force directly proportional to the product of their masses, and because of assumptions about dampening, which need not trouble us now. The lower the orbit the more energy required, since gravitation decreases with the square of the distance between the bodies.

Reference was made earlier to the lost energy that becomes entropic in mass, not convertible back to some form of usable energy. In fact the core of this model, the central mass, is made up of an entropic core at the very centre surrounded by mass and energy. The initial state of the system, with a large core mass, makes it difficult for initial orbits to establish themselves e.g. the first settlements of a town.

In the development of the system (*Figure 1.7*), a small entropic core (not much waste) couples with usable mass/energy and expanding orbits which would be synonymous with a *nascent* state and indicate high rates of growth. In later stages a large entropic core (the debris of the town) with low orbits, increasingly rapid decline, obsolescence and slow change rates, is indicative of a *senescent* state. This life cycle concludes with the whole system tending towards maximum entropy. The normal profile of the system at any given time would be one of large masses in the lower orbits and smaller masses in the outer high change rate orbits, because of the expenditure of energy required to move to, and maintain, a higher orbit.

One last aspect of the model, which is dealt with only briefly, is the addition of the time dimension. Clearly when the orbital model is extended through time, like a coiled spring which is stretched, it describes a helix (*Figure 1.8*). Only the helix, which conserves subjective stability and constant change through continuity, appears to provide a valid representation of transformations, or changes in state, through time.

It is emphasised that although the model is lawful in mathematical and physical terms (within the confines of newtonian physics) it is still a *subjective* model. The particular significance of this is that the 'mass' and 'energy' described in

the essence of the model, more fully developed elsewhere (Aylward and Lapthorne, 1974)[2], the whole system is given mass with the consequent introduction of gravity as described in newtonian physics.

It is not necessary to understand the mathematics of such a model to be able to imagine it in its dynamic form. Principally, we now have a 'planet' of some size (containing mass and energy) orbiting about a core of some mass. The central body exerts a pull on the orbiting body drawing it relentlessly towards destruction (*Figure 1.6*). This represents the forces of obsolescence, which, in order to be overcome, require that the orbiting mass should exert energy to maintain its desired

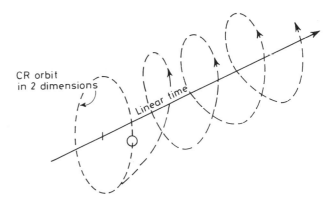

Figure 1.8 The CR orbits 'stretched' through normal linear time = helix: converts 'stability' or circle into 'steady state' of helix

5

the model are real when describing the physical environment, and to some extent the activities within it, but it is also able to call upon the resources that are appreciated by new perceptions of what is possible. This qualitative component is essential in dealing with the interaction of people and things, how they change and how they are valued.

The first, and natural, question is, 'what use is all this modelling?' 'Does it provide any insight as to what is changing and what is stable?' In the particular context of this book, 'what does it tell us about conservation and rehabilitation?' Before examining these questions in terms of design strategies to cope with decay and change, a number of observations that begin to answer such questions are introduced.

Implications of the Model

Hypotheses and comments on rehabilitation and conversion based upon the model for change are:

1. The energy required to reinvigorate an obsolete building/ activity system, if it is in an area of like condition, is far too great for money alone. The decline towards entropy will be accelerating, assisted by the size of central mass that represents the decrepit state of the whole area. A primary hope is to draw in energy from as wide a source as possible, in particular, the efforts of the inhabitants and their perception of what is worth investing their life in, and the energy infused by changed perceptions of value in the system by outsiders. This is a crucial hypothesis.

2. As much energy as possible should be released from the existing fabric and the mass of the system reduced so that it may more easily adopt higher change rates and move to a nascent phase. In practical terms this means that nothing should be replaced which is not absolutely necessary and the latent qualities that have value to the inhabitants should be capitalised on. For an architect this could mean simply, 'don't flush-panel the doors'! For example, an existing vertical circulation in a house subdivision should be used, and only those walls removed that do not have a principal structural role.

3. A small withdrawal of energy will speed obsolescence (positive feedback to a decaying orbit nearer the core) far more than the addition of the same unit of energy for nascent growth (negative feedback where the natural direction towards obsolescence is being opposed). Thus the loss of 'energy' in a damaged roof, say as a result of a storm, will commit the building to final decay; the withdrawal of an active resident can have an equal effect. Conversely, the replacement of defective windows or a decrease in rateable value may have only marginal benefit.

4. The potential energy that resides in the site may be greater than the building that stands on it, thus the pressure to demolish

is strong. Quite often it can be that the building has potential but it has not been appreciated — it is perceived as being useless, or, in model terms, it possesses too much mass.

5. If necessary energy is thinly spread throughout an area in a state of decay, it may be built up to new peaks in some of the building stock by restructuring the land use pattern. For example, if a defunct rail marshalling yard could be converted to landscaped open space, (it probably was originally), the adjacent buildings benefit in amenity and increase in demand. The energy that was in the yard has, in effect, been swept to new peaks at its perimeter. Such major changes can trigger rehabilitation through market forces which is far less demanding on the public purse.

6. Energy also resides in the historical significance of a building. It is judged that this energy value is fairly constant, thus benefitting smaller building and making only a minor difference to larger ones. Thus, an architecturally significant cathedral or railway hotel has a far harder time surviving than a modest residence or small shop. This historical energy in several adjacent buildings does appear to create a web of self-supporting energy in which individual components may not be strong but when woven together, are formidable. Piecemeal destruction should therefore be strongly resisted, even if an individual component may be unusually weak in respect to its historic significance.

7. The inputs of energy to improve a property should, as far as possible, take place at the same time. Piecemeal rehabilitation runs the danger of being drained of its energy to support the rest of the mass. Minimising the mass of the system at the same time as maximising the infusion of energy is thus very important. In rehabilitating tenements, for example, a bathroom should not be put in one year, rewiring carried out another, structural defects made good in another, and so on; it should be timed to be much more intensively rehabilitated.

8. Since the external perception of improvement is important, a property should be seen to be more vital and thus given energy by people's subjective judgement of worth. Rehabilitation should be visible. A simple upgrading of internal spaces reduces the likelihood of long term success in overcoming the entropic pull of obsolescence. Energy input, both real and abstract, must be maximised.

9. 'People energy', as individuals and organisations, must be realised. The inhabitants, or potential inhabitants, must be motivated to contribute to sustaining any improvements. In terms of Rodgers and Shoemaker's adopter categories, 'laggards' must develop in the direction of 'innovators' (Rodgers and Shoemaker, 1971)[13]. Since age is substantially characterised in the categories, an infusion of young people or organisations should be encouraged. What is lacking in money energy may very often be offset by idea and effort energy. It is a common experience in public housing that when a flat falls empty it

declines rapidly and the 'plague' mark of blocked-up windows soon appears, affecting the value of the whole district in the broad sense of lost energy — another example of exponential decay.

10. In a slum-like area where the system has little or no energy available to reverse the accelerating drift to entropy, only an infusion of energy from outside the system, commensurate with the high mass of the system can hope to reverse this drift.

11. As a building deteriorates, the cost of public services increase, but the tax revenue available also reduces as the cost of urban maintenance increases (Cowan, 1965)[6]. The building struggling to pull itself out of the entropic slum thus has increasing mass as well as the high 'gravitational' pull (of entropic core) to contend with. The same building, in a thriving area of low mass, low entropy and high change rate, would either require less energy to maintain a given value, or would experience a rise in value for the same energy input. Even a building in an advanced state of decay would experience a similar subjective rise in value, even though no energy was being expended to arrest decay.

12. The most adaptable form of building is one which can assume a new change rate orbit, or maintain an existing one, without using external energy, by relying entirely on its own internal energy field. This implies not only that the fabric of the building should be easily manipulated, as in the case of the 'Thick Wall Pattern' (Alexander, 1968)[1], and that the fabric should be kept out of the way (Weeks, 1969)[14], but it also implies the need for a variety of spaces, a quality that is often present in existing buildings.

13. Maintenance is equally as important as capital investment. The forces which are tending to reduce the system to an entropic state immediately start to decay the orbit and must be kept at bay by constant infusions of energy. Although only a slight drag when the CR is high and the mass small, when the building moves to a lower orbit as for instance when a house 'filters' down the social scale (Lowry, 1960)[9] then the energy required to resist entropic drain increases. Again, using the model, this decline increases at an exponential rate. An example of this can be seen in the Blackburn Central Library project (Scott, Chapter 8), where the existing building was experiencing rapidly increasing decline until this was arrested by rehabilitation.

Reactions to change and strategies for stability

The formulation of a design strategy to manipulate the resources of a building/activity system which will provide us with our illusion of stability has the three component tactical parts mentioned earlier (physical, organisational and behavioural). Each contains concepts and ideas that will enable a particular change range (orbit) to be maintained.

As a reaction to the impinging agents and instigators of change, a building/activity system should try to utilise its resources in the most effective way commensurate with its own perceived level of stability. Its aim is efficiently to tap all its available energy when it is needed and to convert and/or reconvert mass to energy. This is the essence of change-coping strategies, particularly if resources are limited.

There are six tactical components of any strategy, being

Form;
Dependence,
Capacity,
Utility,
Fixity and
Modularity.

These have elsewhere been developed more fully for general application (Aylward and Lapthorne, 1974)[2]. The tactics apply to the organisation of activities, as well as the organisation of space and building. In the context of rehabilitation and conversion, each tactic imposes constraints and suggests opportunities. Some of the constraints are rigid, while others may be modified or turned to advantage. Examples of all such cases are given. It is clear that, given the fabric of the building, in most cases the stress of change imposed on an activity fitting into the established spatial order of this fabric is absorbed largely by the people rather than the building. This point will recur in the examples to be analysed.

The descriptions of reactions to change are simplified by focussing on the problem of initial reactions when new or modified activities and existing space come together; of less concern here are subsequent events and reactions.

Form

The shape of a building imposes a pattern of potential connections between activities. The significance of this constraint is, of course, largely influenced by size. A small one or two-unit building can adopt a very wide range of small scale activities and it is these buildings that are consequently easier to re-use and conserve. Large, multi-storey buildings are another matter. A common form of 'conservation' in these cases is to destroy completely all but the facade. The building form and old structure just do not conform to current ideas of large scale open space which is multi-divisible.

Form is, in essence, the structure of movement patterns, the organisation of routes. Forms that do not get in the way of activity patterns will naturally help the flux of an organisation and in effect utilise the energy of the building more fully in respect to form at least. The simple basic forms of 'compact', 'linear' and 'matrix' types tend not to exist in any pure way. Most old buildings, because of structural limitations, are transformed into some pattern of multi-cellular form.

In terms of adaptive potential there are certain qualities of form that should be examined. The first would be the mean travel distance (probably weighted for importance), testing to see to what extent actual travel diverges from ideal travel distance. The second is connected to the first, namely, focus versatility. Here it is important to see whether different hierarchies of movement and the concomitant foci can fit into the building form. Last is the number and variety of potential physical connections available to the activity. Other matters related to form such as available perimeter for expansion tend to be less important in existing, perhaps historic buildings. Existing buildings may well be silted up with the many *ad hoc* arrangements of connections built up through time.

It is probably very important to stand back and design an ideal configuration for an activity and then to modify this ideal in the light of the constrictions imposed by the existing fabric. The constraints of old, multi-cellular forms are likely to place heavy burdens on communications, either personal or electronic. However, the value placed in the image and stability of old buildings will often outweigh such considerations, especially since the currently observed pattern of activities may be known to be temporary in terms of the life of the organisation.

If activities are examined more closely and alternative means of communication explored, it may well be that the inadequate building form could be made to be compatible with revised notions of organisational form. The creation of self-contained units of activity may prove to work in many different patterns of association. The compact form does have alternatives.

The larger the unit of activity the more mass that it is likely to contain. The IBM Company is a case in point: although successful, it did not 'take off' until greater autonomy was given to smaller units; the energy that this released in individuals, coupled with the smaller mass, enabled high change rates to be adopted. An activity may prefer to invest in new, more adaptable personnel; rather than invest in substantial changes to the mass of the building it reduces the mass of its organisation. At Wellbury Boys Home (Farrell, Chapter 5) a complete reappraisal of the organisational form, as well as the form of the building fabric, prevented unnecessary rehabilitation of marginally useful buildings and encouraged an efficient and more tightly knit organisation.

Dependence

All building fabric is zoned in some way through the disposition and composition of its elements — the structure, external envelope, vertical circulation, etc. The object is to optimise on a low level of interference between fixed and fluid areas, related in turn to the location of activities that are exerting pressures for change on the physical fabric (Lynch, 1958)[10]. The element of structure is obviously very important in determining the size of fluid areas, uninterrupted space being a common means to obtain flexibility.

With an existing building the principal dependencies are 'locked' in the fabric. In particular, the non-framed structures impose a heavy dependence between subdivision and structure. A dilemma is that this very construction may impart the substantial character, and therefore energy, of the building, yet it also contains the mass that is such a burden to carry. It is likely that, in many old buildings, fluid areas will be limited and at a premium, since those activities requiring these areas will naturally have to use such spaces; as a consequence, there are likely to be strains in operational links. Aside from the response of activity to overcome such problems, the choice quickly narrows to one of creating more fluid areas in the building.

A 'golden rule' in providing adaptable buildings is to reduce dependence between elements in order that changes can be made without interference between these elements. Nowhere is this more true than in services. Traditionally the dependence between environmental control and structure is very close, the thick external wall acting to even-out the vagaries of climate, while tall windows allow deep penetration of light. Such benefits may be retained, though additional services will undoubtedly be required to meet new life style standards, particularly of environmental control.

Following the tactic of system separation, new or additional services must either be very small or self-contained in order to reduce interference between services and other systems. Thus, electricity can wind through the structure and air conditioning can use 'plug-in' units. The obsolescence rate (increasing mass) of services is much faster than the building fabric and renewing it is thus made easier if systems are separated. Thus in Glasgow's Theatre Royal (Frewer and Sugden, Chapter 7) new services were run above the cornice in an unobtrusive way and electric radiant heaters used in preference to bulky ductwork.

Concentrating new development in one area reduces the dependence between old and new, localising disruption. If the new elements are very different in character the independence may be quite marked, as with the service tower to the student hostel in Sussex Gardens (Farrell, Chapter 5), which facilitated not only the construction of the new but, in the case of this heavily serviced element, it minimised disruption to the old fabric.

This 'independence' tactic is of particular importance because, as an energy releasing agent, it has a far longer life than 'form' since the cumulative interference can be kept quite low between components and systems through time. Communication has a substantial role in determining dependence between activities. Unnecessary dependence chokes effective communication or masks effective use of resources, thus contributing to the entropic mass of the organisation. The compromise allocation of existing space to activities will be made easier if all dependencies within the activity networks are scrutinised to determine the magnitude, type and frequency of information flow.

Capacity

The fabric of a new building is never utilised to the full: a corridor maintains its width although traffic density will vary; the space between a column and a wall can create 'dead' space. In an old building which is unlikely to be tailored to new activities this wastage, or unused capacity, can be quite marked. It is a common problem that the excess volume in an old building is a tremendous drain on maintenance resources.

The spare capacity and freedom given by uninterrupted space is comparatively rare in old buildings of heavy load-bearing type structures. When such opportunities do arise they may be used with imagination, as with the new theatre in the old Manchester Corn Exchange, or, more commonly, in the multiple uses given to old churches — everything from community centres to garages. However, capacity resides not only in space but in all building elements; structure, services, and the external envelope for example. Fortunately many old buildings can be carved about because they are well endowed with extra capacity in wall thickness and floor structures, warehousing being a classic example, such as the proposed scheme to convert Liverpool Docks for Liverpool Polytechnic (Greenslade and Saxon, Chapter 12).

In the future, it is likely that old buildings, built in more recent times, will have been built to reduce capital (energy) cost and will be much more closely tailored to minimum needs of activity enclosure and thus not have this spare capacity in the building elements. The ease with which lime mortar masonry and timber can be modified means less energy expended, whereas to modify reinforced concrete presents a major problem. A most significant source of capacity resides in furniture and equipment; this is closely related to some of the other tactics.

The intensity with which an activity uses a space is partly a function of the personnel, and partly the equipment they use. All too often the latent energy in such hardware cannot be released because the organisation does not have the capacity to manage and realise it. The most frequent abuse of this resource is in 'flexible' partition systems: they cost much to buy but remain fixed for periods longer than their design warrants.

The capacity of an organisation to adapt to rehabilitated surroundings is probably more important than the changeability of the physical fabric. What needs to be determined is the break-even point where over-capacity 'slack' in potential staff energy becomes an operating loss: or, conversely, overworked staff become inefficient. The ability of people to adapt is a precious energy source. It is probably far more economic in many instances to release the potential energy to adapt that is within people, rather than simply to invest in more hardware.

In a nascent growth situation there are natural pressures to make the best of existing resources, capitalising on the energy within the system. In obsolescent or declining states it is common practice to reduce energy rather than mass — by the sacking of expensive research staff for example. Using the model it is obvious that a better policy is to slough off mass, such as outmoded procedures and production patterns.

Utility

Included in this tactic are such concepts as: variety, multi-purpose, homeostasis (self-regulation) and polyvalency (multiple fit). Put simply, utility is the extent to which any space or activity can serve many functions. Certainly one of the most important in existing buildings is 'variety'. Viewing the spatial provision as a whole, it is built around the idea that if a mix of different environments is provided then a greater range of activities can be housed.

It has already been noted that the small subdivisions of older property can structurally 'get in the way'. An alternative approach to wholesale demolition is to analyse the needs of the activities within an organisation and look for the optimum fit of activities to space. Clearly some degree of misfit will always be present but, given any kind of experimental activity, or loosely defined activity, a misfit will soon arise even from closely tailored spaces.

It is interesting to note that the variety of room sizes in a large organisation such as a hospital is in fact quite small (Weeks, 1973)[15]. An analogy may be drawn with a city; it has many 'rooms' where activities buy the best 'fit' for their money, moving when appropriate. An existing building, particularly a large one, is less likely to have the kind of open multi-purpose space of long span structures. Variety-of-use could well be a key concept. Thus, the energy retrieval options are kept open; perhaps the space will never be fully utilised in any one place but never lost to add to the dead entropic 'weight' of mass that will hasten obsolescence.

Polyvalency expresses the robustness of fit between activities and space: a space that is not uniquely fitted to one activity but is potentially suited to several. It is probably true that such qualities reside in the secondary elements of equipment and furniture rather than in the space itself. Such a concept is particularly appropriate for existing, converted space since it is far easier to vary equipment than existing enclosure and subdivision. Energy is not wasted unnecessarily by modifying the structure.

Making the best use of people and space through time requires that the organisation should monitor its needs. Ideally, a self-regulating equilibrium state, a homeostatic environment, would constantly adjust the location and needs of activities, modifying space only when absolutely necessary. The energy within the activity/space system is constantly re-evaluated and re-interpreted rather than left redundant. This is the antithesis of the 'throw-away' approach. Old buildings should be closely scrutinised for what they can offer and not forced into a mould in which they are expected to behave and look like new buildings. This may put a greater stress on activities, but many similar stresses so arise in new buildings when new and changing patterns do not fit the initial spatial provisions.

Fixity

Nothing is fixed; in time everything is moved. What makes something immobile is its usefulness, weight, continuity of structure, disturbance caused, and the time and energy required to move it. It is probably not complexity, since things are often made complex to achieve mobility. Because of the need for stability, people and organisations often become more fixed than they really should. Mobile groups, able to operate in many locations, reduce dependence on space and this makes them better suited to inhabiting old structures.

Generally, the investment in mobile artifacts and people able to move in the short term requires a greater investment in energy (money), though this may well be preferable to 'one-shot' investments that are narrowly adapted. The later approach implies more of the disposable aspect of fixity which, unless it is an investment to overcome a unique and short life problem, is going to be a drain on resources. With rehabilitation the need is to consume and make use of energy within the system as much as possible.

As with most of the tactics, the scale at which any one of them can be applied can vary. Mobility in the context of existing building fabric is most likely to reside in small scale elements such as temporary floor finishes, heaters, furniture and partitions. The build-up of units of varying mobility, can, if not controlled, cause even more rigid environments through the cumulative resistance of many small units – a silting process.

Short and long term costs can be measured in energy and mass; in the short term the entropic mass of the component is small, growing larger in the longer term. Further, the energy is at least used to maintain a desired change rate, while mass increases the drag towards obsolescence. Solutions that minimise mass and maximise usability will surely be worthwhile investments. To some extent this explains the value of temporary and mobile structures for tentative and intermediate phases of growth and decline. If such elements are not re-usable, investment in them is probably of low value, and of high value if they are re-usable.

In the change model it is expected that a system that is trying to stave off decline would minimise mass but not have the energy (money) to invest in its re-use. Under growth conditions the option is more likely to be taken to minimise mass by building in convertibility of the temporary/mobile element for another future use, for example, by employing high-value personnel for short periods rather than low-value, less able, people for longer periods, or, re-usable partitioning in preference to short-life timber framed subdivisions.

Modularity

The interchange of parts of buildings is made more simple if the components are fabricated to some optimum size. The brick is modular but it is too small to make much sense of this tactic. It is more appropriate to a new building of regular and co-ordinated dimensions than a converted building.

Nevertheless, if there is sufficient tolerance built into the components, then the fit of standard size units to many situations would be possible. The most obvious example is the standardised bathroom unit that can fit many houses.

Similar spaces in old buildings are likely to vary greatly in their dimensions but with some appropriate tolerances this can be overcome. The advantages are that the energy required to modify a 'one-off' situation is usually higher than a unit produced in quantity. If, for example, all the windows in an old building had to be replaced, where each opening may vary slightly, it would be better to standardise on the smaller opening and detail a variable sized window frame/opening junction, than to make each one tailored to fit each opening.

The modularisation of the organisation could enable it to separate and connect units more easily – this may permit a better use of spaces not specifically designed for that organisation. However, it does imply some repetitive over-supply of skills that could not be sustained by an organisation struggling to survive.

Conclusion

There are many countervailing pressures at work in the environment. The awareness that energy cannot be squandered has caused a new look to be taken at the city fabric we possess. However, to preserve blindly limits the evolutionary options for a city. Re-using warehousing along the River Clyde is nowhere near such a good idea as the environmental improvement that has actually taken place. Society can rehabilitate everything, but at what cost? We are far from such a situation, but the cost could be one of apparent ossification that is not attractive to new firms, new jobs and more wealth for a city. On the other hand the wealth that does exist in the built environment must be appropriately utilised.

What all this shows is that what appears to be obsolete may in fact not be so if the ideas and will are there to realise the potential for revived use. A more sensitive understanding of qualitative, stable environments as perceived by the users is what is required, coupled with the conservation of all types of resources, people and places. Perhaps more experiment should be undertaken to test ideas for alternative uses since our predictive techniques are so bad.

The image and the reality of what is and what might be must be matched. Although some controls and centralisation are inevitable, without the energy of the communities affected the virtual obsolescence of whole city units is unavoidable. As with narrowly adapted buildings, if a city does not diversify into several possible future roles and respond flexibly to those that succeed, then it too will go the way of 'Dodo-like' buildings and organisations. Rehabilitation must be seen to occur so that perceptions of decay and obsolescence can be changed for those inside and outside the system being improved.

Almost total flexibility can be achieved but at the cost of virtually all resources, a sort of 'super nova' before the ashes of failure. What we need is resource husbandry. The mass of the building/activity system must be reduced. Inflow of new energy should be of the kind that is capable of re-interpretation and re-use: in short, reclaimable and not adding to the mass of the system in the long term.

The size scale at which such an approach is relevant will run from the design of furniture to the planning strategy for open space in the city. Many older buildings have 'energy' due to the value placed on their symbolic and cultural value. Often they have considerable potential in their capacity to be easily moulded. The capacity for change in a modern building probably lies in the neutral qualities of similar spaces and minimum structure, whereas an old building is endowed with 'soft' structure that can be easily carved, and a variety of spaces that could suit a large proportion of most activities. These qualities in old buildings occurred quite by chance as a legacy of past levels of construction and environmental technology. However, the realisation of their potential does call for more careful 'design' of activity systems to fit such structures, avoiding the assumption that neutral spaces are the only answer.

We require stable environments, that is, with a steady state illusion of comfortable change. We need continuity with time past and a sense of direction for the future. Utilising the buildings and the activities that we have goes a long way to meet these needs, but is not enough. Rehabilitation also implies, in a general sense, continuity into a viable future which involves an infusion of new structures and activities to provide the future's past.

A simple model of the change process has been described; it tries to incorporate the dynamics of the environment into a useful design analogue. It is in need of calibration, though in its existing form it is a useful design aid by virtue of the questions it raises and the interdependencies it begins to explain. For example, a small withdrawal of energy for a massive building in the last stages of decay will commit it to demolition very quickly; the same amount of energy added to the same building will make very little difference. The 'pull' towards entropy, that is, obsolescence, increases exponentially during the life of a building if the investment in maintenance is constantly below that required to offset this pull.

The drain of energy from a rehabilitated building in an area of blight and decay will be at a higher rate than the same building in a prosperous area, because the 'value' energy given to a building will be depressed. The implication of this is that rehabilitation must take place over a significant area sufficient to affect a lasting change in the perceived value of an area.

Finally, the investment or design strategies should be broadly based in activity design as well as fabric design. The balance between the amount of unusable mass in the building/activity system, and the energy it needs to support its desired change rate is crucial. Ideally any new investment, while it is likely to be kept low, is better utilised if the energy that is contained in the mass can be easily converted.

The fabric of old buildings today has, in some large measure, this potential energy that can be released. It is suspected that the minimum investment strategy currently practised will produce old buildings of the future that will not be endowed with this important potential.

References

1. Alexander, C. 'Thick Wall Pattern', *Architectural Design,* **38,** pp.324–326, (July 1968)
2. Aylward, G. M., Lapthorne, K. 'Designing for Stability in Designing for Change', Working Paper 3, *Technical Research Division, Department of Architecture, University of Cambridge,* (June 1974)
3. Bachelard, G. *The Poetics of Space,* Orion Press, New York (1964)
4. Becker, H. S. 'Personal Change in Adult Life', in *The Planning of Change,* (Edited by W. G. Bennis, K. D. Benne and R. Chin), Holt, Rinehart and Winston, London (1971)
5. Canter, D. 'Need for a Theory of Function in Architecture', *Architects' Journal,* **151,** No. 5, pp.299–302, (4th Feb. 1970)
6. Cowan, P. 'Depreciation, Obsolescence and Ageing', *Architects' Journal,* **141,** No. 24, pp.1395–1401, (16th June 1965)
7. Habraken, N. J. *Supports: An Alternative to Mass Housing,* Architectural Press, London (1972)
8. Le Gros Clark, W. E. and Medawar, P. D. (Editors), *Essays on Growth and Form Presented to D'Arcy Wentworth Thompson,* Oxford University Press, Oxford (1945)
9. Lowry, I. S. 'Filtering and Housing Standards', *Land Economics,* pp.362–370, (Nov. 1960)
10. Lynch, K. 'Environmental Ability', *Journal of the American Institute of Planners,* **24,** No. 2, pp.16–24, (Feb. 1958)
11. Lynch, K. *What Time is This Place?,* MIT Press, Cambridge, Mass. (1972)
12. Rapoport, A. and Kantor, R. E. 'Complexity and Ambiguity in Environmental Design', *Journal of the American Institute of Planners,* **33,** No. 4, pp.210–220, (July 1967)
13. Rodgers, E. M. and Shoemaker, F. F. *Communication of Innovations,* Collier-Macmillan, London (1971)
14. Weeks, J. 'Multi-Strategy Buildings', *Architectural Design,* **39,** pp. 536–540, (Oct. 1969)
15. Weeks, J. 'Hospitals', *Architectural Design,* **43,** No. 7, pp.436–463, (July 1973)

A Time-Space Odyssey

Analyses and appraisal techniques for design-in-use

Thomas W. Maver

This chapter is based in the premise that there is no inherent difference between the methodologies relevant to the design of new buildings and to the re-design, conversion, or 'design-in-use' of existing buildings. Indeed, the point will be made that the explicit methodology of design decision making should be available throughout the life span of the building for use by the building owner or user, or his architectural advisor.

Development of appropriate techniques for design and 'design-in-use' is in its infancy and no claim is made for the degree to which this chapter presents a unifying view of design method, let alone a unifying view of the contribution to this book as a whole. It does however touch on some case study material which exemplifies the use of the methodology in practice and it anticipates a future in which design-in-use methodology will shape our existing building stock.

Characteristics of architectural design

Three characteristics, taken together, uniquely distinguish architectural design from other fields of design endeavour. They are, firstly, the magnitude of the 'solution space' (e.g. there are some 700 000 000 ways of arranging 12 spatial units within a 3 × 2 × 2 unit envelope), (*Figure 2.1*), secondly, the multi-variate nature of the design objective (e.g. the need to satisfy structural, servicing, functional, aesthetic and other

performance requirements), (*Figure 2.2*), and, thirdly, the temporal variation in objectives over the lifetime of the building (e.g. the sixty-year building life compared with the design life of other artefacts which can range from Concorde to the toothbrush), (*Figure 2.3*).

A reluctance, or the inability, to face the problems arising from these characteristics has led, respectively, to the following practices:

1. a retreat into stylism (the magnitude of the solution space being thus reduced to a sub-set representing the arbitrary but currently accepted concensus among the self-appointed cognoscenti);

2. a strict hierarchial ordering of design decisions (in which 'form' is crystallised prior to, and independent of, structure which in turn is crystallised prior to, and independent of, service distribution, etc.);

3. a perverse commitment to a single concrete 'statement' in terms of built form (resulting in buildings in which the mismatch between need and provision starts the day after the building is opened and increases daily thereafter).

The concept of temporal variation in the functional requirements of buildings — the key issue of this book — has been

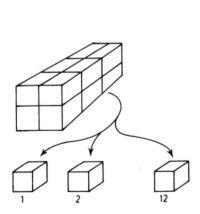

Figure 2.1 Magnitude of the solution space

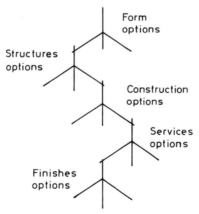

Figure 2.2 Multi-variate nature of the design objective

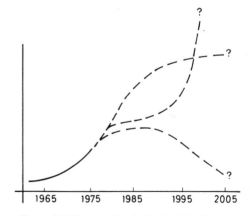

Figure 2.3 Temporal variation in objectives

enjoying unprecedented currency in recent years: no self-respecting architect would discuss modern design rationale without mention of 'flexibility', obsolescence', 'improvisation', 'indeterminancy' or one of the other current neologisms to describe his understanding of the concept or the account he takes of it.

These understandings, however, seem to be individualistic rather than mutual and the account taken of them attitudinal rather than rational. This chapter proposes neither a philosophical overview of the concept nor a catalogue of predetermined solutions; what it does attempt is a modest account of the relevance of explicit analytical and appraisal models to the problems posed by architecture's three distinguishing characteristics, with special attention to the problem of temporal variation in use of educational buildings.

In educational buildings the temporal variation in spatial requirements is significant at three levels:

1. within a single cycle of the educational time-table (which normally has a duration of one week but may be longer) a large number of disparate behavioural settings have to be accommodated; in a comprehensive school, for instance, every period of forty minutes represents a unique configuration of spatial use;

2. as teaching methods, curricula and technology improve, the nature of the periodic activities which make up the educational time-table change; this change is not cyclic but progressive and has to be satisfied spatially;

3. occasionally the case arises for more fundamental change: the conversion of another building type into an educational building or the conversion of an educational building into another building type.

The activity/space/time interface problem in educational establishments is, therefore, one of designing a building (or redesigning an existing building) within which a large variety of disparate activities take place cyclically, the composition of the cycle itself changing progressively over the life-time of the building or at least until it ceases to function as an educational building.

Techniques of analysis

Analysis, in the context given here, is defined as the collection, collation and correlation of the information relevant to the design/redesign activity. The analytical techniques described deal, in turn, with the generation of an initial schedule of accommodation, the transformation of one schedule into another, the specification of the physical attributes of accommodation schedules, and the use of some of these techniques in practice.

The schedule of accommodation

A 'snapshot' of an education establishment at any instant in time would reveal a specific set of behavioural settings: in a secondary school for instance, the 'snapshot' could reveal 90 pupils engaged in the study of English (say in three groups of 40, 30 and 20), 72 pupils engaged in the study of Mathematics (say in four groups of 20, 20, 18 and 14), 53 pupils engaged in Gymnastics, etc. A snapshot taken forty minutes later would reveal the same broad categories of activity – English, Maths, PE, etc., but each involving perhaps a different number of pupils, differently subdivided, from the previous snapshot.

By collating these snapshots it is possible to produce a histogram of the spatial requirements over any period, for any group of pupils and for any subject or group of subjects. *Figure 2.4* shows such a collation for an existing school with class size recorded on the horizontal axis and frequency of occurrence, i.e. number of periods in the cycle (in this case a week), recorded on the vertical axis; in this example a summation

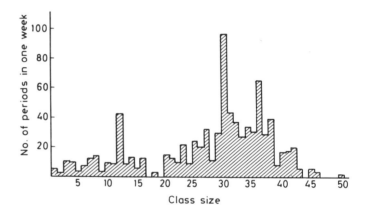

Figure 2.4 Histogram of class size

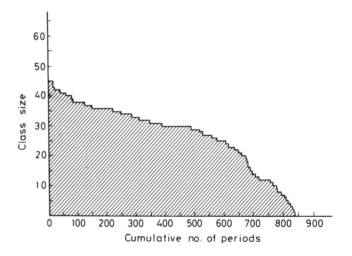

Figure 2.5 Histogram translated into Activity Pattern

has taken place over all years in the school and over all 'non-specialist' subjects. Immediately apparent from this is the variability in class size — from one pupil to fifty pupils — which is typical of secondary schools of comprehensive intake and structure. Somehow or other the spatial configuration in the school must reflect this variety in group configuration.

The matching of spatial provision to spatial need is promoted if both need and provision can be expressed in the same format. One way of achieving format compatibility (University of Bochum, 1968)[10] is to reconstruct the data in *Figure 2.4* in the manner shown by the shaded area of *Figure 2.5*, i.e. class size plotted vertically, number of periods plotted accumulatively on the horizontal axis, with the columns of data arranged in order of decreasing height. This profile, labelled 'activity pattern', envelopes an area proportional to 'pupil-periods' and thus represents the number of pupil-places required. It is not surprising, therefore, that, by the simple device of dividing the horizontal axis by the number of periods in a timetable cycle

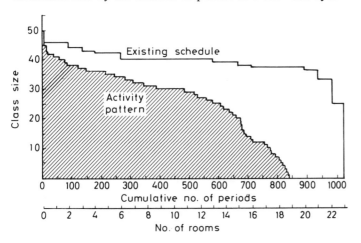

Figure 2.6 Activity pattern compared with existing schedule of accommodation

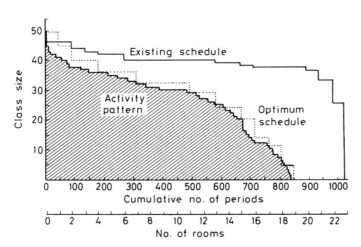

2.7 Production of 'optimum' schedule of accommodation

(in this case 45), the existing schedule can be represented in the same format as shown in *Figure 2.6*.

The plotting of the activity pattern and the actual schedule of accommodation in the school on the same graph, as shown in *Figure 2.6*, affords the opportunity of determining the spatial overprovision or mis-match, as represented by the difference in area between the two profiles. The overprovision in this case (approaching 100%) is by no means atypical of the current generation of modern school buildings.

Commonly, when such a gross overprovision is identified, an attempt is made to justify it on the grounds of 'flexibility', or provision for 'growth or change'; more likely it is a measure of the inadequacy of the analytical techniques used at the design stage. Quite clearly in this case, and in the case of some forty or so comprehensive schools studied by the Building Performance Research Unit at the University of Strathclyde (Building Performance Research Unit, 1972)[3], there are too many rooms and most of the rooms are of the wrong size; the nature of the overprovision is not appropriate to an increased need of the existing kind, let alone a future need (increased or decreased) of another kind. There seems little hope of catering for future need if existing need is so ineptly provisioned.

With the activity pattern displayed as in *Figure 2.5*, it is a relatively simple matter to generate on the diagram an 'optimal schedule' (*Figure 2.7*), i.e. one in which the schedule profile matches the activity pattern profile as closely as is feasible, given the constraints of modular decrements in class size.

The matching of need and provision (i.e. of activity pattern and schedule) can be made even closer by arranging for some rooms to be sub-divisible. *Figure 2.8* shows the principle of

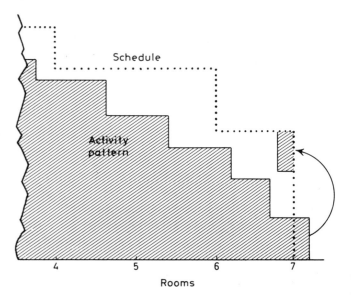

Figure 2.8 Economy of schedule resulting from sub-divisions

dividing the smallest room to accommodate an activity which would otherwise have required an additional room.

The graphical approach outlined in *Figures 2.4 to 2.8* is in itself helpful in producing an initial schedule of accommodation for a homogeneous sub-group of activities within an educational establishment. To consider aggregates of student groups and of subjects (with differing per-student space standards) and to consider alternative operating policies (i.e. 'straight-through' comprehensive as compared with an upper/lower school split), a more manageable procedure is required.

A computer program ECOLE 1 (Davies and Th'ng, 1975)[9] — and its predecessors SPACES 1 (Davies and Th'ng, 1972)[7] and SECS A (Maver, 1972)[19] — has been developed to allow architects and educationalists to co-operate in exploring the spatial implications of varying curricula, student rolls, teaching methods and operating policies.

Data files for ECOLE 1 are prepared by having educationalists complete the pro-formas shown in *Figure 2.9*. Table (a) lists subjects and Table (b) lists spaces (class room, lecture theatre, seminar rooms, individual study carrels, laboratories, project areas, etc.). Table (c) is the main curriculum statement, specifying the number of periods for which each group of students, within each year, studies each subject. Unit teaching space allocations and the desired maximum utilisations are set down in Table (d) and the unit ancillary space allocation in Table (e).

For any desired configuration of year groupings, subject groupings and space type groupings, the program outputs a schedule of unshared accommodation (*Figure 2.10*) and shared accommodation (*Figure 2.11*). The indices of seat and space utilisation and of unit cost (a comparative figure only) guide the program users in the search for an appropriate and economical schedule of accommodation.

Additional output provides information on the summary schedule (*Figure 2.12*), staffing requirements (*Figure 2.13*) and ancillary accommodation (*Figure 2.14*).

Schedule transformations

The program ECOLE 1 deals effectively with the accommodational implications of a single cycle of the educational timetable at one point in time. Provided educationalists are prepared to hypothesise possible future educational scenarios, the data files of ECOLE 1 can be modified accordingly and the corresponding future accommodational needs identified. The key design problem, however, is to decide on the most parsimonious investment in physical flexibility which will ensure the robustness of the schedule in terms of current and future needs.

Assume that an optimum schedule has been generated, as already described, for a comprehensive school due to open in 1971, and that an optimum schedule, based on a hypothesised activity pattern pertaining to the year 1991, has been generated in a similar fashion. *Figure 2.15* represents two such schedules.

Three design strategies are then possible:

1. demolish (or substantially remodel) the school designed to the 1971 requirements in the year 1991;

2. initially provide redundant space, equal to the envelope of the two schedules; or

3. inbuild, to the 1971 schedule, sufficient physical flexibility to allow it to transform into the 1991 schedule when required.

Physical solutions to the first two strategies are obvious; the determination of the optimum physical solution to the third strategy is of extreme complexity. Since comparison of the efficacy of the strategies depends on a solution to the third an analytical method has been devised to deal with this.

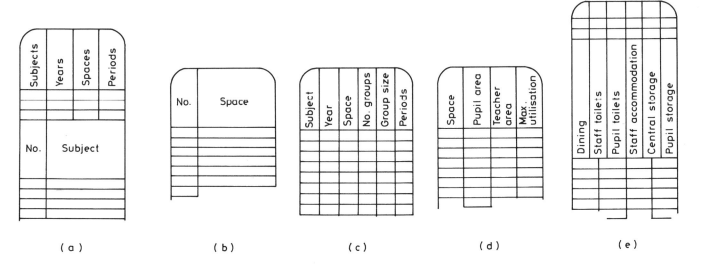

Figure 2.9 Pro-forma for input to ECOLE 1

TEST COMPREHENSIVE SCHOOL

REMAINING SPACES

SUBJECT	SPACE TYPE	NR	SEATS	AREA	UNIT COST	SEAT UTIL %	SPACE UTIL %	TOTAL SEATS	TOTAL AREA	TOTAL COST	COST/ PLACE
FRENCH	PRAC.				145.						
		1	30	63		45	25	30	63	9135.	304.
GERMAN	PRAC.				145.						
		1	12	27		92	10	12	27	3915.	326.
MUSIC	TEACH.				110.						
		1	33	53		69	95	33	53	5830.	177.
		1	10	18		100	20	10	18	1980.	198.
		2	21	35	110.	71	57	43	71	7810.	182.
M. INST	PRAC.				145.						
		1	14	37		89	10	14	37	5365.	383.
GEN. SC	PROJ.				125.						
		1	14	34		100	3	14	34	4250.	304.
GEN. SC	PRAC.				145.						
		1	30	80		60	88	30	80	11600.	387.
PHYS.	PROJ.				125.						
		1	22	51		100	3	22	51	6375.	290.
PHYS.	LECT.				160.						
		1	18	34		68	10	18	34	5440.	302.
PHYS.	PRAC.				145.						
		1	30	80		97	95	30	80	11600.	387.
		1	22	59		68	78	22	59	8555.	389.
		2	26	69	145.	86	86	52	139	20155.	388.
CHEM.	LECT.				160.						
		1	14	32		82	5	14	32	5120.	366.
CHEM.	PRAC.				145.						
		1	30	80		74	68	30	80	11600.	387.
BIOL & H	PRAC.				145.						
		1	30	80		91	95	30	80	11600.	387.
		1	22	59		85	8	22	59	8555.	389.
		2	26	69	145.	91	51	52	139	20155.	388.
BIOL.	PROJ.				125.						
		1	8	21		81	5	8	21	2625.	328.
BIOL.	LECT.				160.						
		1	5	27		100	3	5	27	4320.	864.
BIOL.	PRAC.				145.						
		1	8	22		81	25	8	22	3190.	399.
RURAL.	TEACH.				110.						
		1	19	32		100	5	19	32	3520.	185.

Figure 2.10 Output from ECOLE 1; unshared accommodation

TEST COMPREHENSIVE SCHOOL

GROUP 1

SUBJECT	SPACE TYPE	NR	SEATS	AREA	UNIT COST	SEAT UTIL %	SPACE UTIL %	TOTAL SEATS	TOTAL AREA	TOTAL COST	COST/ PLACE
SHARED	TEACH.				110.						
		1	32	51		95	95	32	51	5610.	175.
		6	30	48		100	95	180	288	31680.	176.
		1	29	47		96	95	29	47	5170.	178.
		1	27	44		98	95	27	44	4840.	179.
		2	26	42		98	95	52	84	9240.	178.
		1	24	39		97	95	24	39	4290.	179.
		2	22	36		94	95	44	72	7920.	180.
		1	18	30		90	95	18	30	3300.	183.
		1	16	27		88	95	16	27	2970.	186.
		1	12	21		98	95	12	21	2310.	192.
		1	10	18		89	95	10	18	1980.	198.
		1	7	14		67	95	7	14	1540.	220.
			23	38	110.	97	95				179.
		19						451	735	80850.	
SHARED	DISC.				115.						
		1	30	35		97	95	30	35	4025.	134.
		1	25	30		76	95	25	30	3450.	138.
		1	12	16		86	95	12	16	1840.	153.
		1	8	11		92	95	8	11	1265.	158.
		1	6	9		83	18	6	9	1035.	172.
			16	20	115.	87	79				143.
		5						81	101	11615.	
SHARED	PROJ.				125.						
		2	30	68		99	95	60	136	17000.	283.
		1	27	62		95	95	27	62	7750.	287.
		1	24	55		94	95	24	55	6875.	286.
		1	22	51		100	95	22	51	6375.	290.
		1	20	46		88	95	20	46	5750.	287.
		1	16	38		94	95	16	38	4750.	297.
		1	14	34		82	95	14	34	4250.	304.
		1	7	19		80	25	7	19	2375.	339.
			21	49	125.	95	87				290.
		9						190	441	55125.	
SHARED	LECT.				160.						
		1	30	41		41	73	30	41	6560.	219.
GROUP AVERAGE			22	38	117.	94	89				205.
GROUP TOTAL		34						752	1318	154150.	

Figure 2.11 Output from ECOLE 1; shared accommodation

TEST COMPREHENSIVE SCHOOL

SUBJECT	NUMBER	%	AREA	%	COST	%
FRENCH	1	1.4	63	1.9	9135.	2.1
GERMAN	1	1.4	27	.8	3915.	.9
MUSIC	2	2.8	71	2.2	7810.	1.8
M.INST	1	1.4	37	1.1	5365.	1.3
GEN. SC	2	2.8	114	3.5	15850.	3.7
PHYS.	4	5.6	224	6.9	31970.	7.5
CHEM.	2	2.8	112	3.4	16720.	3.9
BIOL & H	2	2.8	139	4.3	20155.	4.7
BIOL.	3	4.2	70	2.1	10135.	2.4
RURAL.	2	2.8	96	2.9	12800.	3.0
NEEDLE	2	2.8	86	2.6	12470.	2.9
HOUSE.	2	2.8	125	3.8	18125.	4.2
ART & D.	3	4.2	171	5.2	24795.	5.8
WOOD.	3	4.2	174	5.3	25230.	5.9
METAL.	3	4.2	191	5.9	27695.	6.5
G. E. D.	2	2.8	134	4.1	16080.	3.8
TYPE.	1	1.4	67	2.1	9715.	2.3
AWARD	1	1.4	44	1.3	5500.	1.3
SHARED	34	47.9	1318	40.4	154150.	36.0
TOTAL	71	100.0	3263	100.0	427615.	100.0

Figure 2.12 Output from ECOLE 1; summary schedule of accommodation

TEST COMPREHENSIVE SCHOOL

STAFFING REQUIREMENTS

SUBJECT	PERIODS	TEACHERS	UTIL %
ENG.	270	8	85
GEN. ST	32	1	80
HIST.	137	4	86
ECON.	16	1	40
LAW	6	1	15
SOC. EC	6	1	15
R. E.	128	4	80
GEOG.	152	5	76
MATH & C	200	6	84
F. MATH	14	1	35
FRENCH	113	4	71
GERMAN	54	2	68
LATIN	12	1	30
MUSIC	46	2	58
M. INST	4	1	10
GEN. SC	46	2	58
PHYS.	92	3	77
CHEM.	36	1	90
BIOL & H	54	2	68
BIOL.	15	1	38
RURAL.	14	1	35
NEEDLE	58	2	73
HOUSE.	62	2	78
ART & D.	100	3	84
WOOD.	64	2	80
METAL.	60	2	75
G. E. D.	54	2	68
COMM.	2	1	55
TYPE.	32	1	80
SHORT.	20	1	50
AWARD	16	1	40
CAREER	6	1	15
TOTAL	1941	70	70

Figure 2.13 Output from ECOLE 1; check on teacher utilization

TEST COMPREHENSIVE SCHOOL

NON-TEACHING SPACE	AREA	COST
CIRCULATION	392	39200.
PUPIL STORAGE	428	68480.
CENTRAL STORAGE	143	25740.
STAFF ACCOMM.	147	24990.
ADMINISTRATION	147	24990.
PUPIL TOILETS	238	47600.
STAFF TOILETS	53	10600.
DINING AREA	380	43700.
TOTAL	1928	285300.

(NO. OF TEACHERS: 70)
(NO. OF PUPILS : 950)

Figure 2.14 Output from ECOLE 1; schedule of non-teaching accommodation

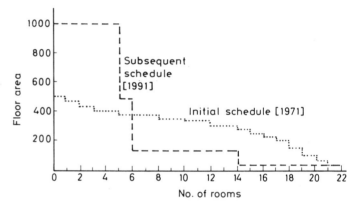

Figure 2.15 2 optimum schedules; one relevant to 1971, one relevant to 1991

In simple terms it is necessary to chop up the 1971 schedule into columns and to snip and glue these columns until the pieces can be combined to give the 1991 schedule. To do this most efficiently a method is required to determine the fewest number of 'snips' and 'glues' to achieve the reformation. Even a small problem tackled this way will drive the victim to sniffing the glue and stabbing the wife with the scissors.

Fortunately, an analytical program is available to cope with this, namely SECS C (Maver, 1972)[18].

The input to SECS C is simply a list of each area in the initial (1971) schedule, followed by a list of each area in the subsequent (1991) schedule, as obtained from the output of SECS A (or SPACES 1 or ECOLE 1). The operation of the program is best explained by reference to the output, of which an annotated version is given in *Figure 2.16*.

The areas in the initial (existing) schedule are recorded in decreasing order of magnitude down the left side of the matrix and the areas of the subsequent (required) schedule are recorded along the top of the matrix, also in decreasing order.

The first search the computer makes is for required areas which are identical to existing areas; if any exist, the computer

Existing areas of initial schedule	Required areas of subsequent schedule																				
	1000	1000	1000	1000	1000	470	120	120	120	120	120	120	120	120	30	30	30	30	30	30	30
500	500	0	0	0	0	0	0	0	0	0	0	0	0	0	0	0	0	0	0	0	0
470	0	0	0	0	0	470	0	0	0	0	0	0	0	0	0	0	0	0	0	0	0
430	430	0	0	0	0	0	0	0	0	0	0	0	0	0	0	0	0	0	0	0	0
400	0	400	0	0	0	0	0	0	0	0	0	0	0	0	0	0	0	0	0	0	0
400	0	400	0	0	0	0	0	0	0	0	0	0	0	0	0	0	0	0	0	0	0
380	0	0	380	0	0	0	0	0	0	0	0	0	0	0	0	0	0	0	0	0	0
380	0	0	380	0	0	0	0	0	0	0	0	0	0	0	0	0	0	0	0	0	0
380	0	0	240	140	0	0	0	0	0	0	0	0	0	0	0	0	0	0	0	0	0
350	0	0	0	350	0	0	0	0	0	0	0	0	0	0	0	0	0	0	0	0	0
350	0	0	0	350	0	0	0	0	0	0	0	0	0	0	0	0	0	0	0	0	0
340	0	0	0	160	180	0	0	0	0	0	0	0	0	0	0	0	0	0	0	0	0
340	0	0	0	0	340	0	0	0	0	0	0	0	0	0	0	0	0	0	0	0	0
300	0	0	0	0	300	0	0	0	0	0	0	0	0	0	0	0	0	0	0	0	0
300	0	0	0	0	180	0	0	0	0	120	0	0	0	0	0	0	0	0	0	0	0
290	0	0	0	0	0	0	0	0	0	0	120	120	50	0	0	0	0	0	0	0	0
250	0	0	0	0	0	0	0	0	0	0	0	0	0	120	0	0	30	30	30	30	10
240	0	0	0	0	0	0	120	120	0	0	0	0	0	0	0	0	0	0	0	0	0
200	0	200	0	0	0	0	0	0	0	0	0	0	0	0	0	0	0	0	0	0	0
150	0	0	0	0	0	0	0	0	120	0	0	0	0	0	0	30	0	0	0	0	0
100	0	0	0	0	0	0	0	0	0	0	0	0	70	0	0	30	0	0	0	0	0
70	70	0	0	0	0	0	0	0	0	0	0	0	0	0	0	0	0	0	0	0	0

Partitions to be added = 13;   partitions to be removed = 13.
Remainder of existing areas = 0;   remainder of required areas = 20.

Figure 2.16 Output from SECS C; transformation of existing to required schedule of accommodation

allocates the existing area to the required area and shows this by printing the value in the appropriate location in the matrix (i.e. column 6, row 2). The next step is to identify the largest value in the list of existing and required areas; in this case it is the value 1000. The search then proceeds for two existing areas which together will exactly make up 1000; in this case there are none so the computer identifies the next largest value in the list of existing and required areas and tries again. Following this pattern, it deals with columns 1 to 4 without success, then tries row 1, without success, row 3 to 16, without success and then, at row 17, manages to find a pair of required areas which together match the existing area of 240. The allocation is made (columns 7 and 8, row 17) and the search continued. The only other similar match occurs in row 19.

The next phase of the operation, in which the previously allocated areas play no part, now commences. The program identifies the largest unallocated value in the list of existing and required areas, which in this case is still the required area (value 1000) of column 1. To this is allocated the largest existing area (500). In effect this leaves a 'remainder' of 500 in column 1 still to be allocated. The program now reverts to the routine described in the previous paragraph, i.e. seeking, for any single value of existing or required area, a pair of required or existing areas, respectively, to provide an exact match. The only difference at this point in time is that the value 1000 at the top of column 1 has been replaced by the remainder value, 500. It is this remainder value 500, which is now allocated to rows 3 and 21. If no exact matching has been possible, the 430 of row 3 would have been allocated

to the remainder 500, changing the remainder in column 1 to 70. If this led to no matching, remainder 70 in column 1 would have been allocated to the 400 in row 4, leaving a 'row remainder' of 330, and so on.

The procedure is an heuristic one – i.e. one of limited search – and does not guarantee an optimum solution; controlled trials, however, have shown that the output is as close to an optimum as to make no practical difference.

The implications for design are fairly obvious. In any row, an entry is equivalent to an area of magnitude equal to the numerical value of the entry; thus two entries in a row mean that an existing area has been divided into two; three entries mean that an existing area has been divided into three. Thus, the number of partitions which must be added to any existing area is the number of entries in the relevant row minus one; the number of partitions which must be added overall is the sum, over all the rows, of the number of entries in each row minus one (in this case 13, as printed out by the computer immediately below the matrix). Similarly, the number of partitions to be removed is given by the sum, over all the columns, of the number of entries in each column minus one.

In this case the minimum number of partitions required is 13; if the column and row values had been different from each other, the minimum number of partitions required would have been equivalent to whichever was the larger of the two.

The final items of output are the remaining spaces left unallocated; in the example given, an additional 20 units will have to be provided, in addition to the 13 partitions, to fully satisfy the subsequent schedule. It will be clear from this part of the output that the program is capable of dealing with initial and subsequent schedules which are different in total area.

If, as opposed to two, say five different schedules have to be provided over the life of the school, the program can be used four times, dealing in turn with schedules 1 and 2, schedules 2 and 3, schedules 3 and 4 and schedules 4 and 5; the requirement for demountable partitions is given by the maximum value over the four runs. Clearly then progressive change can be investigated by making the time intervals relatively small.

A comparison of the economies of the three basic design strategies already mentioned i.e. the 'demolish' strategy, the 'redundant space' strategy and the 'physical flexibility' strategy, is possible by setting the cost of the overprovision of space in the redundant strategy against the extra cost of the demountable partitions over conventional partitions. In all the specific cases explored there is a significant advantage in adopting the 'physical flexibility' strategy of design. It should be said, however, that the minimum number of demountable partitions output by the computer will suffice in practice only if the plan layout arranges those spaces contiguously which are to be divided or amalgamated. It is likely that at plan layout stage an increased number of demountable partitions will be seen to be required but the technique exists for checking if the economic advantage still lies with the 'physical flexibility' strategy.

Of course this 'physical flexibility' strategy can be applied only in buildings when first designed. If the current design problem is the conversion of an existing building with no physical flexibility then remodelling is required. Readers will be interested in the remodelling strategies investigated in Chapter 3 by Frey and the comparison of these strategies to the analytical techniques just discussed.

Spatial and functional specifications

Thus far, the analytical techniques, while matching areal attributes, have taken no account of the other, multi-variate attributes of architectural space. Analytical techniques relevant to this aspect of space planning are underdeveloped, but the portents are good.

Consider the catalogue of attributes — spatial, environmental, etc — presented in *Figure 2.17a* for each element of accommodation in a building. While element *n* may be similar to element *m* in one respect, it may be dissimilar in other respects. It may be useful to attempt 'across-the-board' measures of similarity and it is indeed possible to generate, using appropriate analytical techniques (Bridges, 1977)[2] two symmetrical matrices as shown in *Figure 2.17b*; one matrix incorporates single measures of similarity between elements of accommodation, the other presents measures of similarity between pairs of attributes. Symmetrical matrices can, by multi-dimensional scaling techniques (Kernohan *et al*, 1973)[14] give rise to point plots in 2-, 3-, or *n*- dimensional space (*Figure 2.18*).

The techniques involved are sophisticated and powerful, no doubt, but their relevance, particularly to conversion is, as yet, somewhat tenuous. A major difficulty, obviously, is the basis on which the multi-attribute profiles of any pair of spatial elements are collapsed into a single measure of similarity; the process depends on relative weightings of importance among the attributes — expressed explicitly, or implicitly embodied in the scale of measures adopted.

In Chapter 3 the problem of matching the specification of spatial pairs is thoroughly discussed and reference made to the computer program BAM P-11 which addresses this problem. In any multi-variate design problem, however, optimisation by analysis is possible only by a degree of problem simplification which could result in an outcome which, in terms of the real world is pessimum rather than optimum. In the case of the program P-11, the allocation of functions to spaces takes account of both the physical match between functions and available spaces and the desired spatial relationships between the functions to be located. Both aspects of this allocation procedure are multi-variate in character and cannot be solved optimally in isolation, let alone together, without an exhaustive search of a magnitude which is beyond available computer power (see the first 'characteristic' of architectural design identified at the beginning of the chapter). These reservations apply, of course, to any manual approach to the problem and there is convincing evidence that the computer technique will consistently do better than a more ad-hoc approach. The worry is that, in neither case is it obvious how close the final solution is to an optimum.

Techniques of appraisal

The greatest advances in explicit and rational design methodology have been related to the process of appraisal (Maver, 1971)[17]. Appraisal is defined as the testing of formal hypotheses, i.e. the measurement of the cost/performance attributes of a proposed design solution and the comparison of these measures with agreed criteria. The iterative nature of the appraisal process can be characterised as in *Figure 2.19*.

The designer hypothesises an initial formal solution (following, perhaps, use of appropriate analytical techniques); the hypothesis is subjected to explicit measurement of as many cost/performance attributes as are considered relevant and the cost/performance profile is compared with pre-agreed criteria. The designer makes a subjective value judgement as to the quality of the hypothesis, decides which aspects of cost/performance ought to be improved and attempts to modify the design hypothesis accordingly.

In essence, the process of appraisal is the opposite of the process of analysis. In analysis the criteria and their relative importance have to be specified *a priori* and an algorithm found to generate a solution satisfying these criteria; in appraisal the designer generates the solution in response to his/her own

PROJECT M 1/SFB 63 HOCHSCHULBAU/STUTTGART: BAUFLÄCHENARTEN (BUILDING TYPES)

Space types on the basis of GKW (basic characteristics) and aggregation of IKW (installation characteristics) of the categories Natural Sciences, Construction Engineering, Electrical Engineering and Mechanical Engineering acc. to Ergebn. Bericht 11/1

(Synthesis by Frey/BPRU Department of Architecture & Building Science/1975)

o categories	o natural sc.	o constr. eng.	o electr. eng.	o mechn. eng.	o 302	o 101 height = 3.0 m	o 102 height = 3.6 m	o 103 height = 4.2 m	o 104 height = 6.0 m	o 105 height = 9.0 m	o 106 height > 9.0 m	o – plain floor	o 110 raising floor	o 112/114 grooves.	o 213 extr. op. floor	o 214 extr. op. ceil.	o 215 extr. op. walls	o – normal grid	o 604 larger grid	o 115 up to 500 kg	o 116 up to 750 kg	o 117 up to 1000 kg	o 118 up to 1500 kg	o 119 over 1500 kg	o N norm. install.	o H high install.	o 601 lorry access	o 123/126 foundation	o – daylight unnec.	o 201 daylight nec.	o 202 sunshine nec.	o 120 extr. point load	o 121 extr. roll. load
1.3	x	x	x	x		•						•						•		•					•				•				
5.1			x			•						•						•			•				•				•				
5.4				x		•						•						•				•			•				•				
5.7			x			•						•						•				•			•				•		•		
6.7	x	x	x	x			•					•						•		•					•		•		•				
6.8	x	x	x	x	•	•						•						•		•					•				•				
6.10	x	x	x	x	•	•						•						•		•					•				•				
6.16	x							•				•						•		•					•				•				
6.1	x						•					•						•		•					•				•			•	
8.3	x	x	x	x		•						•						•		•					•				•				
12.50		x			•			•				•						•		•			•		•				•				
16.10		x			•	•						•						•		•					•				•				
16.50				x	•	•						•			•			•		•					•				•				
18.1		x	x	x	•	•						•						•		•			•		•				•				
18.3	x	x	x	x	•	•						•						•		•			•		•				•				
18.16			x	x		•						•						•		•			•		•				•				
18.50				x		•						•						•		•					•				•			•	
22.11		x				•	•					•						•		•			•		•		•		•				
23.3		x			•	•						•						•		•					•				•				
23.4	x						•					•						•		•					•			•			•		
24.5			x				•					•						•		•					•				•				
27.1	x	x	x	x		•						•						•		•					•				•			•	
28.4	x	x	x	x		•						•						•		•			•		•		•		•			•	
28.5	x	x	x	x	•	•						•						•		•					•				•			•	
28.6	x	x	x	x	•	•						•						•		•					•		•		•			•	
28.7	x						•					•						•		•					•		•		•				
49.9		x				•						•						•		•					•				•	•			
49.50				x	•	•						•			•			•		•					•				•	•		•	
53.20				x			•					•			•			•		•					•				•				
57.1				x	•	•						•			•			•		•					•				•			•	
57.50		x			•	•						•			•			•		•					•				•			•	
59.1		x	x	x		•						•						•		•					•				•			•	
59.2				x		•						•						•		•					•				•				•
59.19				x	•	•						•						•		•					•				•			•	
59.21				x	•	•						•						•		•			•	•	•				•				•
63.3			x	x	•	•						•						•		•					•		•		•			•	
64.50				x	•	•						•						•		•					•				•				
66.4	x								•			•						•	•	•					•				•				
66.5	x								•			•						•	•	•					•				•				
67.5	x							•				•	•	•	•	•		•	•	•					•				•				
77.17		x			•			•				•						•		•			•		•			•		•		•	
77.50				x	•			•				•						•		•			•		•			•		•		•	
77.75				x	•			•				•						•		•			•		•			•		•		•	
87.10		x			•			•				•						•		•			•		•				•		•		
88.10		x			•	•						•			•			•		•			•		•				•		•		
90.02	x							•				•			•		•	•		•					•				•		•		
103.50	x							•				•			•			•		•					•				•		•		
104.5			x		•					•		•						•	•	•			•		•				•		•		•
111.1	x								•			•			•	•	•	•		•					•				•	•			
111.4	x									•		•			•	•	•	•		•					•				•	•			
118.14				x				•				•						•		•			•		•				•		•		•
118.15				x				•				•						•		•			•		•			•	•		•		
118.19		x			•			•				•						•		•			•		•			•	•				
118.50			x	x				•				•						•		•					•				•		•		
119.2	x							•				•			•			•		•			•		•				•				
121.22				x				•				•			•			•		•			•		•				•		•		
121.27		x						•				•			•			•	•	•					•				•	•	•	•	•
121.50	x	x		x	•			•				•	•	•	•			•	•	•					•				•	•	•	•	•
125.50	x				•				•			•			•			•		•					•				•	•		•	•
126.50				x	•				•			•			•			•		•					•				•	•		•	•

| Σ 60 | 24 | 22 | 23 | 30 | | | | | | | | | | | | | | | | | | | | | | | | | | | | | |

Figure 2.17a Catalogue of attributes of elements of accommodation

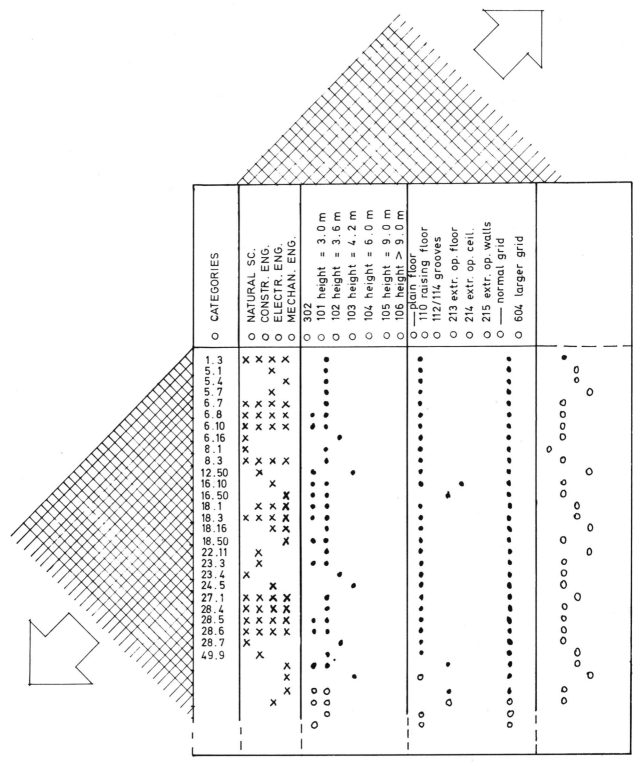

Figure 2.17b Catalogue of attributes converted to association matrices

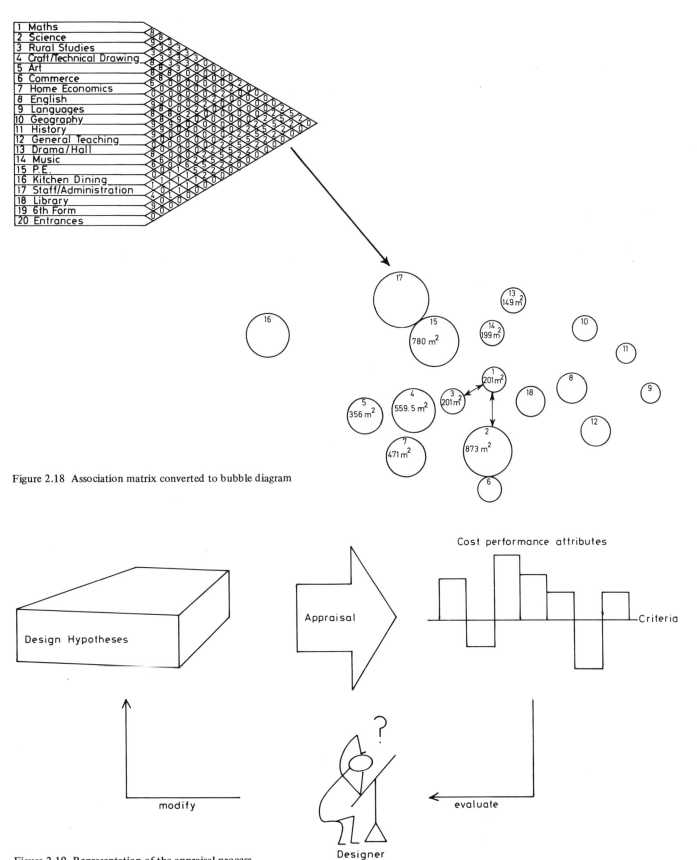

1 Maths																			
2 Science	8	8																	
3 Rural Studies	9	3	3	3															
4 Craft/Technical Drawing	3	3	3	3															
5 Art	8	3	3	3	0														
6 Commerce	8	8	3	3	0	0													
7 Home Economics	6	0	0	0	0	0	2												
8 English	9	8	0	0	0	0	2	2											
9 Languages	8	8	2	0	0	0	0	2	5										
10 Geography	8	8	9	0	0	0	0	2	5	5									
11 History	9	9	9	0	0	0	2	2	5	2	0								
12 General Teaching	9	0	0	0	0	0	2	5	5	2	2	0							
13 Drama/Hall	8	0	0	0	0	2	2	5	5	2	2	0							
14 Music	6	0	0	1	5	5	5	2	2	0									
15 P.E.	0	1	1	1	5	2	2	0											
16 Kitchen Dining	1	0	1	5	2	0	0												
17 Staff/Administration	4	0	1	1	0	0													
18 Library	4	0	0	0															
19 6th Form	9	0	0	0															
20 Entrances	0	0																	

Figure 2.18 Association matrix converted to bubble diagram

Figure 2.19 Representation of the appraisal process

23

views on the relative importance of the criteria. Consequently, the difficulties associated with analysis are obviated in appraisal: multi-attribute situations are quite happily catered for, provided of course the chore of measurement can be coped with. This is as true for redesign as it is for *tabula rasa* design.

Integrated appraisal by computer

A very considerable investment has been made in the development of comprehensive and integrated program packages with which the designer can interface graphically and interactively. The general structure of one such program, ECOLE 3 (Th'ng, 1976)[21] is given in *Figure 2.20*: the site and the design hypothesis — at whatever desired level of detail — are drawn on the screen of the computer terminal; the program outputs economic, spatial, functional and environmental measures. In the absence of mandatory or client-specified criteria, the cost/performance measures can be compared with the mean values collated from the population of previous hypotheses.

The implications for conversion are considerable. Indeed, the redesign potential was realised as a result of the justifiable caution of interested members of the profession who sensibly thought it appropriate to test the software against existing buildings.

Consider an existing building which, after some remodelling, is to be put to new use. The existing site, layout and construction is input as the 'starting hypothesis' and new data files — internal climatic conditions, functional associations, etc — are created for the new situation. Thereafter the designer modifies the existing buildings, using the interactive graphics facilities, by locating activities, moving walls, changing construction, etc as required. Following each step in the redesign activity the program outputs the cost/performance consequences, i.e. the profile of economic, spatial, functional and environmental performance.

Quite clearly such an appraisal process can be applied in the specific case, i.e. a single existing building and a single new use. Equally, however, the process can be used either to test the appropriateness of a single existing building to a variety of new uses, or to test the appropriateness of a variety of existing buildings to a single new use.

Comprehensive and integrated computer packages for design/redesign appraisal do no more, of course, than could be done manually at the drawing-board, given infinite time, patience and money. The facility for rapid, directed and, above all, explicit exploration of many design/redesign alternatives, is, however, of major importance to the designer and client alike.

Use in practice

The use in practice of computerised analytical and appraisal techniques is growing rapidly. No attempt is made here to

document case studies but a broad indication of the extent and efficacy of practical application to the design/redesign activity is given.

Analytical practices

Several local authority architectural departments in the United Kingdom, notably Cheshire County Council and Strathclyde Regional Council, in conjunction with educational advisors, have made extensive use of the programs SPACES 1 and ECOLE 1 to generate robust schedules of accommodation for new schools and re-model accommodation in existing schools.

The summary output from SPACES 1 in a typical application to a new comprehensive school (Th'ng, 1974)[20] is given in *Figure 2.21*. Each column represents a particular operating policy; application of the program SECS C to any selected pair of runs would help identify the minimum possible provision of physical flexibility needed to change from one operating policy to another.

Currently the County Architect's Research and Development Unit in Cheshire County Council is taking stock of the accommodation schedules and their utilisation in ten comprehensive schools by means of ECOLE 1. This stock-taking has been encouraged by the success of a carefully monitored exercise at the existing Frodsham Secondary School (Davies, 1975)[6].

The Frodsham exercise aimed to determine the spatial requirements which would enable the school to operate successfully with an increased roll equivalent to six form-entry, plus 120 sixth form places (in two phases). It involved the creation of a projected curriculum and time-table analysis to meet proposals for the future, a computer aided analysis of accommodation requirements to meet the projected curriculum data, and a comparison of these accommodation requirements with existing buildings and buildings under construction.

The report of the exercise concluded that no extensions were necessary to accept the first phase of the expansion and that the full expansion could be accommodated by undertaking adaptations to existing space together with provision of an additional 656 m². Part of the conclusions, based on the computer output, is given in *Figure 2.22*. The cost savings of adopting the outcome of the computer exercise over the original proposals was certified to be £158 000.

Experience of the application of analytical techniques to more fundamental changes in building use is somewhat difficult to come by. One BArch student (Hogg *et al*, 1977)[12] within the Department of Architecture and Building Science at Strathclyde University does, however, closely simulate a real world application. The proposal to house Liverpool Polytechnic within the Albert Docks has been well publicised and the scheme, with its more subjective aspects of conversion decision making, is described in Chapter 12. The student group, in the course of testing the feasibility of the proposal, carried out a

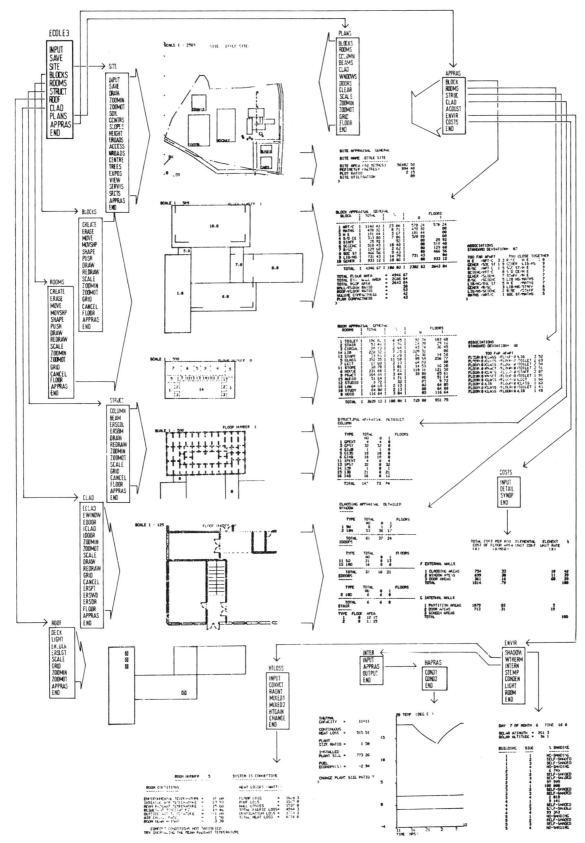

Figure 2.20 Form and structure of the program ECOLE 3

25

SUMMARY OF RUNS

SUBJECT	RUN 1 *Year 1–7* *RU = 85%*	RUN 2 *Year 1–7* *RU = 90%*	RUN 5 *Years 1, 2, 3–7 some shared spcs* *RU = 85%*	RUN 6 *Years 1–2, 3–7 some shared spcs* *RU = 90%*	RUN 11 *Years 1–2, 3–7 some shared spcs* *RU = 85%*	RUN 12 *Years 1–2, 3–7 some shared spcs* *RU = 90%*	RUN 15 *Years 1–2, 3–7 some shared spcs* *RU = 90%*
Maths	474	448	309	309	309	309	309
Science	837	775	837	789	837	789	837
Rur. Sc.	86	86	86	86	86	86	86
Craft/TD	400	400	400	400	100	100	100 } 424
Art	215	215	215	215	91	91	91
Commerce	139	139	139	139	139	139	139
H. Econ.	348	286	448	448	224 + 548	224 + 548	448
English	530	439	937	847	595 } 556	504 } 530	504 } 530
Languages	374	352	400	400	187	187	187
Geography	317	317	295	295	487	487	487
History	317	317	295	295			
R. E.	269	269	269	247			
Drama	249	249	392	392	450	431	249
Music	230	230	278	287			182
P. E.	786	786	786	786	786	786	786
TOTAL	5571	5308	6087	5926	5395	5211	5359

Figure 2.21 Summary of a series of runs of SPACES 1 applied
to a comprehensive school

rigorous analysis of the accommodational requirements of the School of Art and Design and the School of Construction. As a result, their project strategy differed significantly from that of the Polytechnic's architects, who proposed that Art and Design should be located in one of three smaller blocks and that Construction should be located in the other two smaller blocks, a proposal necessitating the addition of a new floor and the conversion of the basement.

The student proposal took advantage of sharing between low utilisation teaching and studio space to the extent that both Schools could be accommodated together, without significant constructional modification, in the single large block of the Dock complex.

Quite clearly, the analytical techniques previously described and exemplified here are appropriate primarily to building types, e.g. educational institutions, in which a formal statement of the space-time requirements is complex, explicit and of major significance. The main areas of application will include a spatial stock-taking of the existing stock of Schools, Polytechnics and Universities and there are indications of a desire by architects and client bodies to undertake such a stock-taking.

In fairness it should be stated clearly that the techniques described are less than wholly appropriate at least to the majority of the case studies presented in this book. It may be argued however that appropriate explicit methodologies could be developed for at least the majority of cases: the principle which requires to be carried over to a repertoire of new techniques is that of mapping need and provision in the same format.

Appraisal practices

The application of computer appraisal packages is even more widespread than the application of computer analysis packages. Notable examples of successful application can be quoted.

Firstly there is the use of the appraisal package PHASE (Package for Hospital Appraisal, Simulation and Evaluation) (Kernohan *et al*, 1973)[13] at the early design stage of District General Hospitals in Scotland and Germany. Currently, the package is being used extensively by the Common Services Agency (Building Division) of the Scottish Home and Health Department, and by a private practice in Edinburgh, in the

Subject	Space Type	Run No	Demand	Space Utilization	Comments
Needlework	Practical	9	1 × 46 1 × 40	95% 535	One 83 cm² space available giving an average 74% space utilization
Housecraft	Practical	9	1 × 70 1 × 55	95% 53%	2 spaces available, each of 88 m² the above proposals for Needlework and Housecraft leave the Homemaking room as excess space based on data supplied (see Conclusions). This provides an opportunity to relate Art to Home Economics by using . . .
Art and Design	Practical	9	1 × 80 1 × 54 1 × 38	95%) 95%) 60%	. . . 1 space 87 m² available 1 space 85 m² available Excess space available in the Homemaking room These proposals would require consideration of the adaptation to a Homemaking area which would release the proposed Art area (Room 16) for other purposes – see conclusions.
Woodwork Metalwork	Practical Practical	9 9	1 × 93 1 × 98	95% 95%	One space 89 m² available One space 102 m² available
Woodwork Metalwork	Practical Practical	9 9	1 × 70 1 × 61	25%) 15%)	One space 107 m² available, joint Woodwork/Metalwork proposed – Low space utilization factor allows removal of part of 95% load from other rooms
Woodwork Metalwork	Practical Practical	9 9	1 × 7 1 × 19	40%) 40%)	6th Form groups – can be catered for in joint space proposed above

Figure 2.22 Typical conclusions based on computer runs, as applicable to Frodsham Secondary School

development of the design of two such hospitals up to development control plan stage.

Secondly there is the use of the appraisal package SPACES 3 (Davies and Th'ng, 1972)[8] at the early design stage of primary and secondary schools in several Local Authorities throughout the U.K. SPACES 3 can be used 'en suite' with SPACES 1, allowing the designer to identify a likely strategy at the analysis stage (SPACES 1) and to test its implications by appraisal (SPACES 3).

An interesting example of the application of computer appraisal in the redesign context is afforded by the exercise carried out jointly by ABACUS (Architecture and Building Aids Computer Unit. Strathclyde) and the British Airports Authority (BAA) at Glasgow's Abbotsinch Airport (Laing and Gentles, 1975)[16]. BAA wished to explore strategies for extending the airport and this necessitated simulation of passenger movement within the existing complex. The program AIR-Q (Laing, 1975)[15] was developed for this purpose. The existing passenger-handling system can be drawn on the computer screen (*Figure 2.23*) and information on throughput, modal split and service amenity input. The program traces the movement of passengers over the period which it is intended to simulate and the designer can obtain output to show, for any selected group of nodes in the system, over any selected time period, the queue history (*Figure 2.24*) and critical journey times. It is a very simple matter to hypothesise future usage conditions (the advent of Jumbo jets, fog, the introduction of passport checks between England and Scotland, etc) and to establish what system changes or system development will be necessary to cope.

The Glasgow Airport example focuses on a particular aspect of building performance – circulation. Increasingly, designers and client bodies are concerned with another aspect of the performance of our existing building stock – energy utilisation. The program ESP (Environmental Systems Performance) (Clarke, 1976)[4], has been developed to provide comprehensive modelling of environmental control in buildings and the resultant energy implications.

As a consequence of regionalisation and of rationalisation of the use of school buildings, Strathclyde Regional Council

27

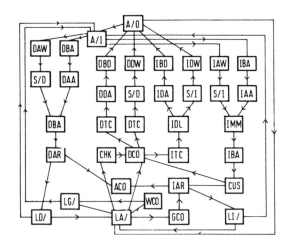

Figure 2.23 Input to AIR-Q; the passenger network is drawn on the computer screen

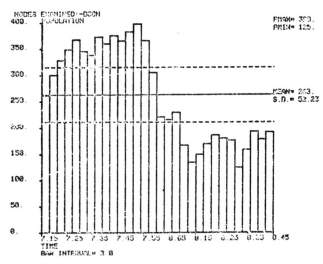

Figure 2.24 Output from AIR-Q; histogram of population changes over time at check-in desk

wished to test the feasibility of using as a New Regional Headquarters, a building recently vacated by the Boys' High School at Glasgow. For each of the five buildings making up the complex, and for which tentative room layout proposals had been made, the Council's engineers used ESP to explore the thermal performance of the building under its new regime and to obtain data on energy consumption, internal temperature, etc for alternative summer and winter plant operating policies. The report (Clarke, 1977)[5] concluded that use of the program allowed a much more rigorous investigation to be undertaken than would have been possible manually, at a fraction of the time normally taken and at roughly half the cost.

The program ESP was also used in the student investigation of the use of the Albert Dock site for Liverpool Polytechnic. The Dock buildings are constructionally massive and devoid of engineering services. Introducing people and lighting gives rise to problems of overheating. Solutions to the overheating problem are constrained by the preservation order applying to the existing buildings. By ingenious use of ESP, the student group was able to carry out a cost-benefit appraisal of alternative glazing policies taking account of usage patterns, plant capital and running costs and, of course, special glazing costs (Hogg, 1977)[11].

As opposed to analytical techniques, those of appraisal are, by and large, generally applicable to each and every building type. Certainly, measures of the physical and economic attributes are generally relevant; current R & D strategies will ensure that integrated appraisal software will include a standard set of physical and economic routines which can be supplemented by routines appropriate to the specific functional attributes of the particular building being designed/redesigned.

It will be clear that the *analytical* logic embodied in the program P11, and already questioned, could be inverted to

28

provide an effective *appraisal*: as the redesigner proposes reallocations of functions to spaces, the appraisal program will measure costs, association etc.

Conclusions and future developments

At the beginning of this chapter three characteristics were identified which, taken together, were claimed to distinguish architectural design from other fields of design endeavour. It is appropriate now to consider to what degree the analytical and appraisal techniques, subsequently exemplified, ameliorate the problems raised by these three characteristics.

1. *The magnitude of the solution space.* Evidence of use of the techniques in practice shows that appropriate analyses may help to put the designer in the right solution zone; they do, at least, as in the case of SECS C, help identify the 'target optimum'. Once in the right solution zone, with a target optimum to use as a criterion, appropriate appraisals rapidly direct the design search.

2. *The multi-variate nature of design objectives.* Analyses are powerful aids in the optimisation of uni-variate problems; as such, and as stated in (1) above, they help identify independent optima on individual cost and performance attributes. Only through appraisal, however, can the best profile of attributes be interactively approached.

3. *The temporal variation in design objectives.* This chapter, has, of course, focused on this problem. Both analytical and appraisal techniques can aid the design, identify the robustness of old buildings for new uses and ensure the robustness of new buildings for future uses.

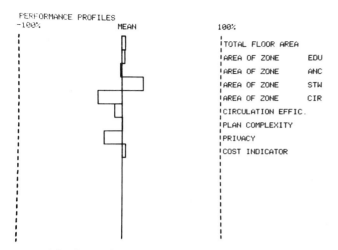

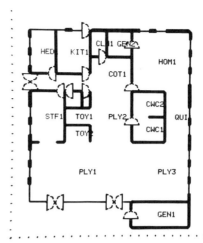

Figure 2.25 Output from the program PARTIAL

Figure 2.27 An 80 place nursery school. Designed by an architect or a nursery school head teacher? (grid interval = 0.9 m)

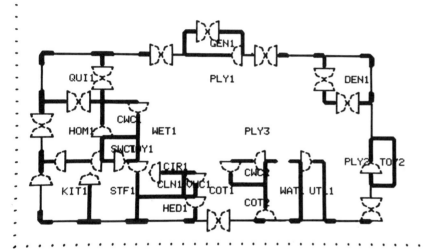

Figure 2.26 An 80 place nursery school. Designed by an architect or a nursery school head teacher? (grid interval = 0.9 m)

This chapter has really been about models; analysis is concerned with modelling logical relationships between elements of the design problem; appraisal is concerned with modelling hypothesised solutions to the design problem. They are complementary, one to the other, and, of course, complementary to the generative skills of the human designer.

As with design skill, the skill necessary in the devising of appropriate models has to be developed. The few examples given are the first tentative attempts within one Research and Development group. It is suggested, however, that the scope for development is effectively unlimited and that, given a modest change in the investment of professional effort from *plan* to *process*, the improvement in the quality of our design product would be phenomenal.

Of paramount importance is the concept of passing on to the client/user organisation not just the design or redesign solution but the analytic/appraisal models which are relevant to the solution, against the day when they will be needed again. Indeed 'redesign' or conversion, while a welcome concept, implies occasional professional intervention whereas the match or mis-match between need and provision changes dynamically. A concept which hopefully will gain increasing currency is that of 'design-in-use' with full participation of the client-user organisation. ABACUS is concerned with the development of computer appraisal programs designed to be operated by building users (Aish, 1977)[1]. Experience with nursery school teachers indicates that, given access to appropriately interfaced software, the teachers, guided by the performance profiles output by the program (*Figure 2.25*), can generate solutions not readily distinguishable from those designed professionally (*Figures 2.26 and 2.27*).

29

References

1. Aish, R., 'Prospects for Design Participation', *Journal of Design Methods and Research,* **11,** 1 (1977)
2. Bridges, A. 'Interim Report of On-going Work on Analytic Techniques', University of Strathclyde, Glasgow (1977)
3. Building Performance Research Unit, *Building Performance,* Applied Science Publishers, London (1972)
4. Clarke, J. 'ESP – Environmental Systems Performance', *ABACUS Occasional Paper No. 48,* University of Strathclyde, Glasgow (1976)
5. Clarke, J. New Regional Headquarters (Strathclyde Regional Council): Application of ESP, *ABACUS Occasional Paper No. R33,* University of Strathclyde, Glasgow (1977)
6. Davies, M. 'Frodsham County Secondary School (Cheshire County Council): Application of SPACES 1', *ABACUS Occasional Paper No. R32,* University of Strathclyde, Glasgow (1975)
7. Davies, M., and Th'ng, R. 'SPACES 1: A Program for Use in Accommodation Scheduling of Schools', *ABACUS Occasional Paper No. 22,* University of Strathclyde, Glasgow (1972)
8. Davies, M., and Th'ng, R. 'SPACES 3: A Program for the Appraisal of School Building Designs', *ABACUS Occasional Paper No. 24,* University of Strathclyde, Glasgow (1972)
9. Davies, M., and Th'ng, R. 'ECOLE 1 – The Basis, Structure and Format of a Computer Program for Accommodation Scheduling in Educational Environments', *ABACUS Occasional Paper No. 40,* University of Strathclyde, Glasgow (1975)
10. Die Universitat Bochum *Gesamtplanung,* published by Der Minister fur Landesplanung, Wohnungstan und Offentliche Arbeiten des Landes Nordrhein/Westfalen, Bonn (1968)
11. Hogg, D. 'Thermal Performance Study', *B. Arch. Thesis: Individual Study,* University of Strathclyde, Glasgow (1977)
12. Hogg, D., McGregor, D. and Maxwell, T. 'Albert Dock Development: Liverpool Polytechnic', B.Arch. Design Thesis, University of Strathclyde, Glasgow (1977)
13. Kernohan, D., Renkin, G., Walters, R. and Wallace, G. 'PHASE: An Interactive Appraisal Package for Whole Hospital Design', *Computer Aided Design,* **5,** No. 2, April (1973)
14. Kernohan, D., Renkin, G., Walters, R. and Wallace, G. 'Relationship Models: Analytical Techniques for Design Problem Solving, *Architectural Design,* 43 (May 1973)
15. Laing, L. 'AIR-Q: A Flexible Computer Simulation Model for Airport Terminal Building Design', *DMG-DRS Journal,* **9,** No. 3 (July–Sept 1975)
16. Laing, L. and Gentles, J. 'AIR-Q Validation Study: Glasgow Airport', *ABACUS Occasional Paper No. R34,* University of Strathclyde, Glasgow (1975)
17. Maver, T. W. 'Computer Aided Design Appraisal', *Architects Journal* (28th July 1971)
18. Maver, T. W. 'The Space-Time Interface', *Architectural Design,* 43, pp.44–46 (January 1972)
19. Maver, T.W. 'Spatial Environment in Comprehensive Schools', *Operational Research Quarterly,* **23,** No. 3 (September 1972)
20. Th'ng, R. 'Witham Rickstones Comprehensive School (Essex County Council): A Schedule of Accommodation – SPACES 1', *ABACUS Occasional Paper No. R5,* University of Strathclyde, Glasgow (1974)
21. Th'ng, R. 'ECOLE 3 – Package for Modelling and Appraisal of Buildings', *ABACUS Occasional Paper No. 63,* University of Strathclyde, Glasgow (1976)

CHAPTER THREE

Building Conversion

A system for the prediction of capital cost

Hildebrand Frey

It is suggested that fewer new buildings will be constructed in the foreseeable future than during the past years of extensive economic activity, the main reason for this being the current limitations on economic growth, combined with a growing appreciation of the quality of historic buildings and, as Farrell points out in Chapter 5, increased knowledge of the economic value of the existing building stock. Unfortunately, statistics do not identify the amount of construction output devoted to conversion work, so it cannot be presented as a percentage of the annual value of construction work carried out.

At the same time, the demand for suitable building space is likely to continue and will, therefore, be increasingly met from the available building stock. Consequently, existing buildings will be required to last longer than envisaged some years ago, necessitating more frequent rebuilding or rehabilitation. However, the decision to convert a building is dependent upon a reasonably accurate cost estimate, which is not possible at present unless based upon a detailed survey and design proposal. This is a laborious, inflexible and expensive process, and gives rise to the need to develop methods which allow a faster, yet sufficiently accurate, cost prediction of building conversion in the early stages of design.

Building obsolescence may be caused by degeneration of structure, services and fittings (Terborgh, 1976)[20] or by change of objectives demanding a different use from that for which the building was designed (Switzer, 1963)[19]. In the latter case the building may still provide the environmental standard appropriate to its original use. The new use, however, demands a different standard, thus requiring the conversion of the building. Some buildings do not need to be converted, because decreases in standard can be compensated for by change of use to one which requires lesser standards. However, in this chapter, only cases where obsolescence is overcome by the conversion of the buildings are studied.

A prediction system for the costs which result from such adaptations of buildings to new functional requirements should be both general, to allow quick decisions in the early design stage, and accurate — preferably as accurate as the cost prediction of new work at the same stage. Furthermore, such a system should permit the prediction of costs for the conversion of individual spaces, as well as for entire buildings. The scope of the system developed covers all building types except housing. As time and economic resources were limited, the development of a framework only was possible and at present the system lacks the comprehensive data bank required for general use, though it has of course been tested. Furthermore, conversion work involving extensive structural changes are excluded on the basis that the economic merit of conversion over new construction lies in the existence of a sound loadbearing structure. The case studies described in other chapters seem to confirm this. External works are also excluded.

As a consequence of these exclusions, a building must undergo preliminary examination in order to clarify whether or not it is generally suitable for conversion and for the proposed new use. Criteria for this examination include structural soundness, sufficient total building area, storey height, loadbearing capacity of the building structure, clear span, access to the building and main services supply. If these criteria are not met, then either the objectives have to be changed or the building is not suitable for conversion.

Development of the system

New building work is estimated in the very early design stage by use of cost units per square or cube metre building area volume. The cost units are specific for each building type and have been collected in long-term analyses of construction costs. They are based on detailed information about the spaces and their standard occurring in such building types. Hence the data allow fairly accurate cost predictions, even without sketch designs. A knowledge of the total building area involved is sufficient.

Current cost prediction practice in conversion work, however, is necessarily dependent upon a fairly detailed description of the work in terms of quantities and qualities of material and labour. Such a description requires detailed drawings (*Figure 3.1*). The disadvantage of this procedure is its limited flexibility, as early estimates of costs are not possible. If the estimate

31

		Planning process		
		Stage 1 (space program)	Stage 2 (sketch design)	Stage 3 (design)
Cost estimate	New work current procedure	basis: building type cost: per m² building area	basis: space type cost: per m² floor area	basis: building element cost: per quality & quantity of material & labour
	Conversion work current procedure	not possible no data available	not possible no data available	basis: building element cost: per quality and quantity of material and labour
	Conversion work proposed system	basis: aggregated information space types to building types cost: per building type	basis: aggregated information element types to space types cost: per space type	basis: element types (space & building) cost: per element type (quality & quantity of material)
		long-term objective	short-term objective	short-term objective

◯ formal cost prediction method new work and conversion work

⟨◯⟩ informal cost prediction method new work

⟨◯⟩ proposed system for cost prediction of conversion work

Figure 3.1 Planning process and cost estimate

proves too expensive, or the client's objectives change, then the whole procedure must be repeated. A further disadvantage is that specific design decisions cannot be repeated without some modification, so the cost data obtained are not reusable.

The proposed system is based on the definition of quantity and quality of labour and materials involved in the conversion, in much the same way as the design-based estimation procedure. The objective is, however, to systematise these definitions in such a way that, once gathered, conversion data can generally be applied in any conversion case, thus allowing the development of a conversion data bank and, ultimately, the aggregation of individual data to allow a cost prediction procedure similar to that used in the early design stage of new work.

Objectives

In order to meet the short-term objective, the definition of conversion work must be based on a unit which occurs in

32

identical form and standard in as many conversion cases as possible. The remodelling of such a 'repetitive unit' into one having an alternative form and standard repeatedly generates the same type and extent of conversion work, as a consequence of the invariable difference between initial and respective alternative structure. The 'repetitive unit' should be as comprehensive as possible, to avoid the necessity for the description of conversion work in detail.

It has been suggested that 'building types' could be regarded as such repetitive units. However, more detailed examination shows that their standard varies considerably within the spatial sub-division, the combination of space types differing from building to building, even of the same use category. Accordingly, each modification of the standard of an entire building produces a different type and extent of conversion work and thus cannot lead to the deduction of generally-valid information.

It has been argued that 'spaces' are a more appropriate unit because they occur with the same functional purpose in quite different building types e.g. offices. However, if spaces are analysed they rarely prove to be identical; furthermore, if their conversion is described, it refers not to the space as a whole but to its individual elements, such as floors, ceilings, walls, installations and fittings. Thus, in spite of the objective being to develop a fairly general system, the repetitive unit is, in fact, the element and the space only in so far as it is the combination of such elements. The term 'element' here stands for a part of a construction in the same way as in the BCIS or CI/SfB element lists; the definition, however, is qualified later.

If individual elements are systematically defined, and their conversion into alternative forms methodically derived and listed, then the information gained is applicable in any situation which includes such elements and their conversions, because the occurrence of elements and their conversions can be described independently from any building or space type.

Therefore, one of the fundamental differences between the proposed system to those already in use, is that it is based on this systematic definition representing generally applicable information. Another fundamental difference is the consequent allocation of conversion cost to these elements, and via elements to spaces, or to the building, depending upon the nature of the elements.

Comparison between the existing and the required standard is a precondition for a systematic definition of conversion work. The demands of activities on their environment are directed to individual spaces, but the required environmental properties are created by the individual space elements and their characteristics. The required standard is therefore the definition of characteristics which elements should contain, in order to create a space with certain environmental properties. Efforts to define the interdependence between activities and space element characteristics have led to extensive data collections in several institutions (Bartke *et al*, 1974)[1]; (Gorhely *et al*, 1976)[5]; (HISBAU, 1973)[8]; (Legge, 1975)[10, 11]; (Musgrove, 1970)[13]; (PfI, 1971)[14]; (SFB 63, 1975)[17, 18] many of which have been made available for use in the development of this system (Bartke *et al*[1]; Gorhely *et al*[5]; PfI[14]; SFB 63[17, 18]); (UCL, 1975)[21].

Existing spaces can be described only in terms of materials and construction principles, their standard depending, therefore, on the specifications of their elements. Obviously required and existing standards are not directly comparable, because they are defined on different levels and in different 'languages'. As in any other design process, the demands on elements must be transformed into element specifications, with the required characteristics. This transformation, an essential and cost-influential part of the planning process, cannot yet be based on a data collection and is subject to the designer's experience alone. There are, however, attempts to systematise the transformation (Legge,[10, 11]); (Deutsche Bau-Dokumentation, 1977)[4].

After transformation, both existing and required element standards are defined in terms of specifications and are therefore directly comparable; the differences can be noted and allow decisions to be made on type and degree of conversion work necessary.

Cost data

The conversion of a space is consequently the adaptation of its set of elements to a higher standard, either by removal, restructuring or addition. This definition of conversion work is comparable with that used in a bill of quantities, but performed on a more detailed level.

The cost data for this conversion work can be obtained by analysis of completed work. This technique has been used to derive cost data for several case studies. It would appear, however, that most cost data for new work could also be used for conversion work, in a slightly modified form.

The systematic comparison of element types with their alternative versions produces an element-conversion-work and cost-data bank. As the data are neither dependent upon building types, nor on space types, they will be generally applicable in any conversion case.

To guarantee applicability at any time, data must be kept up-to-date. This is no problem with regard to element-conversion data, where new information has only to be added to the collection whenever it becomes available, and obsolete data are simply ignored. The up-dating of cost data, however, demands not only the addition of information about new element types, but also the constant adjustment of the cost in relation to the economic situation. As data are not collected in aggregate form, the up-keep is, technically, not complicated, the actual data adjustment being handled in the same way as that of data for new work.

The systematic definition of element types, and the derivation of data on their conversions into alternative element types, represents the primary data bank upon which the prediction system is based (*Figure 3.2*). Naturally, the elements do not occur individually, as collected on Aggregation Level I, but in combination. Information about such combinations to space types in relation to certain space uses is, therefore, a pre-condition for the aggregation of element-conversion data to space-conversion data (Aggregation Level II). This information is usually obtained by survey of spaces and the activities they allow; in more sophisticated systems the survey is combined with the questioning of the space user, to guarantee the definition of optimal environmental conditions for each activity-set using the minimum number of elements (Bartke *et al,*[1]; Görhely *et al,*[5]; Legge,[10, 11]; PfI,[14]; SFB 63[17, 18]).

The data aggregation on space level (*Figures 3.1 and 3.2*) represents a considerable simplification of conversion work definition and cost prediction and enables the procedure to be expedited. However, as the number of unique combinations of element types actually occurring is very large, an extensive space data bank is absolutely essential.

If it is possible to further analyse the typical combinations of space types to building types, the space conversion data are transformed into building conversion data on Aggregation Level III. This last form of aggregation, the long-term objective for this system, would then allow a conversion cost prediction similar to the one described for new work in its very early design stage. The number of building type analyses necessary is equally as large as that for space types.

Elements and their costs

Before conversion and cost prediction can be described in more detail, it is necessary to examine and describe the conversion unit 'element', because it influences the system as a whole. Basically, three groups of elements and, accordingly, of element conversion, can be distinguished:

1. The ***space elements***, i.e. elements which can be allocated to individual activity spaces (boundaries, installations and fittings). Their conversion refers to the space only and generates 'space cost';

2. The ***building elements***, i.e. elements which cannot be allocated to one space alone (distribution systems). Their conversion is necessitated by the requirements of activity spaces and refers to several of them at the same time, therefore generating 'building cost';

3. The ***building-related space elements***, i.e. elements which can be allocated to individual spaces (central supply systems) but the conversion of which results from demands on individual activity spaces, therefore generating 'building cost'.

These three main groups of elements are shown in detail and hierarchical order in *Figure 3.4*. Further distinctions must then be made with regard to the quality and quantity of the elements within these three groups.

With regard to the *qualitative* classification, not all elements need to be described with the same degree of detail. In this respect, two groups of elements can be distinguished. Those of Group A (space boundaries) represent combinations of different materials; their quality depends accordingly on that of their individual components, in the same way as the thermal insulation value of a wall, for instance, is the sum of the insulation values of all its parts. The definition of floor, ceiling and wall types, therefore, must include the classification of their 'main construction', 'secondary construction' and 'finish'. (*Figure 3.3*).

The quality of elements of Group B (all others except structural and external elements, the conversion of which has been excluded) is not dependent upon different components but is a function of the specific element type in the same way as, for instance, 'radiator', 'convector', or 'storage heater' are different qualitative types of the element 'space heating'. The definition of alternative types of installations, fittings, distribution systems and central services, therefore, already includes a qualitative classification.

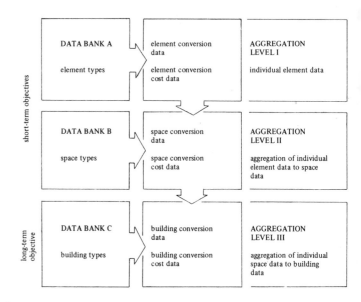

Figure 3.2 System structure, necessary data collections and aggregation levels

Main construction	Secondary construction	Finish		Type number
MC5	SC0	F0	none	28
		F3	sound-absorbing board	29
		F7	plywood	30
		F9	texture	31
	SC3	F0	none	32
		F1	paint	33
		F3	sound-absorbing board	34
		F5	vinyl sheet	35
	SC4	F0	none	36
		F1	paint	37
		F5	vinyl sheet	38

MC5 = timber framed

SC0 = no secondary construction
SC3 = 13 mm plasterboard
SC4 = 25 mm non-combustible board

Figure 3.3 Definition of boundary elements as combination of components (example partitions)

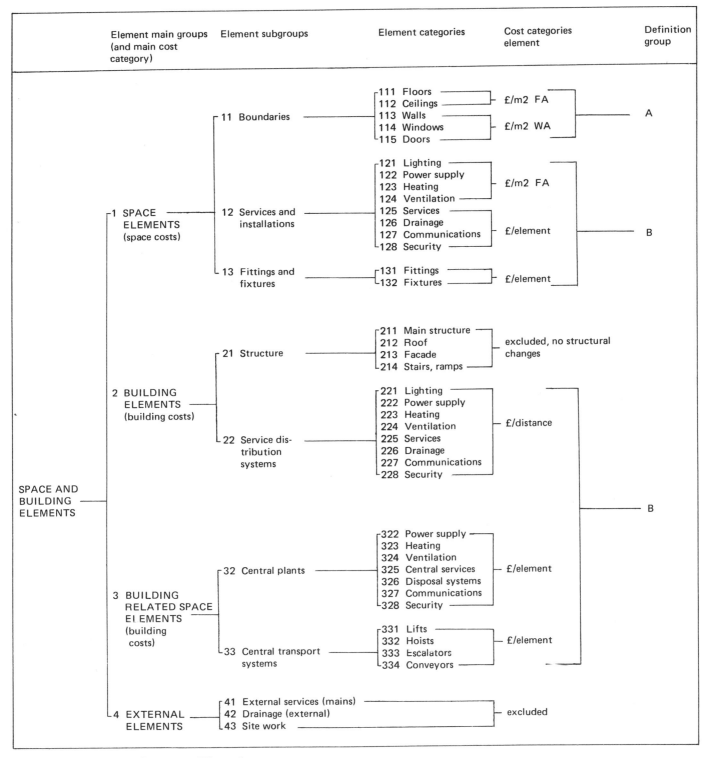

FA = floor area   WA = wall area
Definition group A = elements which need detailed description as combination of finishes, secondary and main construction.
Definition group B = element type description is sufficient for qualitative classification.

Figure 3.4 Element and element cost hierarchy

Following the qualitative definition of the elements, their *quantity*, i.e. their size or capacity, must be determined as an essential part of a comprehensive classification of the conversion unit 'element', and is a further precondition. Again, two basic groups can be distinguished, those elements the quantity of which is a characteristic of the element type, and those the quantity of which depends upon a geometry factor.

To the first group belong the central plant and transport systems, some of the space installations (services, communication and security installations) and all fittings. The capacity of the central plant results from the total area or volume of the spaces served, that of the transport systems from the number of persons using them, or from the quantity of goods being transported. Fittings are produced in standard or special sizes, the only necessary quantitative statement other than the definition of their type, being the indication of the number of occurrences per space.

The second group of elements must be sub-divided also. The quantity of service distribution systems is a function of the distance between served areas and supply systems, and is thus dependent upon a layout. The quantity of other space installations (lighting, power supply, heating and ventilation) is dictated by the size of the space and is therefore defined as a function of the floor area. The quantity of the boundary elements is either directly related to the size of the space (floor and ceiling elements) or is related to the wall area (wall, door, window elements), and consequently is a function of size, height and shape of the space. As the cost of an element itself is a function of its quality and quantity, the following cost categories can be distinguished (*Figure 3.4*):

1. *Unit cost of element type per number of elements* for central services and transport facilities, for some of the space installations (services, communication and security installations) and for all space fittings;

2. *Unit cost of element type per distance* between supply point and served space, for all distribution systems;

3. *Unit cost of element type per floor area* for floor, ceiling and some of the space installations (lighting, power supply, heating and ventilation);

4. *Unit cost of element type per wall area* for walls, windows and doors.

The unit costs of boundary elements represent the aggregation of costs for the individual element components.

Element conversion and conversion cost

As the definition of the two basic groups of elements (*Figure 3.4*) suggests, there are also two groups of element conversion. The conversion of elements in Group B generally involves the addition of a new element type or the replacement of one

36

element type by another. The element itself is not normally changed or restructured.

As well as replacement or reconstruction of the whole element, the conversion of elements in Group A, involves the restructuring of the element in the form of an addition or replacement of element components (finish, or secondary construction and finish). The decision about the degree of conversion depends upon the difference between existing and required specifications. In the same way as the definition of such elements has been based on the combination of components (*Figure 3.3*), the conversion work can systematically be described in terms of removal and/or addition of finish, secondary construction and finish, or of the whole element (*Figure 3.5*).

Elements and element components are not necessarily removed when they are not required. They may be retained as redundant elements or element components; the space in this case is then under-utilised. The decision on removal or retention depends upon the performance demanded from the respective element. In this context, the importance of the possibility of a systematic transformation of a set of specifications into sets of characteristics, or vice versa, again becomes clear, not only with regard to the decision about possible or required space use, but also with regard to the decision about redundancy or conversion of individual elements and, finally, to an optimal cost solution of conversion.

From Type	To Type	Removal of			Construction		
		MC	SC	F	MC	SC	F
28	29	–	–	–	–	–	F3
28	30	–	–	–	–	–	F7
–							
34	36	–	SC3	F3	–	SC4	–
34	37	–	SC3	F3	–	SC4	F1
–							
31	23	MC5	–	F9	MC4	SC3	F5
31	25	MC5	–	F9	MC4	SC4	F1
–							

Note: All partition types involved are defined in Figure 3.3 except type 23 and 25:

Type 23	MC4	= 100 mm metal framed partition
	SC3	= 13 mm plasterboard
	F5	= vinyl sheet
Type 25	MC4	= 100 mm metal framed partition
	SC4	= 25 mm non-combustible board
	F1	= paint

Figure 3.5 Systematic definition of element conversion in terms of removal and/or construction of element components and whole elements (example partitions)

In conjunction with the types of element conversion are two basic groups of conversion costs. The conversion of elements in Group B generally involves costs for the addition of new elements, and costs for the removal of existing elements in cases of replacement by another type. The derivation of cost data for construction or removal of elements in Group B is not the real problem as analysed costs, as well as those for new work, can be applied with certainty. The difficulty lies rather in the definition of the quantities of the elements, for instance that of the actual size of distribution systems, without going into detailed description of the layout (which in most cases is not defined in the early design stage and sometimes not even in the detail stage) or in the definition of the inter-dependence between total amount of served-space and size or capacity of central installations. Some general rules have been developed, but further analysis is required to answer respective questions.

The conversion of elements in Group A involves costs for the construction of elements, and costs for the removal of existing elements, with the addition of costs for the construction of element components, as well as for their removal. As these elements are defined to a high degree of accuracy in terms of quality and quantity of components, cost data can be derived for their demolition and construction, which can then be aggregated to a unit cost per conversion of an element type.

Thus, the systematic comparison of element types, the definition of the necessary conversion work with regard to element components or whole elements, and the derivation of cost data for these conversions, leads to an element-conversion-cost data collection (*Figure 3.6*).

to element type	From element type 28	29	30	31	32	33	34
28	–	4.48	2.91	1.12	2.24	3.14	6.05
29	–	–	2.24	1.12	2.69	3.59	6.50
30	–	4.48	–	1.12	2.91	3.81	6.72
31	–	4.26	2.24	–	2.69	3.59	6.50
32	–	3.81	1.79	1.12	–	0.90	3.81
33	–	3.81	1.79	1.12	–	–	3.81
34	–	–	2.24	1.12	–	–	–
35	–	3.81	1.79	1.12	–	–	3.81
..	....	....	....	....	....	....	....

Remark : The conversion cost unit is £/m2 partition area.

The matrix is ordered vertically. It is not possible to read it horizontally as cost data would then be incorrect.

Figure 3.6 Conversion cost matrix, (example partitions)

ACC	SIZE in M	ELEMENT TYPES Floor	Ceil.	Walls ext.	Walls int.	Doors	Wind.	Inst.	Fitt.
A	2M	14	9	10x	33x	A	2	2	–
B	2M	15x	7	10x	33x	A	2	7	–
C	2M	17x	8	10x	33x	A	2	3, 4	–
D	3M	15	9	10x	33x	A	2	3, 6	–
E	3M	14	7	10x	33x	A	2	–	–

FU	SIZE in M	ELEMENT TYPES Floor	Ceil.	Walls ext.	Walls int.	Doors	Wind.	Inst.	Fitt.
U	1M	17	11	11	34	A	2c/d	2, 4, 7, 8 9, 12, 14 20, 22, 26	3, 8, 12 13, 16, 22
V	2M	14	10	14	33	A	2	3, 4	12
W	3M	15	10	14	35	A	2/2c	2, 4, 6, 12 14, 19, 26	–
X	3M	17	11	16	34	A	2c/d	2, 4, 6, 8 9, 22, 26 27, 30	3, 8, 9 12, 16
Y	2M	17	14	16	45	A	2c	2, 4, 7, 11 22, 26, 27	3, 6, 8 12, 13 17, 22
Z	1M	15	10	10	33	A	2/2c	2, 4, 6 26, 27	3, 7

ACC = acceptors, existing spaces
FU = functional units, required space standard
M = space module (11.52 m2 floor area, h=3, 0 m, shape 2, 4 x 4, 8 m)

Figure 3.7 Definition of existing and required spaces as combinations of element types (example)

Space conversion and space conversion costs

Space having been defined as a combination of elements, its conversion is, accordingly, the conversion of its set of elements in Groups A and B. If it is known which element type occurs in which space type, the collected data can be applied for the definition of space conversion work and cost.

The collection of space data by survey is an essential instrument for the systematic aggregation of data. The sets of element types in existing spaces can be surveyed. The definition of a new space-use leads, with the help of the space typology, to the definition of the appropriate set of element types. Thus, the comparison of existing and required space becomes possible and the necessary element conversion work and cost can be selected from the element data bank (*Figure 3.7*).

Floor area m²	Wall area s = 1 : 1.0		Wall area s = 1 : 1.6		Wall area s = 1 : 3.0	
	m²	ratio	m²	ratio	m²	ratio
1	12.00	1 : 12.00	12.30	1 : 12.30	13.86	1 : 13.86
5	26.90	1 : 5.38	27.60	1 : 5.52	30.96	1 : 6.20
10	37.90	1 : 3.79	39.00	1 : 3.90	43.80	1 : 4.38
15	46.60	1 : 3.09	47.80	1 : 3.19	53.70	1 : 3.58
20	53.60	1 : 2.68	55.20	1 : 2.76	62.00	1 : 3.10
25	60.00	1 : 2.40	61.60	1 : 2.46	69.30	1 : 2.77
30	65.80	1 : 2.19	67.20	1 : 2.24	75.90	1 : 2.53
35	71.00	1 : 2.03	72.90	1 : 2.08	82.00	1 : 2.34
40	75.80	1 : 1.90	78.00	1 : 1.95	87.60	1 : 2.19
45	80.50	1 : 1.79	82.70	1 : 1.84	93.00	1 : 2.07
50	84.80	1 : 1.70	87.20	1 : 1.74	98.00	1 : 1.96
55	89.00	1 : 1.62	91.40	1 : 1.66	102.80	1 : 1.87
60	92.90	1 : 1.55	95.50	1 : 1.59	107.30	1 : 1.79
.						
.						
.						
100	120.00	1 : 1.20	123.20	1 : 1.23	138.50	1 : 1.39
	− 2.7% ⟵ ± 0.0% ⟶ + 12.4%					

Figure 3.8 Ratio floor to wall area for shape factors 1:1.0, 1:1.6 and 1:3.0 and a constant height of 3.0 m

Cost categories

According to the previous definition of cost categories, space conversion cost is a function of fixed costs per element, unit costs per square metre floor area, and unit costs per square metre wall area. If the relationship of all three cost categories to one comprehensive definition unit (e.g. square metre floor area) were defined, the costs for all individual elements could be aggregated to one overall space-cost. This would simplify the conversion cost calculation on space level considerably, and allow space conversions to be placed in order of their cost importance.

There is, however, no relationship between fixed cost and space size. On the other hand, the relationship between floor area and wall area depends heavily upon size, shape and height

38

of the space. Even if the shape factor is of little importance and could be disregarded, there remains the difficulty of changing height and size of one and the same space type. A generalisation of the factor size alone would lead to extensive deviations, particularly in the range of sizes of the majority of spaces (up to 25 m²). See *Figure 3.8*.

It has been suggested that typical sizes of space types (e.g. office: 6.0, 12.0, 18.0, 24.0 m² etc) and average height and shape factors should be defined, which would then enable the pre-calculation of the conversion cost of a certain space type for all sizes in question, and thus operate with a total conversion cost per space only. The main disadvantage of such a procedure is the multiplication of conversion data, with the ensuing difficulties of data handling and up-keep. In addition selected sizes would cause, in some cases, a considerable deviation from the space sizes actually occurring, leading to a lower degree of accuracy of the cost estimate.

It has been further suggested that this inaccuracy could be tolerated, because the proposed accuracy of the definition of quantities would seem exaggerated, if compared with the low degree of accuracy of the cost data. This argument is not valid, because inaccurate cost data and quantities would multiply the error to a much greater degree of deviation than that produced by the inaccuracy of the costs alone. If an attempt is made to minimise the degree of deviation, then the inaccuracy of all components will be minimised. As it is inevitable that certain components (such as cost) are inaccurate, the other components should be defined as precisely as possible, in order to minimise the deviation and to maintain control over the factor responsible. Both suggestions have accordingly been ruled out.

An aggregation of the three cost categories to one overall cost category is therefore not possible. The space cost equation is accordingly:

$$C_{space} = (aFa) + (bWa) + (c + d)$$

where

a = the aggregated unit cost per floor area related elements as qualitative statement (£/m²);

Fa = the size or floor area as quantitative statement (m²);

b = the aggregated unit cost per wall area related elements as qualitative statement (£/m²);

Wa = the wall area as quantitative statement (m²);

c = the aggregated fixed cost for non-floor area related installations incorporating qualitative and quantitative statement (£);

d = the aggregated fixed cost for fittings incorporating qualitative and quantitative statement (£).

As space conversion involves the adaptation of the distribution systems and the central supply system, the total cost for space elements, building elements and building-related space elements is:

$$C_{total} = \underbrace{[(aFa) + (bWa) + (c+d)]}_{\text{space cost}} + \underbrace{[(eDi) + (f)]}_{\text{building cost}}$$

where

e = the aggregated unit cost per distribution systems as qualitative statement (£/distance);

Di = the quantity of the distribution systems (actual length) as quantitative statement (distance);

f = the aggregated fixed cost for central supply systems as qualitative and quantitative statement (£).

The aggregation of the costs in the first bracket to the total space cost, and of those in the second bracket to the total building cost, is only possible if qualitative and quantitative statements for all elements involved are given. Thus, the only valid overall criterion for all individual elements is cost.

Space conversion

The cost calculation of space conversion follows the definition of all existing and required elements in terms of quality (as element type) and quantity (dependent on or independent of the space geometry). To systematise this calculation process, a matrix has been developed which permits the entries of all elements on one sheet, and thus the calculation of all the individual element conversion costs and their aggregation to space cost. (*Figure 3.9*).

The calculation produces specific information on costs for the conversion of one space type into another space type having a particular geometry. This information can then be generalised according to space-cost function by calculating unit costs per floor area, wall area and fixed costs per space.

Similar matrices have been developed for the calculation of the conversion costs of building elements (distribution systems), and for that of building-related space elements (central plant and transport systems), the results of which can be aggregated to the total conversion cost.

Application for cost prediction

The system can, in its present form, be applied in all cases of building conversion without any further modification or addition, provided the necessary element and space data are available. As a mere cost prediction system, however, it presupposes planning decisions about the proposed new use of a space or building and about the layout or, more precisely, about the allocation of activities to the existing building spaces. Hence the quality and economic acceptability of a solution is not controlled by the cost prediction system but requires an independent appraisal.

In cases of the conversion of individual spaces in a building, the geometry of the existing spaces or 'acceptors' (so-called because they 'accept' the required functional unit) is fixed and cannot be changed, as this would affect adjacent spaces which are not part of the conversion programme. Thus, no activities or functional units other than those requiring the same, or a similar, space geometry, can be allocated to the individual acceptors (within the definition of maximum deviation of size, etc).

The main criterion for the definition of type and degree of conversion is, consequently, the comparison of existing and appropriate environmental standards. This comparison enables a decision to be made about the necessary space element conversion and, subsequently, that of the conversion of building elements and building-related space elements. This space comparison, in the form of comparison of element types, follows exactly the procedure previously described; the actual conversion of individual spaces makes use of the collection of element data and the element conversion matrices (*Figures 3.5 and 3.6*), as well as that developed for the calculation procedure (*Figure 3.9*).

If several existing spaces can be used for one and the same function, their geometries being equal or similar, a decision is then required about the allocation of the functional unit to one of the acceptors. This decision having been made, the cost prediction for the space conversion then follows the prescribed pattern. Accordingly, feasibility of the solution depends upon the allocation decisions.

The conversion process becomes more complex when a set of functional units has to be allocated to a set of acceptors, i.e. if a whole set of spaces is to be converted. In this case, not only the environmental standard of the individual acceptor spaces must be compared with the required standard of the functional units, but the geometry of both sets of spaces must be compared. The first working step is, accordingly, the definition of all possible acceptors for each functional unit, on the basis of their geometry alone. With regard to geometry there are basically three types of acceptors:

1. acceptors with fixed geometry (e.g. with loadbearing walls);

2. acceptors as an undivided area (e.g. an entire floor);

3. acceptors with non-loadbearing partitions, which can be demolished or shifted.

It is to be expected that, in a normal conversion case involving a set of spaces or an entire building, all three types of acceptors will occur in combination. If the geometry is fixed, the conversion of these spaces will be the same as for that of individual spaces, as described above. If, however, there is no space subdivision, or the existing subdivision can be

39

A		From Type	To Type	%	±	Size m²	Cost/ m²	Cost/ space	Sub-Total	Total £	Cost type	
£/FLOOR AREA	FLOOR	(14)	(17)			11.52	10.31	118.80	413.80	413.80	35.92 £/m²	a (£/m² Fa)
	CEIL.	(9)	(11)			11.52	16.37	188.60				
	INST. 1–9	2	2, 4, 7, 8, 9			11.52	9.24	106.40				
£/WALL AREA	WALLS N	(10x)	(11)	40		2.88	26.68	76.80	610.00	681.70	15.78 £/m²	b (£/m² Wa)
	WALLS E	–	(34)	100		14.40	8.97	129.20				
	WALLS S	(33x)	(34)	100	−2m²	5.20	3.81	19.80				
	WALLS W	(10x)	(11)	100		14.40	26.68	384.20				
	DOORS N	–	–			–	–	–	38.80			
	DOORS E	–	–			–	–	–				
	DOORS S	wall (33) →	window A		2m²	(2,00)	(19.40)	38.80				
	DOORS W	–	–			–	–	–				
	WINDOWS N	(2)	(2d)	60		4.32	7.62	32.90	32.90			
	WINDOWS E	–	–			–	–	–				
	WINDOWS S	–	–			–	–	–				
	WINDOWS W	–	–			–	–	–				
£/SPACE	INST. 10 –	–	12, 14, 20 22, 26					262.80	702.00	702.00	702.00 £/space	c + d (£)
	FITT.	–	3, 8, 12 13, 16, 22					439.20				
Σ		A1	U			(11.52)				1797.50		

Figure 3.9 Matrix for the calculation of space conversion cost (example: conversion of A1 into U)

altered, then the geometry of the acceptor spaces must be determined. This requires the development of a general layout pattern indicating all possible locations of partitions and thus, all possible acceptors and their combinations. In most cases, the layout pattern will be dictated by the existing building structure.

Once all possible acceptors are defined, their geometry can be compared with that required by the functional units. On the basis of this comparison, all possible acceptors for each functional unit can be defined, and a decision taken about the actual layout, by the choice of one allocation case.

The allocation, chosen on the basis of space geometry alone, then permits a comparison to be made of the environmental standards of functional units and acceptors, and the definition of the required conversion work of space elements and, consequently, of building elements and building-related space elements, in the same manner as described above.

The system developed has been applied in two case studies, in order to examine the validity of all assumptions and the process. To organise the studies on a realistic basis, it was necessary first of all to collect element and space data.

A small quantity of data was specially derived for the case studies by analysis of a well documented conversion project which had already been carried out. This collection, though small, comprised 21 floor types, 15 ceiling types, 45 wall types, 4 window and 4 door types, 44 space installation elements and 30 fitting elements, i.e. 163 space element types in all, with the addition of 15 building-related space elements. For all 178 elements, cost data were derived for boundaries as an aggregation of individual costs of element components. Furthermore, cost data for distribution systems were analysed, mainly for lighting, power supply, sewer and drainage, water supply, sound distribution, telephone, fire alarm, emergency lighting, fire fighting, earthing and main power cables.

Within the limits of the available material, the conversion of boundary element types into all possible alternative forms was systematically listed and costed, producing the following numbers of possible conversions: floor elements 158, ceiling elements 85, wall elements 426.

This data collection, comparable with the primary data bank on Aggregation Level I (see *Figure 3.2*), was supplemented by the collection of all combinations of element types in spaces occurring in the conversion project analysed, giving 150 unique combinations of element types or space types (Aggregation Level II). Element and space material was subsequently used in Case Studies I and II, described briefly as follows.

Case Study 1

The purpose of Case Study I was to check the structure of the system developed, i.e. the adequacy of the definition of quality and quantity of element conversion, the aggregation of the element information to space information, and the calculation of element, space and building conversion costs. If the cost prediction system is used in the calculation of a project for which comprehensive documents are available, then any discrepancy between the predicted cost and the actual conversion cost would indicate a failure in the system. It was, therefore, decided to select a building, the conversion of which was analysed to produce the data for the case study.

The building, the property of the University of Strathclyde, consists of nine floor levels and about 130 activity spaces. The building was converted to its present standard and spatial subdivision from an old tobacco warehouse. For a case study, the building as a whole was too large. One floor level was, therefore, selected containing the maximum variety of space types, thus requiring the maximum number of types and degrees of conversion work. (*Figure 3.10*). All partitions are new; the floor level was originally one open space, with the exception of an office, lifts and a toilet, all of which had to be demolished as they did not fit into the chosen layout pattern, or were obsolete.

Previous and existing standards for each space were defined in terms of element types, according to the system. The

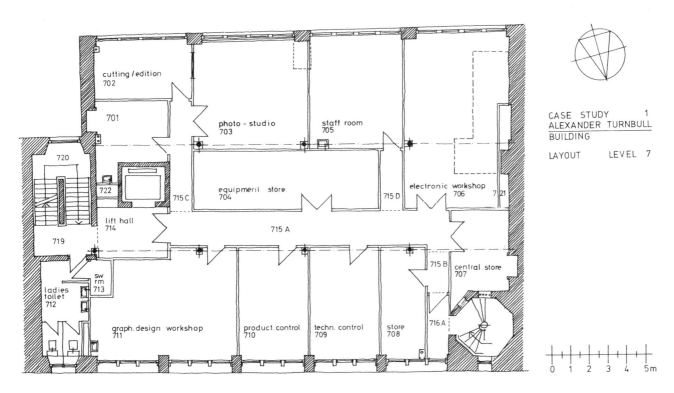

Figure 3.10 Floor plan Case Study I (Level 7)

quantity and quality of conversion material in the case study was, therefore, identical to that involved in the actual conversion of this floor level. The cost data used were those derived from the building analysis and were thus comparable with the conversion costs obtaining. Any differences in newly-calculated conversion cost from the actual conversion cost of the chosen floor would, therefore, indicate faults in the definition and/or aggregation of qualities and quantities of materials by the system developed, or in its cost-calculation and cost-aggregation process.

The result showed a deviation of the total conversion cost of 0.2%, thus confirming the accuracy of the definition and calculation system.

Case Study 2

Case Study 2 was undertaken to test the system in a situation of an entirely new conversion project, for which no documents existed. A further objective was to compare the system's approach, using the data derived from the first case study, with conventional methods of quantity surveying.

For this study a different type of building was selected: an old church which had already undergone building conversion by division of the open space with a new floor level and partitions. It is proposed that the conversion should provide new facilities including a crèche, a chaplaincy centre and chaplain's flat, student club rooms, night-line offices, overnight accommodation etc.

Again one floor level only was selected and a plan was produced for the chaplaincy, night-line offices and a mature student's club. This layout (*Figure 3.11*), together with a survey of the existing building, was the basis for both conversion cost estimates. The existing and the required standard for each space was defined as a combination of element types, allowing the calculation of qualities and quantities of demolition, construction and repair.

It was established that, when using the new system, the definitions of qualities and quantities of materials do not differ substantially from those of the Quantity Surveyor, but are more detailed and 'space orientated'. The Quantity Surveyor uses building-level information which represents the aggregation of the individual space-level information of the prediction system.

There was a substantial deviation between the cost estimate based on conventional quantity surveying methods and the cost estimate produced by the system. This deviation was to be expected, since (as previously discussed) the cost data used in the system are derived from the analysis of a single project and are not, therefore, statistically valid. However, this deviation does not invalidate Case Study 2, since the objective was to compare the methodology of the proposed system and the traditional method, rather than the accuracy of the cost prediction.

Nevertheless, it confirmed the validity and applicability of the cost prediction system. It also showed that the system's approach is based on the general methods used by the Quantity Surveyor, but that it systematises the definition in such a way that, once acquired, the information becomes repetitive and can be applied in any conversion case.

However, data analyses are required which produce reliable element conversion costs, with the necessary statistical security. Further research is essential for the system to become capable of general application.

Application including cost optimisation

The fact that the system neither influences nor assists design decisions, particularly with regard to layout development, also indicates that there is no control over the type and extent of subsequent conversion work, nor is there any control over the quality of the solution with regard to cost. Therefore, the manner in which the decision making process in building conversion work can be systematised, enabling the optimisation of conversion cost on the basis of the proposed system, is now discussed.

If individual spaces are the focus of building conversion, and if, for each functional unit for which the appropriate environmental standard must be provided, only one possible acceptor space exists, then no alternative allocation of the unit is possible and cost optimisation is not required. If, however, several acceptors are available for the same functional unit, then alternative allocations are possible and cost optimisation, in this case, means determining the allocation which causes the minimum conversion work and, consequently, the minimum conversion cost.

This optimal solution can only be found if the environmental standard of all possible acceptors is compared with that required by the functional unit, i.e. if the functional unit is theoretically allocated to all acceptors, and the respective conversion work and cost for each allocation is determined and calculated. Comparison of the results for all allocations will lead to the solution entailing minimum conversion cost. Thus, the principle of cost optimisation is the comparison of all possible allocations and the selection of the most economical solution.

The optimisation process includes both the space and building-element conversion costs. This means that the overall optimal solution with regard to cost is not the optimal space-conversion alone, but the allocation which results in the lowest total conversion cost as the sum of space-cost and building-cost (*Figure 3.4*). The conversion cost of the central plant and transport systems remains constant and has no influence upon the optimisation process.

The optimal solution does not automatically represent the aggregation of the optimal space-cost solution and the optimal

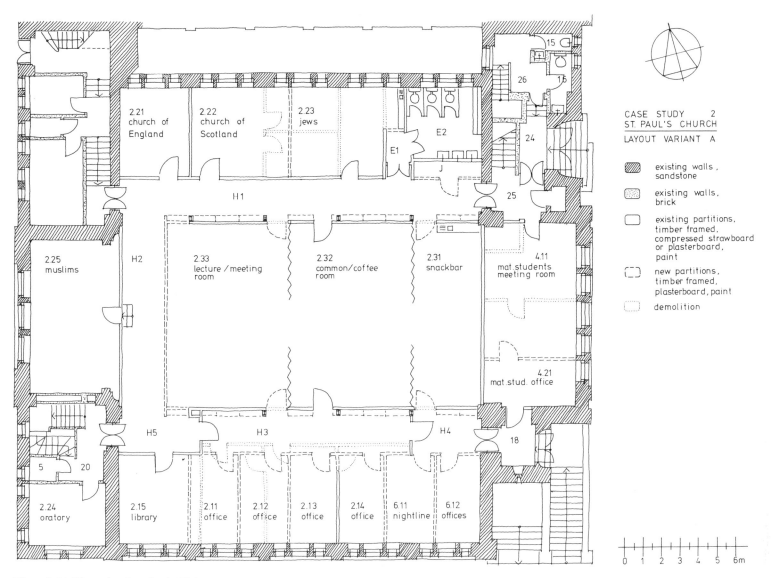

Figure 3.11 Floor plan Case Study III (ground floor level)

building-cost solution, because neither may coincide in the same layout. The solution must be selected from all individual layouts, their space conversion cost and their resulting building cost, aggregated to the total conversion cost.

Spaces and cost optimisation

In principle, the same procedure has to be followed, whether the conversion target is a set of spaces or whether it is an entire building. However, the required number of comparisons and calculations will be much larger, and the process more complex and time consuming, as the number of possible allocations grows, rapidly with the increasing number of spaces involved in the conversion case. This process is explained in the following paragraphs.

The first step is the definition of all possible acceptors, as explained earlier, because it has to be assumed that the three distinct types of acceptor geometry — fixed, sub-dividable and changeable — occur in combination in the set of spaces to be converted. The layout pattern thus derived (influenced by the existing building structure) indicates all fixed and moveable partitions and their locations, as well as the positions of new space subdividing partitions (*Figure 3.12*).

Following the definition of all possible acceptors, comparisons can be made with the functional units which have to be housed. The criterion for the comparison at this stage is the geometry of acceptors and functional units only. Thus, for each functional unit all possible acceptors are defined and, consequently, all alternative layouts (*Figure 3.13*).

43

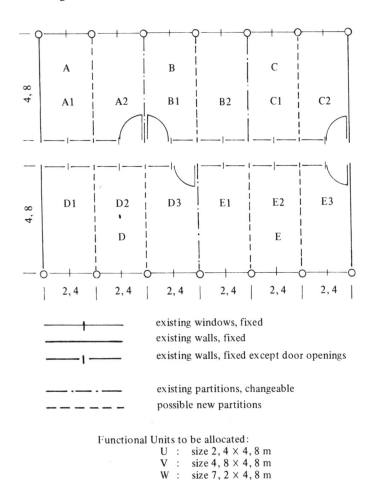

existing windows, fixed

existing walls, fixed

existing walls, fixed except door openings

existing partitions, changeable

possible new partitions

Functional Units to be allocated:
U : size 2,4 × 4,8 m
V : size 4,8 × 4,8 m
W : size 7,2 × 4,8 m
X : size 7,2 × 4,8 m
Y : size 4,8 × 4,8 m
Z : size 2,4 × 4,8 m

Figure 3.12 General layout pattern, definition of acceptors and their geometry (See Figure 3.7 for definition of acceptors and functional units)

U–A1	V–B	W–D	X–E	Y–C	Z–A2	(1)
,,	,,	W–E	X–D	,,	,,	(2)
,,	V–C	W–D	X–E	Y–B	,,	(3)
,,	,,	W–E	X–D	,,	,,	(4)
U–A2	V–B	W–D	X–E	Y–C	Z–A1	(5)
,,	,,	W–E	X–D	,,	,,	(6)
,,	V–C	W–D	X–E	Y–B	,,	(7)
,,	,,	W–E	X–D	,,	,,	(8)
U–B1	V–A	W–D	X–E	Y–C	Z–B2	(9)
,,	,,	W–E	X–D	,,	,,	(10)
,,	V–C	W–D	X–E	Y–A	,,	(11)
,,	,,	W–E	X–D	,,	,,	(12)
U–B2	V–A	W–D	X–E	Y–C	Z–B1	(13)
,,	,,	W–E	X–D	,,	,,	(14)
,,	V–C	W–D	X–E	Y–A	,,	(15)
,,	,,	W–E	X–D	,,	,,	(16)
U–C1	V–A	W–D	X–E	Y–B	Z–C2	(17)
,,	,,	W–E	X–D	,,	,,	(18)
,,	V–B	W–D	X–E	Y–A	,,	(19)
,,	,,	W–E	X–D	,,	,,	(20)
U–C2	V–A	W–D	X–E	Y–B	Z–C1	(21)
,,	,,	W–E	X–D	,,	,,	(22)
,,	V–B	W–D	X–E	Y–A	,,	(23)
,,	,,	W–E	X–D	,,	,,	(24)

Figure 3.13 Possible allocation cases – alternative layouts (for fixed walls between acceptors A–B, B–C and D–E of Figure 3.12)

Information about all possible acceptors for each functional unit permits the comparison of existing and required environmental standards (*Figure 3.7*), the definition of the necessary type and degree of conversion of the acceptors caused by the allocation of all possible functional units, and the calculation of the conversion cost for each allocation. The conversions can be ranked in order from low to high cost, forming an order of priority for each particular allocation (*Figure 3.14*).

Each space allocation initiates not only different space conversion costs but also different costs for the conversion of the distribution systems, due to the different location of the served space in the building. The conversion costs for central plant and transport systems are independent from the layout and as they are element-type costs they remain constant. The overall optimal conversion-cost is, consequently, that with the lowest total conversion-cost, as the sum of space and building costs. It can only be found by the comparison of all conversion costs produced by the alternative layouts (*Figure 3.15*).

The total number of allocations can, of course, be limited by pre-allocation of functional units (e.g. stairs, lifts, duct spaces, etc) or by introduction of association-values regulating the location of the functional units to each other, on the basis of their mutual functions. As the chosen example clearly shows however, the number of possible allocations for only a few spaces is already quite large and becomes increasingly larger when only a few spaces are added. It becomes consequently more and more difficult to deal with all layout alternatives in the traditional way due to the 'explosive' nature of combinatorial problems (Maver, 1977)[12] and (Scott, 1971)[16]. Accordingly, it is necessary to develop or adopt methods which will deal with the magnitude of the operation comprehensively and quickly.

Assignment of functional units to acceptors
The derivation of an optimal solution, therefore, involves a large number of calculations. The methods that have been developed are usually applied for cost optimisation in large scale allocation problems occurring, for instance, in production

Allocation of FU .. to ACC ..		Conversion cost	Priority of allocation
1	U — A1	£ 1797.50	(6)
2	U — A2	£ 1497.50	(4)
3	U — B1	£ 1390.80	(1) !!
4	U — B2	£ 1429.60	(2)
5	U — C1	£ 1481.20	(3)
6	U — C2	£ 1771.70	(5)
7	V — A	£ 362.00	(2)
8	V — B	£ 443.30	(3)
9	V — C	£ 356.90	(1) !!
10	W — D	£ 793.40	(1) !!
11	W — E	£ 1018.10	(2)
12	X — D	£ 1863.70	(1) !!
13	X — E	£ 2065.10	(2)
14	Y — A	£ 1805.50	(2)
15	Y — B	£ 1802.40	(1) !!
16	Y — C	£ 1831.30	(3)
17	Z — A1	£ 437.30	(5)
18	Z — A2	£ 398.50	(3)
19	Z — B1	£ 340.20	(1) !!
20	Z — B2	£ 379.00	(2)
21	Z — C1	£ 450.30	(6)
22	Z — C2	£ 411.50	(4)

Result: Absolute minimum target value: £ 6547.40 as aggregation of all allocations with first priority.

Figure 3.14 Possible allocations of functional units and conversion costs

plants where transport costs between functional units represent a considerable part of the running costs (according to Rockstroh, 1969[15], between 20% and 50%) and where, consequently, the quality of the layout is of considerable importance. There are basically two different groups of methods, (Baurri)[2]:

The *analytical methods* are based upon the evaluation of all possible allocations (total enumeration). This method — already described in principle in its manual application — produces the optimal solution or solutions but it does not reduce the amount of calculation work. In spite of the use of computers, the calculation times become, with increasing numbers of functional units, extremely long and expensive. Analytical methods, therefore, are not applicable for large scale problems.

Understanding of the fact that, even with reasonable effort and expenditure, practically no computer program can be developed which produces with absolute certainty the most economic layout of a large number of functional units, has led to the development of *heuristic methods* which do not aim to produce optimal solutions, but which try to reduce the costs (for transport, conversion, etc) as much as possible within certain constraints.

There are two types of approach:

The *exchange methods* start with an arbitrary allocation. The resulting transport costs (and, if included in the program, conversion costs) are calculated. Through exchange of functional units attempts are then made to minimise the costs until no further improvement can be achieved. These methods are less laborious and produce good layouts.

The *constructive methods* start with a 'nucleus' to which functional units with highest association value (or similar environmental standard) are added. These methods, however, are generally not applicable for pre-given floor plans, because they produce irregular layout shapes; they cannot, therefore, be used in building conversion.

Preliminary studies of existing and available programs showed that they were all developed for the optimisation of transport costs only and not for the optimisation of conversion costs, which incorporates quite different problems. After further search, however, one program was found which has been developed to cope with both problems: the computer program BAM P11 (Hiller *et al*, 1974)[7]. It has been developed by BAM (Bureau for Applied Mathematics) in Stuttgart and can be used for all general allocation problems, but in particular for optimal allocation of functional units to existing acceptors with minimum conversion cost, minimum transport cost and with minimum cost penalties for un-allocated functional units and un-used space installations. Acceptors and functional units can be defined by their geometry, by their location in the building and by 'physical attributes', in much the same way as developed in the cost prediction system.

The program BAM P11 is based upon the exchange method. It operates with partial systems which are heuristically selected from the total allocation problem (several small groups of functional units and acceptors, their size being decided by the program user). The optimisation process tries to allocate functional units within these partial systems by 'limited enumeration', i.e. the exchange process is controlled by the user through indication of the calculation time in seconds, the number of partial systems and the relative minimum benefit of the cost function.

In order to find out whether BAM P11 would be fully applicable for the cost optimisation of conversion work on the basis of the prediction system, an example was calculated. This at the same time tested the applicability of the structure of the system developed i.e. the compatibility of the system with electronic data processing.

The cost prediction system

For this study, an example was developed which incorporates all the general problems of conversion and allocation. The

Layout	Space cost	Distribution System						Central plant + transport	Total Cost £	Cost Prior
		water		telephone		intercom				
		m	£	m2	£	m2	£			
1	7328.7	25.2	406.7	190.1	298.4	131.0	117.9	–	8151.7	22
2	7352.4	,,	,,	,,	,,	,,	,,	–	8175.4	23
3	7213.4	,,	,,	,,	,,	,,	,,	–	8036.4	19
4	7237.1	,,	,,	,,	,,	,,	,,	–	8060.1	20
5	7067.5	22.8	368.0	,,	,,	115.2	103.7	–	7837.6	14
6	7091.2	,,	,,	,,	,,	119.6	107.6	–	7865.2	15
7	6952.2	,,	,,	,,	,,	115.2	103.7	–	7722.3	11
8	6975.9	,,	,,	,,	,,	119.6	107.6	–	7749.9	12
9	6821.2	,,	,,	,,	,,	109.4	98.5	–	7586.1	7
10	6844.9	20.4	329.3	,,	,,	115.2	103.7	–	7576.3	5
11	6790.3	22.8	368.0	,,	,,	118.1	106.3	–	7563.0	4
12	6814.0	20.4	329.3	,,	,,	,,	,,	–	7548.0	3
13	6821.2	22.8	368.0	,,	,,	103.7	93.3	–	7580.9	6
14	6844.9	18.0	290.5	,,	,,	115.2	103.7	–	7357.5	2
15	6790.3	22.8	368.0	,,	,,	118.1	106.3	–	7563.0	4
16	6814.0	18.0	290.5	,,	,,	,,	,,	–	7509.2	1 !!
17	6915.2	22.8	368.0	,,	,,	106.6	95.9	–	7677.5	9
18	6938.9	15.6	251.8	,,	,,	115.2	103.7	–	7592.8	8
19	6999.6	22.8	368.0	,,	,,	118.1	106.3	–	7772.3	13
20	7023.3	15.6	251.8	,,	,,	,,	,,	–	7679.8	10
21	7244.5	22.8	368.0	,,	,,	106.6	95.9	–	8006.8	17
22	7268.2	15.5	251.8	,,	,,	115.2	103.7	–	922.1	16
23	7328.9	22.8	368.0	,,	,,	118.1	106.3	–	8101.6	21
24	7352.5	15.6	251.8	,,	,,	,,	,,	–	8009.0	18

Result: Overall lowest cost solution is Case 16: £7509.20; Cases 11 and 15, the minimum space cost solutions, are rank 4 and £53.80 (0.7%) more costly.

Figure 3.15 Calculations of optimal conversion cost by comparison of costs for alternative layouts 1–24 (Figure 3.13)

geometry of acceptors and functional units (*Figure 3.12*) is based on a modular space unit, in order to allow a large number of alternative allocations with a relatively small number of spaces.

Using the data derived for the other case studies, each acceptor and functional unit represented a different space type, in order to guarantee a different type and degree of conversion work for each possible allocation, and, consequently, different conversion costs.

Allocation and cost optimisation procedure was planned in three stages:

1. with fixed partitions between the existing acceptors, limiting the number of alternative layouts to 24 (*Figure 3.13*);

2. with demountable partitions, but pre-allocation of one functional unit, allowing 60 alternative layouts. (By cancelling the pre-allocation the number of layouts could be increased further);

3. with variable number of layouts, controlled by demountable partitions, pre-allocation of one functional unit, and the association matrix indicating the inter-relationship between functional units.

The conversion costs for all twenty-four alternative layouts of stage one were manually calculated and the optimal solution was derived (*Figure 3.15*), in order to allow a comparison of the quality of cost optimisation by BAM P11.

Though the logic of the data structure of both systems is practically identical, the data input of the example developed showed immediately the difference between the definition of 'conversion work' in the cost prediction system and the existing version of the program BAM P11. The system's definition of conversion is necessarily based upon comparative matrices of conversion costs, as shown in *Figures 3.5 and 3.6*, due to the fact that space conversion includes addition, removal and *re-structuring* of elements, with different cost functions for each conversion in the latter case.

In BAM P11, however, space conversion operates, in the original program version, with the principle of addition and — via 'negative addition' — removal of elements, and does not include comparative matrices of conversion costs for the restructuring of elements. Therefore, the program only allows statements about the existence, or non-existence, of elements in a space, and is not able to cope with the much more detailed level of element standard comparison, as used by the prediction system.

In an attempt to adapt BAM P11 to this particular problem of element comparison, the basic form of an additional sub-routine was developed by BAM, permitting the incorporation of the required matrices of conversion costs into the optimisation process. To simplify the development of this sub-routine, the data structure of the example was reduced by pre-allocation of two functional units, producing only the first eight out of the twenty-four layouts in *Figure 3.15*. After this modification of program and data, two optimisation tests were then performed, each with different initial layouts. Both tests produced the optimal solution in a very short time (20.25 and 7.26 sec). This result indicates that BAM P11 is adaptable for cost optimisation of conversion costs, as developed in the prediction system.

The fact that the test runs produced optimal results is due to reduction of the problem to only eight possible alternative layouts. This result should not obscure the fact that no program can be developed, within reasonable resources, producing optimal solutions of large scale allocation problems. Consequently, sub-optimal solutions, as produced in all exchange programs, must be regarded as satisfactory.

The quality of the solutions of large scale allocation problems with BAM P11, operating in its original program version, has been shown in other test runs — for instance, with 100 functional units and 73 acceptors in the case of a university hospital, producing a reduction of transport and conversion costs of about 4% compared with the initial planning solution, representing a very substantial cost saving per year (Bayer *et al*, 1976[3]).

The BAM P11 is, therefore, applicable for cost optimisation

in building conversion if it is adapted to the special structure of element comparison, on the basis of the sub-routine already developed. Accordingly, there is no doubt of the merit of the program. Furthermore, this test has demonstrated that the structure and nature of the data, as developed for the cost prediction system, can be applied directly and without modification in the computer program, if the additional sub-routine is fully developed.

The system as a planning instrument

The cost prediction system as defined represents a useful planning instrument. If the conversion program, i.e. the activity space brief, is selected, the individual activity spaces can be classified as space types with the help of the space data bank and are, thus, automatically defined as combinations of standard element types, the conversions of which are collected in the element data bank. The survey of the spaces to be converted leads, in the same way, to the classification of the existing spaces as space types, by comparison of the combination of existing element types with those occurring in the space typology. The comparison of existing and required space types is then only a question of the application of the conversion data, and results in the derivation of the space conversion cost. Cost optimisation is possible by comparison of alternative allocations and by selection of the allocation case producing the lowest conversion cost, or by use of an 'exchange method'-based computer program.

Consequently the system can be used for:

1. the selection of space types which allow the performance of a particular set of activities;

2. the definition of the space conversion required, in order to allow the performance of a particular set of activities;

3. the selection of a set of activities which can be performed in particular space types;

4. the selection of activities which can be performed in particular spaces, the standard of which can be improved by spending a given amount of money;

5. the selection of all space conversions which cost a given amount of money and which allow the performance of a particular set of activities.

A slight disadvantage is the fact that the space conversion cost cannot be pre-calculated unless the required geometry of the space type is defined. Nevertheless the possibility of also using the system for planning is a good reason for its further development. Not only is cost prediction possible but also the prediction of building space and building use.

Conclusion

The system described covers all the individual working steps which are required in order to methodically estimate conversion cost, to derive generally applicable data, to aggregate these data and, finally, to optimise conversion cost. However, to allow the unlimited application of the system for building conversion, the comprehensive derivation and analysis of element and space data and particularly of generally valid cost data for element, space and building conversion, is required. Furthermore, the computer program BAM P11 has to be adapted to the particular problems of element comparison, in order to enable cost optimisation in large scale conversion projects. Without extended development, the system remains an interesting though not an applicable framework.

References

1. Bartke, A., Görhely, T., Lenz, H-J., Lohkamp, Ch., Nicolai, M. and Pfitzer, S. 'Bautechnische Flächenarten, Ergebnisbericht Naturwissenschaften' (Building Area Types, Report Natural Sciences), Texte und Daten zur Hochschulplanung 11/1–11/4. SFB 63–Hochschulbau, *University of Stuttgart* (1974)
2. Baur, K., 'Verfahren für die räumliche Zuordnung von Betriebsmitteln in der Fabrikplannung.' (Methods for the spatial assignment of functional elements in factory planning). *Institut für Industrielle Fertigung und Fabrikbetrieb (Institute for industrial production and factory management), University of Stuttgart,* wt.–Z. ind. Fert. 61, No. 1. (no date)
3. Bayer, W., Seibert, H–U. and Weisbord, M., 'Grundriss–optimierung mit Computerprogram P11, dargestellt am Beispiel der Vorplanungsunterlagen für das Klinikum Heidelberg' (layout optimisation with the help of the computer program P11, demonstrated through the example of the University Hospital Heidelberg). *PMU, Planungsstelle für Medizinische Universitätsbauten (planning group for University Medical Buildings) and BAM, Stuttgart* (1976)
4. Deutsche Bau-Dokumentation (German Building Documentation), *Bauteilkatalog (Building element catalogue, floors, partitions, ceilings, internal and external doors, windows),* Heinze Verlag, Celle (May 1977)
5. Görhely, T., Nicolai, M., Polacek, V. and Schaaf, J. 'Bautechnische Flächenarten, Ergebnisbericht Ingenieurwissenschaften', (Building Area Types, Report Engineering Sciences). Texte und Daten zur Hochschulplanung 19. SFB 63–Hochschulbau, *University of Stuttgart. Verlag Dokumentation München* (1976)
6. Hiller, M., Kolbe, O., Bayer, W. and Ruhrmann, I. *Heuristic Solution of General Allocation Problems in Administration and Regional Planning.* IFAC Symposium of Large Scale Systems Theory and Applications. Udine (1976)
7. Hiller, M., Kolbe, O. and Ruhrmann, I. 'General Allocation Problem Solver-Gaps, *BAM Büro für Angewandte Mathematik (Bureau for Applied Mathematics), Stuttgart* (1974) User Manual
8. HISBAU System – 'Dokumentation zur Raumdatei, Bestandeserfassung', (System documentation for the space data collection, building stock survey). *Hochschul-Informations-System GmbH (University Information System Ltd.), Hannover* (June 1973)
9. Kolbe, O. 'Ein fuzzy Algorithmus zur Behandlung von komplexen Zuordnungsproblemen', (A fuzzy algorithm for the solution of complex assignment problems). *Institut A für Mechanik, University of Stuttgart* (no date)
10. Legge + Legge Architekten 'Erfahrungsbericht aus dem Aktionsprogramm NW 75 (Report of the action programme Nordhein-Westfalen 1975), *Bonn/Aachen* (1975)
11. Legge + Legge Architekten 'Standardisierung ' (standardisation). Aachen (1975)
12. Maver, T. W. Activity/Space/Time: allocation and re-allocation. Paper for the symposium 'New into Old'. *University of Strathclyde, Department of Architecture and Building Science, Glasgow* (1977)
13. Musgrove, J. and Doidge, Ch. 'Room Classification', *Architectural Research and Teaching,* I No. 1, pp.31–36 (May 1970)
14. PfI, Planungsgruppe für Institutsbaudes Landes Baden-Württemberg (Planning group for University Institutes of the land Baden-Württemberg), 'Raumstandards für Naturwissenschaftliche Fachbereiche', (Room standards for Natural Sciences), Karlsruhe (1971)
15. Rockstroh, W. *Technologische Betriebsprojectierung – Gesamtbetrieb (technological planning of plants-master plan development),* Berlin (1969)
16. Scott, A. J. *Combinatorial programming,* London (1971)
17. SFB 63 Hochschulbau (Special field of research 63 University building), Ergebnisbericht Mai 1975 (working report 1975); 'Teilprojekt M1 Bautechnische Flächenarten' (Project M1 Building Area Types), pp.121–134. *University of Stuttgart* (1975)
18. SFB 63 Hochschulbau, Ergebnisbericht Mai 1975 'Teilprojekt M2 Kostenplanung, Kostenrichtwerte', (Project M2 Cost Planning, Cost Standards), pp 135–167. *University of Stuttgart* (1975)
19. Switzer, J. F. Q. 'The Life of Buildings in an Expanding Economy', *The Chartered Surveyor,* 96, No. 2 (1963)
20. Terborgh, G. W. 'Business Investment Management', *MAPI (Machinery and Applied Products Institute) Study and Manual,* Washington (1976)
21. University College London, University College Environmental Research Group, Unit for Architectural Studies: Data of Oxford Polytechnic, *Personal Communication* (1975)

CHAPTER
FOUR

Housing Rehabilitation

A challenge to the profession

Jim Johnson

The conversion and rehabilitation of buildings and, in particular, housing is a key area in which the working relationship of the architect to society is coming under scrutiny. Some of the pressures for change in that relationship are being tested in practice and new patterns are emerging which have both a relevance beyond the field of conservation and implications for the architectural profession's ideologies and organisation.

The profession is under considerable pressure at the moment, both from society and from within its own ranks. The economic recession of the 1970s has hit the building industry and, with it, the profession, harder than at any time since the depression of the 1930s. Although this is not a direct criticism of architects by society it does reflect a pattern of national priorities that underlines the weakness of an industry normally divided into warring factions, with a fundamental division between design and construction, and in which the professionals have opted out of industrial management.

In the last few years public criticism of architect's work has become commonplace and been given wide publicity. In particular there has been the growth of a large and articulate preservation/conservation movement which seems to reflect a public belief that the actions of architects and planners almost invariably lead to a deterioration in the quality of the environment, particularly in our city centres: that any old building, however tatty, is probably preferable in its character and 'humanity' to its proposed modern replacement. This attitude is certainly unfair and selective, but it is based on many well known cases where areas of historic and architectural quality have been destroyed for commercial gain or through an over-zealous belief in the necessity for change and the building of a brave new world. In addition it has become apparent that urban renewal does not favour all sections of the community; usually it is poor communities that bear the brunt of the disruption, in some cases due to deliberate policy. Burns writes: 'one result of slum clearance is that a considerable movement of people takes place over long distances, with devastating effect on the social groupings built up over the years. But, one might argue, this is a good thing when we are dealing with people who have no initiative or civic pride. The task surely is to break up such groupings even though the people seem to be satisfied with their miserable environment and seem to enjoy an extrovert social life in their own locality' (Burns, 1963)[2].

Within the profession it has become apparent that many younger architects are suspicious that the Royal Institute of British Architects and Architects Registration Council of the United Kingdom codes of conduct and engagement are devices to protect the livelihood of the profession rather than their avowed purpose of protecting the 'public interest'. This suspicion has expressed itself for the first time in organised opposition (rather than by individual 'dropping out') to RIBA/ARCUK by the setting up of the Architect's Revolutionary Council and the New Architecture Movement. Meanwhile older members have brought the profession into disrepute through a series of corruption cases, and their competence has been questioned after a number of major building failures.

The professional institution's response to these pressures has been both positive and negative. The negative one has been to close the ranks against criticism and reiterate the traditional professional values. Some aspects of the 1976 RIBA Conference illustrate this attitude: 'The positive objectives of the Conference were to celebrate, gather together and assess the many diverse skills of British architects, reasserting their value to society' (Goldstein, 1977)[7]. The positive one has been a search for new approaches, new ways of working, and a call for improvements in education to eliminate incompetence (at least in a technical sense).

However, most of these initiatives have ignored basic shifts in the relationship between architects and their clients or patrons. Whilst the profession has been preoccupied with trying to change the *content* of architecture, i.e. the knowledge and skills that are the basis of the profession's contract with society, it is the context that has been changing more rapidly. Architects working in housing rehabilitation have felt these changes most keenly and their experiences can provide some understanding of the new directions in which the profession should progress.

49

But before examining some cases that illustrate this it is necessary to consider the reasons why houses are being rehabilitated.

Reasons for housing rehabilitation

The first and most obvious reason is that it is cheaper to rehabilitate than to rebuild. In the present economic situation no Government is going to ignore the fact that it may cost £5000–£7000 to improve an inner city house or flat whereas it would cost two or three times that sum to demolish and rebuild (even ignoring the cost of a three year temporary housing loss during the demolish/rebuild process as opposed to a three month period for rehabilitation). A second reason is that in a period when housing needs are being re-assessed due to the unexpected changes in the projections of population growth, rehabilitation for a nominal thirty year life may give valuable breathing space. The conservation movement has also added support to rehabilitation, both in its historical sense and from the wider point of view that all resources now need conservation. Existing buildings are a resource in this sense as Farrell, in Chapter 5, has said: 'In many cases old buildings will last as long as or even longer than new ones, and in that sense they are an economic resource to be conserved just like our coal and oil' (Farrell, 1977)[5].

However the primary move towards rehabilitation came not from economic or resource considerations but from a reaction to the views of Burns, quoted earlier, and the results of such policies. The realisation slowly dawned that the best interests of our cities and citizens would not be served by totally reconstructing them if, in the process, the intricate network of social and economic relationships in the so-called 'deprived areas' was smashed. The buildings could be replaced but the social life could not be, at least not for several generations (Gans, 1962)[6], (Wilmott and Young, 1957)[23] and (Jacobs, 1962)[13]. Thus the catchword became 'gradual renewal' – the small scale replacement and refurbishment of the environment. Gradual renewal has proved difficult to achieve in practice (not because of technical or architectural difficulties but because of the clumsy nature of the administrative machinery) so the choice has now become primarily a straight dichotomy between renewal and rehabilitation.

This commitment to the retention of the existing community is emphasised by the levels of grants given in the 1974 Housing Act. Rehabilitation is focused on the more deprived areas by the provision of 75% grants for Housing Action Areas against the 50% elsewhere, and within the Action Areas the grant can be raised to 90% in cases where the owner is in financial hardship. This clearly implies the intention to retain as many of the existing residents as possible. Unfortunately, the provisions for commercial property in these areas has not been marked with similar sensitivity with the result that many

small shopkeepers dependent on low cost property may find themselves in difficulties due to rising rents or sudden demands for contributions towards the cost of repairs as the fabric of buildings that they share with housing is rehabilitated.

Munciple rehabilitation

Clearly architects and other professionals will have to understand something of the nature of the communities in which they are working if the process of rehabilitation is not to produce the very break-up of social networks that it is designed to prevent. A cautionary tale from Glasgow will illustrate this. In 1969 Glasgow Corporation, in the first flush of enthusiasm for the 1969 Housing Act, declared a substantial block of tenements at Pollockshaws (known as the 'Old Swan' after a pub on the corner) to be a Housing Treatment Area. A poor response to a rather half-hearted attempt to involve owners in the improvement of their own flats caused the Corporation to decide to acquire all the flats and prepare a rehabilitation scheme, this being seen, superficially, as the most economical way to go about the building work. All the flats were to be emptied, and a large contractor would carry out the work in one contract. Maximum standardisation was aimed at in the architectural scheme, with the ground floor 'closes', which gave direct street access to the stairs, being blocked off in order that the new bathroom/kitchen unit could be repeated on all four floors. Applying the normal technical and professional criteria, this seemed the most efficient and economical way of tackling the project.

The reality turned out to be something different. Although many owners sold out willingly and were rehoused elsewhere by the Corporation, a small core of owner-occupiers, anxious to retain their houses which they found comfortable and convenient, and into which many had sunk all their capital, wanted to organise their own improvement and went so far as to prepare alternative schemes to show how this could be done. However, this was not judged to be compatible with the Corporation's scheme and, after a protracted period of negotiations (during which two families were left alone in an otherwise empty tenement and had to virtually fight-off marauding scrap-merchants and vandals who threatened to strip everything valuable from the empty houses), the Corporation eventually obtained 100% ownership.

Building work on the rehabilitation started in 1974, with costs considerably increased because of vandalism and decay during the protracted period over which residents were moved out. The block was re-occupied in 1977. It is not known how many of the original families moved back, though it seems unlikely that many did, given the six or seven years that they had been 'decanted'. So the social networks of the area have inevitably been disrupted – not just in the block itself, because adjacent areas are affected when a large area of housing stands empty for any length of time. The final cost of the exercise is not known but, even if it is deemed a success on economic grounds, it must be adjudged a failure on social ones. The disruption in the neighbourhood would have been no worse if the block had been demolished and redeveloped. (In fairness to Glasgow Corporation, now replaced by Glasgow District Council, it is well aware of these problems, and has now adopted an entirely different and forward looking policy of rehabilitation through locally based Housing Associations).

Community based rehabilitation

As a contrast to The Old Swan approach, ASSIST, which is an action/research unit of the Department of Architecture and Building Science of Strathclyde University, Glasgow, specialising in housing rehabilitation, developed a different policy when it took on the improvement of a mixed ownership block of 220 tenement flats in Govan. Working from the premise that the existing community should be maintained as far as possible it was proposed that costs be kept as low as possible to help maintain the 30% owner-occupation.

'Improvement' was interpreted as giving the chance for each family to improve its housing conditions in whatever way that family thought best — possibly by the addition of a bathroom and hot water supply to their house, but equally possibly by the chance to move out to a local authority scheme, or to move around the block into a larger or smaller tenement flat, or to enlarge their flat by acquiring a room from an adjacent one, or even by staying as they were if housing conditions came low on their list of priorities. Thus the first stage in the work was essentially a community development job, helping residents to articulate their needs, to organise themselves and negotiate with the Local Authority over re-housing, grants, etc.

The practicability of the scheme was demonstrated by a show house, a 'live' one with the owner around to greet visitors and tell them that it was the best two hundred pounds worth she had ever had! The improvement scheme was a piecemeal one, taking each tenement in turn, and using various standard bathroom designs as flexibly as possible to meet the requirements of the residents of that 'close' (co-operation is essential in tenement improvement where vertical plumbing stacks have to be inserted into the four storey buildings).

An alternative form of 'social ownership' in the form of a locally based Housing Association was set up to acquire and improve property from owners wishing to sell up. An ASSIST office was set up adjacent to the improvement area. This provided a service that went far beyond the normal bounds of architecture; it included obtaining grants and loans for owners, negotiating with lawyers, arranging re-housing and moves around the block; in general, trying to keep everyone happy.

Such an attitude to the community does not only lead to extensions of the architect's normal service, but also to re-thinking the appropriateness of that service. For example, there was a clear need for low-income owner-occupiers to know exactly how much the proposed improvement of their flat would cost. An estimate, followed by an exact figure after tendering, would not be adequate, as a possible 10% increase could make all the difference to someone whose income would be stretched to the limit to meet weekly repayments. A system of negotiated prices for a range of work items was developed, enabling the architect to put a precise cost on the job at the end of his survey of the flat — this cost could then be discussed with the occupier and adjusted to suit his pocket.

This system was only achieved in the face of some severe misgivings arising from its conflicts with normal professional procedures, but it led to a simple and flexible system which was accepted by three builders who competed on quality and efficiency rather than cost. It is sad to note that, with the intervention of the Housing Corporation and the increasing bureaucratisation of Glasgow's improvement programme since the 1974 Housing Act, this system has had to be abandoned and there has been a reversion to competitive tendering.

ASSIST was not unique in the problems it encountered. Rod Hackney, working from his house in Black Road, Macclesfield, helped his neighbours to organise themselves to get the threat of clearance lifted from their homes, and then to rehabilitate them and the surrounding environment using much of their own labour (Knevitt, 1975)[14]. On a smaller scale, Hackney's work echoes the ASSIST experience: a local base, intense involvement with residents, the need for organisation and the acquisition of resources by the community before any architectural work, in the traditional sense, could start, and the highly labour intensive nature of the work. In both Govan and Macclesfield, architects operated as catalysts for community action and self-help.

A more conventionally organised and long established practice, Edmund Kirby & Sons, commissioned by the owners, a family trust, to rehabilitate the Flower Streets General Improvement Area (GIA) in Liverpool, found it had to adopt similar methods. It appointed liaison officers, based in a show house in the area, to co-ordinate the decanting and rehousing, to keep tenants advised on the progress of the work, and to advise people on the redecoration and refurnishing of their improved houses. Construction supervisory staff also worked from a site office. Edmund Kirby's recognised that the *process* of improvement was as important as the end *product*, that tenants disgruntled by unexplained delays, or arbitrary changes in programme, and perhaps given less than adequate temporary accommodation were not likely to welcome the improvements, however good they were, nor were they likely to care for their improved homes.

Who is the client?

These examples clearly indicate that the architectural profession will have to re-examine its mode of operation and its outlook if the objectives of housing rehabilitation are to be achieved.

The key issue is the relationship of the architect to his clients but before this can be discussed the client must be defined. A useful distinction has been made between *user* and *sponsor* clients which applies to all modern housing apart from the one-off family house (Harms, 1972)[11]. The user client is the resident who feels a proprietory interest in his house or flat albeit only rented; the sponsor is the provider of funding and, therefore, usually the controller of standards. The interests of the two are often at variance. The sponsor will be concerned with such issues as value for money and ease of maintenance, the user with the convenience of the internal layout and the flexibility of the dwelling in meeting his changing family requirements. Traditionally the architect has primarily served the interests of the sponsor client (who pays his fees), serving the users only through intermediaries such as housing managers or social scientists who interpret the needs of the 'mass client'. It has been argued that we can only move to more humane housing if the architect changes his allegiance and serves the users direct (Turner and Fichter, 1972)[19].

The user client

However, this dichotomy oversimplifies the case. To take the current organisation of Glasgow's rehabilitation programme as a fairly typical example, it can be seen that the client has many heads. Firstly, there is the tenant who in many cases returns to the same flat after improvement and may have lived for forty years or more in the same tenement. Understandably he (or usually 'she' in the Glasgow culture) has views on how it should be improved for his benefit. He is the person who has to put up with the disturbance of builders in the flat or temporary removal, and will see no point in co-operating with an improvement programme which is not clearly beneficial to him. Tenants have their own order of priorities too. A bathroom may seem an obvious necessity if the home lacks one, but to the occupant the insertion of a bathroom within a fixed shell may lead to the loss of valuable storage or sleeping space and on balance it may be perfectly rational for him to prefer a weekly visit to the local bath house.

The second level of client is the local community based Housing Association. Many of these have been set up in Glasgow following the 1974 Housing Act. Each has an area containing some 1000–2000 flats to improve; they have elected management committees of local residents (mainly tenants or future tenants of the Association) and employ their own staff to acquire and manage property and organise the improvement programme. In addition to improving their own property they act as the local authority's agents by providing a technical and administrative service for owner-occupier improvements.

One of the reasons for the promotion of these community based Associations by the Housing Corporation and Glasgow District Council was to bridge the gap between sponsor and user client — in other words, by letting the community set its own standards and organise its own rehabilitation work the

end results should be more acceptable to tenants. The local management committee was to be both user and sponsor client. However, these committees have many responsibilities and have, perhaps inevitably, become preoccupied with the mechanics of running the Association. Short term organisational and programming problems can displace the longer term objectives of community control. In addition there are legitimate differences of interest between the committee and tenants; whilst the committees are mindful of tenants' wishes for choice in the layout and finishes of improved flats, they have to balance these against the equally strong pressures for speed in the improvement programme and for the long term 'lettability' of flats which are to have a thirty year life. Pride in the development of their Housing Association sometimes leads committees to press for their improved tenements to have a standard image — external colour schemes are a rich source of controversy in this respect.

There may also be differences in outlook between the local management committee and their staff, who tend to have a 'professional' outlook and to have expectations of a professional career structure. Management committees may have a healthy distrust of professionals, especially when both their basic salaries and fringe benefits such as annual increments and pension schemes may well be better than those enjoyed by many on the committee. Although many staff believe in the ideas of community control and the decentralisation of resources and power implicit in the establishment of the community based housing associations, there are pressures on their role to see personal advancement measured in tangible achievements such as the number of units improved. There may be other divergent aims which stem from individual responsibilities, i.e. maintenance managers see all rehabilitation in terms of future ease of maintenance and hence tend to promote standardisation where possible. (It may be noted in passing that many of these potential strains are absent in the more traditional type of nationally-based housing associations which tend to have professional or middle-class management committees more remote from the user-client.)

The sponsor client

The next layer of client in the Glasgow situation is the Housing Corporation which clearly lies on the sponsor side. Although having initiated and supported the community-based Associations, as a dispenser of public funds it has a legitimate concern with the value being obtained for that money, and with the establishment of minimum standards for thirty-year life improvement. Thus the standards for the local housing association are set by the professional advisers in the Housing Corporation, and, as in so many public building fields, severe cost restraints mean that minimum standards become also the maximum, i.e. the one and only standard, from which any deviation has to be argued as a special case.

The final layer consists of the Scottish Development Department (SDD) of The Scottish Office in Edinburgh. Representing central government, and having ultimate financial control through the system of housing association grants, allowances and subsidies, SDD are concerned with levels of expenditure across Scotland. Hence another potential level of standardisation is imposed as the average level of improvement costs in Glasgow may be considered high as compared to, say, Edinburgh or Dundee, regardless of the standard being achieved or the condition of the property before improvement.

The architect's response

Thus the architect in housing rehabilitation is working in a complex situation with many potential areas of conflict between the different levels of client. The number of clients, and the representation of the user client both informally, in that the tenant has a say in how his flat is to be improved, and formally, in the shape of the management committee, make the architect's position significantly different from that involved in, say, designing new local authority housing, or even in local authority modernisation schemes where there is generally only a minimum of tenant consultation.

The conflicts of views affect the architect in his everyday work. The layout of the kitchen in an improvement scheme for a flat may, for example, involve a decision whether to accept a fairly narrow and cramped kitchen in an existing scullery, or whether to demolish the scullery wall and expand the kitchen at the expense of the adjacent room. The tenant will have his priorities — he may wish to keep the adjacent room in its traditional role as a living/dining room, in which case he will prefer to retain its shape and size, or he may wish to change his living pattern, have a separate decent sized kitchen and use the adjacent room for sleeping. The Housing Association may decide that the small kitchens, though tolerable now and requested by the tenant, have a limited life, and their retention may make the flat difficult to let once the original tenant leaves. The Housing Corporation, in turn, may favour the bigger kitchen but baulk at the cost of demolishing and rebuilding the wall and request the architect to look for an alternative solution.

In the end the architect has to do the drawing — what part is he to take in the decision making process? Is he to adopt a strictly professional view and stand back until the Housing Association makes a decision and briefs him? Is he to regard the tenant as the 'real' client and support his views? Is he to argue for the broad economic view that in order to use resources to the full the maximum standardisation must be achieved in order to get the speed and cost efficiency resulting from large contracts? Or, is he to back the Housing Association and its tenants (perhaps by advancing arguments for positive discrimination of resources) even if he knows their requirements will inevitably be rejected by the cost controllers in the Housing Corporation and at government level in the short term?

Broadly speaking the architect can adopt one of three positions. He can side with the user clients represented by tenants and the Housing Association committee (though, as has been shown, there may well be conflicts within that group) and risk forfeiting the confidence of the resource controllers, with whom, in the long term, it is necessary to have reasonable working relationships (and on whom he may be dependent for future work). Alternatively, he can side with the resource controllers, forfeit the confidence of the user client, and perhaps help to injure the local community as badly as if its homes were to be demolished and redeveloped. Or, most likely, he will take up a compromise position, mediating between the various parties until a solution acceptable to all is produced. In this case he is open to the charge of being a professional 'fixer' — essentially the velvet glove on the iron fist of authority, softening the harsh impact of controls and perhaps winning small battles here and there for the users.

Community involvement

So far we have discussed the problems from the rather blinkered architectural viewpoint of sponsor and user clients — service to the 'client' being the cornerstone of the profession's ethical code. However the discussion has a wider and more political dimension. Clearly the promotion of community based housing associations and co-operatives in inner areas of Glasgow, Liverpool, Belfast and other cities has been done for a number of motives, but figuring large amongst them was a desire not only to help retain local communities but also to regenerate the areas and help to arrest the decline of the inner cities. The Liverpool Inner Areas Study Team (Department of the Environment, 1977)[4] for example argue that:

'The aim of policy for inner Liverpool should be for its regeneration in the interests of its present and future residents. It should be to enhance the status of the inner area, recognising local values and *giving to the people who live, work and invest there a greater commitment* to its future . . .'

The team propose that the City Council should be responsible for the implementation of this programme but note that '. . . (it) would require major changes in decision making and administration to satisfy the basic requirements of *positive discrimination, local involvement and decentralisation*'.

Later in the same report the Birmingham Study Team recommend:

'That community organisation in inner areas be actively encouraged, with the aim of greater community self-reliance so that residents may influence decisions which affect their lives. Local authorities should stimulate organisation by the provision of a catalyst where none exists . . . community groups should have direct access to the city's policy-making system . . . the lack of such contracts in Small Heath (the study area) have meant that residents' organisations have, at times, seemed in danger of disintegrating through a sense of their own futility'.

Here we see considerable support for the involvement of the local community in the regeneration of the inner cities. There are many other instances, indeed the notion has become so popular that lip service at least is paid to 'participation' in practically every inner city initiative. In the Glasgow East End project which is in the hands of an alliance of the Regional and District Councils, the Scottish Development Agency and the Scottish Special Housing Association, each of these four bodies has appointed community development or liaison officers and so much 'participation' is going on that the few remaining local residents are hard put to attend all the meetings!

But in these areas, where until recently most residents have been forced into attitudes of apathy or fatalism by the apparent incoherence of the policies which affect their homes and environment and their inability to influence these policies, it is a difficult task to build strong local groups (it is tempting to make the analogy with the de-colonisation of the British Empire since World War II). Groups must be given some real power and resources, and nurtured and supported, and the primary role for professionals involved with them is an educational one. An attitude of 'leave it to me, I know best', though well meaning, defeats the purpose of the exercise.

This is a difficult shift of role for most professionals. Accustomed to having their work interfered with from above, so to speak, by their governmental or local authority paymasters and from the host of bureaucratic gatekeepers in building control and planning departments, they now have an added ingredient, a user client who may be suspicious not only of their competence but also their attitudes and motives. Confidence has to be won by performance, by a high level of accessibility and frankness in discussion and most of all by a clear commitment to the community's well being.

On the other hand, in a more positive light, the rewards of establishing a good working relationship are enormous both to the local group and the architect. The community can achieve tangible results from its work (in contrast to the 'consultations' or perhaps negative results such as the cancellation of proposed road works which are the more usual results of community action). Architects gain the stimulus and challenge of an identifiable and interested client for their work which, for many, more than compensates for the limited nature of the work in conventional architectural terms.

Thus if we return to the three positions which can be taken by the architect when operating with such a community based organisation, it can be argued that he will be doing a positive disservice to that organisation unless he clearly supports their

54

viewpoint. This is not to argue for an attitude of 'my housing association or community group, right or wrong!'; the Association, particularly a new one, will need to understand the restraints under which it has to work, and the underlying reasons for these. Only in this way can it make the decisions which both in short and long term will be to the benefit of its local community. The architect can play a major role in the development of this understanding, but only if he has an attitude of mind which has sympathy for the delicate social structure of the area, attaches importance to the local community and values the contribution of residents to the solution of their problems.

Professional ideologies

It must be recognised that professional attitudes, and ultimately such practical controls as codes of conduct, are based on the architect's ideology — the system of beliefs and attitudes which tacitly support his manner of working and his relationships with clients, builders and professional colleagues. Before proceeding to discuss ways in which the architect's ideology could change to reflect these new relationships to his clients, it may be useful to set down the two existing principal ideological positions of the profession, and contrast them with a new and emerging one. The three positions are summarised in Table 4.1 for comparative purposes.

The first position could loosely be termed the traditional professional one which is enshrined in the RIBA/ARCUK Code of Conduct and whose apotheosis is private practice. It views society as being controlled by a business/professional elite which the architect serves. Professional work is seen as being a-political. The architect is seen as the upholder of aesthetic values in a largely philistine or apathetic society, and the outlook in general is pragmatic in nature.

The second ideology can be seen as a development from the first, perhaps epitomised by Sydney Webb's address to the RIBA in 1917 (Webb, 1964)[21] when he forecast that the profession's role would be as a watchdog on aesthetic and environmental matters and as a servant to *all* sections of society, particularly in the field of housing and community buildings where the then newly started local authority architects' offices would take an increasingly important role. The utopian architect looks forward to a better society and sees his buildings both as directly influencing their users and as symbolising his view of society.

The third, or radical, ideology has emerged from disillusionment with the perceived failures of the first two ideologies to cope with the pressures leading to the decay of the urban environment, and with the ecological crisis, and as a retreat from the traditional political attitudes which are seen as sterile. Explicit political attitudes are seen to permeate the architect's work and not be reserved for the ballot box or

Table 4.1 *Ideology*	*View of Society*	*Attitude to Political Action*	*Attitude to Aesthetics*	*View of Architect's Role*	*Attitudes to Client*	*Attitudes to other Professionals*
Traditional Professional RIBA/ARCUK	Society controlled by a business/ professional elite	If active, these actions not integrated with work (Work is *a-political*)	Architect is up-holder of aesthetic values and tradition in a philistine society	To interpret clients requirements into a building form and be "leader of the building team"	Responsibility is to *sponsor* client	Mutual support in long-term self-interest
Utopian	Sees society as unified and architect's interests as self-evidently same as society's	*As above* but architecture also seen as symbolic of a new society	*As above* but architect may also have duty to 'educate' the public	*As above*	Responsibility is to society as a whole	*As above*
'Radical' Architect	Society made up of interest groups with conflicting views — architect should take sides through his work	Political beliefs directly influence work and working methods. Planning & Architecture seen to be, at root, political activities	Disregards aesthetics — "form follows partici-pation" (Puritan View)	Catalyst, one of a team, 'Midwife' to community's ideas	Responsible primarily to *user* client	Iconoclastic view of profession — believes it is exploitive. Believes in the de-mystifi-cation of profession

spare time activity. There is a strong belief in the decentralis-ation of power and resources to a local level and an iconoclastic view of the profession.

These are necessarily simplifications, even caricatures, and it is not suggested that architects can be pigeon-holed neatly into one or other category. Whilst based on personal obser-vation and experience, the positions proposed have some support. Lipman has emphasised the idealistic 'supra-client' aspirations of some architects 'to foster sociability and engender community-like relations among building users' (Lipman, 1976)[15]. Campbell has distinguished two main dimensions by which architects' values can be differentiated (Campbell, 1971)[3]. The first is a pragmatic or traditionalist dimension, where the architect will be conservative in the emphasis he places on institutions and will resist change in professional organisations and roles. He sees the architect as leader of the building team, and tends to despise principles but works on a set of informal rules or habits which constrain his actions. The contrast is an idealistic or rationalist dimension, where the architect will tend to be more interested in the mechanics of producing a solution than in the quality of the solution proposed, and will want to change the system where it contradicts his principles. His political standpoint will tend to be left-wing or utopian, and he will show a tendency to believe in deter-minism — that the environment influences behaviour so that the architect can control and manipulate physical objects to produce his social ends.

Service or solidarity

The crucial point of difference between the radicals and the two other ideologies is that the former are rooted in what has been described as the 'service ethic' (Williams, 1958)[2] whereas the radicals wish to move towards its alternative, the working-class ethic of solidarity:

'In our own day we have two major interpretations (of community). These are the idea of service, and the idea of solidarity. These have in the main been developed by the middle class and the working class respectively. From Coleridge to Tawney the idea of function and thence of service of the community, has been most valuably stressed, in opposition to the individualist claim. The stress has been confirmed by the generations of training which substantiate the ethical practice of our professions, and of our public and civil service. As against the practice of laissez-faire, and of self-service, this has been a major achievement which has done much for the peace and welfare of our society. Yet the working-class ethic, of solidarity, has also been a major achievement and it is the difference of this from the idea of service which must now be stressed . . .

A very large part of English middle-class education is devoted to the training of servants. This is much more its characteristic than a training of leadership, as the stress on conformity and on respect for authority shows. In so far as it is, by definition, the training of upper servants, it includes, of course, the instilling of that kind of confidence which will enable the upper servants to supervise and direct the lower servants . . .

The idea of service, ultimately, is no substitute for the idea of active mutual responsibility, which is the other version of community. Few men can give the best of themselves as servants; it is the reduction of man to a function. Further, the servant, if he is to be a good servant, can never really question the order of things; his sense of authority is too strong. Yet the existing order is in fact subject to almost overwhelming pressures. The break through, into what together we want to make of our lives, will need qualities which the idea of service not only fails to provide, but, in its limitations of our minds, actively harms'.

Williams uses 'community' here in the sense of a community of interests rather than in the narrower interpretation of this chapter and the crucial point for the architectural profession, which has been grasped by the radicals, is that if architects are to work successfully with the emerging local groups in the inner cities they must move from a position of primary allegiance to their profession to one of allegiance to their client community. Most architects believe that their contract with society is based on their skill and knowledge allied to adherence to an ethical code which guarantees a disinterested service to the client. Thus they see themselves primarily as members of a professional community to whom they look for support and approbation for their work. They serve clients in a temporary or peripatetic way, and in extreme cases (too often the avant garde of the profession) the client is seen as a necessary evil with their 'best' work being done for imaginary or idealised clients.

The alternative approach, solidarity with the client community, postulates an alternative social contract. While still based on knowledge and skill, these are allied to a clear commitment to sharing the values and aspirations of the community. The professional ethic of service to the client is redefined as a new way of working with a clearly chosen client: a client who is affected by and uses the building rather than the client who controls the resources. This is in essence the stance adopted by the examples of successful rehabilitation described and can be further illustrated by the manner in which ASSIST works with residents' groups in Glasgow on environmental improvement schemes for tenement backcourts.

The first job is to help the community to organise itself and obtain resources. The system of grants and the need for a representative body are discussed, and visits to other schemes are arranged. The discussions develop into an analysis of the problems in the area and the priorities for improvement. The architect speaks with experience and knowledge but does not impose his values and solutions. This is a very difficult process because often local people defer to the architect's knowledge, and are very reluctant to criticise his ideas. He has to encourage an open and relaxed style of meeting where people are not afraid to put forward half-formed or daft-sounding ideas because these will often spark off trains of thought in others. Sometimes alternatives are prepared and shown to the group to help get ideas flowing, at others the architect deliberately refuses to suggest any solutions until the group put forward theirs (sometimes little happens at such meetings until they

begin to break up, whereupon someone diffidently produces a meticulously detailed scheme from his back pocket).

Often the architect may feel that the group's aims are too low — they merely wish to re-establish old boundaries long since missing, and tidy up the area. He may argue for a more ambitious and imaginative scheme but must not pursue his views in the teeth of sustained opposition — unless the scheme has support in the area it will not be an improvement nor last very long. Local people and the architect may get involved in self-help schemes such as the demolition of dilapidated washhouses, and in self-build schemes as in Black Road (Knevitt, 1975)[14].

To the more radically minded, such a procedure is not only seen as meeting the short term goals of improving a small part of the environment, but part of a much more important and longer term process of community development; that the community should not only better its living conditions but also gain confidence in dealing with officialdom, gain understanding of some of the forces which have lead to the decay of their environment and to their own poverty and lack of job opportunities, and regain the belief that by concerted action they can begin to change some of these things. Thus any project involving physical improvements can be seen as a catalyst for community development rather than an end in itself; the aim of all professionals involved in the project should be to see that not only is the environment improved but the community left stronger too.

Dilemmas of the architect's new role

Even if this extra political dimension is set aside, life is still not easy for the 'radical' architect. At the moment they have to act in a political milieu with which they are at odds; apart from situations such as the Glasgow community based housing associations described above, user clients do not have any control over resources. Hence it is difficult for architects acting for such clients to get support.

At its inception ASSIST was fortunate in getting backing from an independent source, the Wates Foundation, which in turn triggered off more money from government sources. These grants were given with 'no strings attached' allowing ASSIST freedom to experiment within the limits of responsibility set by its own commitment to the district in which it was working. Such a situation is rare, and ASSIST has recently gone through the severe strains, in another district, of trying to keep the confidence of both residents for whom it is working and of the local authority on whom it is dependent for support, in a situation where the residents are using ASSIST's work to attack the authority. Such situations are not comfortable and make nonsense of much of the rubbish written about 'community architecture' in the press.

For example, in an article on Birmingham's decentralised project teams which are carrying out improvements in the city's Housing Action Area (HAA) and GIA programme, the comment was made (Building Design, 1977)[1] on the role of architects in such teams:

'It places the architect in a fascinating position: he is there not only to carry out the Council's policies, but to carry them out in a way that all the local residents find acceptable. He must allow them to take the decisions and must, therefore, advise and inform them of all the possible advantages and disadvantages of particular decisions that are taken'.

The confusion of thought is matched by the confusion of syntax; is the architect to advise on the advantages and disadvantages before or after the decision is taken? What happens if the council's policies conflict with the resident's decision? Is the architect to try and influence the council's decisions in the light of local feeling, or is he to 'steer' local opinion in the required (council's) direction? A fascinating position indeed! This comment reflects the false assumption underlying the Skeffington Report (Ministry of Public Buildings and Works)[17] — the belief that if the professional does his job properly a consensus view will emerge which will be the 'right' plan for an area. Experience shows that there is more likely to be fairly irreconcilable differences of view amongst local people, and between them and the local authority, and the architect or planner will be in the middle of the cross-fire.

Architects who wish to move towards this new relationship with the client are also discouraged by the codes of behaviour which now purport to uphold the professional ethic. These codes were originally designed to protect the public, and the profession, in an era of laissez-faire capitalism, and they emphasised the separation of the professional from other members of society. Recently an alternative definition of professionalism has been proposed which places more emphasis on knowledge and skill rather than on an ethical code and it is argued that professions exist where the application of knowledge that is socially important cannot be reduced to rules and procedures because cases are different, and that in such situations responsibility is entrusted to *persons* rather than *procedures* (Malpass, 1975)[16] and (Hillier, 1977)[12]. This move to a knowledge base rather than a socially defined one by the profession would free the architect to act in the best interests of the community, which, it can be argued, is really the true interpretation of the profession's ethical code.

The radical position also calls into question the rigid demarcation between architect and builder. Young architects, increasingly frustrated by such divisions, are moving into various types of community based builder/designer/self-help organiser roles, often in the housing rehabilitation field where they can provide the low-income owner with an all-in service, making use of improvement grants. In doing so they are responding in a direct way to the community's needs, providing a service which is more appropriate in the circumstances than the traditional architect/contractor relationship, and, as a bonus, re-acquiring the lost skills of craftsmanship and the organisation of building work from which the architectural profession cut itself off a hundred years ago.

The wider viewpoint

In this chapter some of the challenges encountered by architects involved in housing rehabilitation have been described, some of the profession's assumptions have been questioned and a new approach to the relationships between architects and society has been postulated. Can these arguments be extended to a wider field than rehabilitation? Surely they can. Architects have always prided themselves on standing for quality in the environment but this has usually been interpreted as wresting some kind of aesthetic quality out of buildings within our current social and economic system. The question now is to what extent this is still possible. The organisation of society and the means of production is conducted on such a large scale that it has become increasingly difficult for the individual to relate in any meaningful way to the physical artefacts which are the expression of this organisation. This is particularly evident in housing and in urban design. The change in position of Professor Habraken illustrates the problem. In 1961 he believed that it lay in the architect's power to produce more humane housing by designing support structures and a kit of parts from which individual tenants could fashion their own dwellings (Habraken, 1961)[9]. By 1976 he had reached the conclusion that architects were helpless victims of a system for the provision of housing which has placed all the power in the hands of professionals and bureaucrats and none in the hands of the users of the dwellings (he calls the latter a 'fine-grained' exercise of power as against the 'coarse-grained' public power). He says:

'The signs point out that our actions can give less and less an answer to the questions which are put to us. If we listen to the criticism which is expressed on all sides regarding the built environment . . . do we really believe that we can provide an answer within the presently operative, one-sided power structure?' (Habraken, 1976)[10].

It is significant that many of the most highly regarded modern housing schemes are small in scale. Quality is very difficult to maintain in large schemes. There are the exceptions but their rarity demonstrates that the level of skill required is hard to come by, and relies essentially on the manipulation of forms and the celebration of every incident, however trivial, on the existing site, to give an impression of the variety and richness achieved naturally under a less centralised patronage system. Thus we reach a position where it can be argued that unless there is a fairly fundamental change in the way society is organised we cannot achieve the more humane architecture many are calling for. Many people have argued that society must move towards a 'smaller-grained' exercise of power, and more localised control of resources (Schumacher)[18]; (Turner)[19]; (Ward, 1974)[20] and (Goodman, 1968)[8]. We appear to be at what could be an important turning point — society is at once pulled towards larger organisation (e.g. the European Economic Community) and towards more decentralisation (the movements towards devolution within Great Britain and the increasing commitment to local decision-making in the rhetoric of the inner-city reports).

What role have architects to play in this? Habraken is clear that they must speak out:

'It no longer makes sense to look for new dwelling types to provide the answers, but one must . . . look for new process forms, new management forms, new financing forms, and new production methods. But above all it is . . . time to speak soundly and openly about the . . . introduction of the fine-grain exercise of power' (Habraken)[10].

Architects can only speak out if they have prepared themselves for the alternative manner of operation, and have explored the contradiction and dilemmas inherent in their organisation and accustomed ways of operating when faced with different, smaller and more localised clients. The argument here is for the development of a new relationship between architects and their clients, based on the experience of housing rehabilitation in an inner-city context. It is doubtful whether architects (and other professionals) will be able to contribute with any success to the alleviation of inner-city problems unless they do move to such a new working relationship — success in this context being measured from the local area's point of view rather than in terms of the architect's reputation and professional acclaim. However, it would be futile to expect the profession to change its attitudes overnight — many architects have sincerely felt objections to the changes proposed. But the need has been demonstrated and the profession is ill-prepared at the moment. In the long term the potential for change lies in architectural education but this can only be achieved by change both in attitudes to design and to the client inculcated into students, and in the technical skills taught. In the shorter term, relaxations in professional codes are required to enable architects who wish to work for local communities to respond to those communities' needs in the most appropriate way.

References

1. Building Design *Refurbishment & Maintenance Supplement, Building Design* (July 1977)
2. Burns, W. *New Towns for Old,* Leonard Hill, London (1963)
3. Campbell, S. *Ideological Dimensions in Design Decision Making,* MSc Thesis, Strathclyde University, Glasgow (1971)
4. Department of the Environment *Inner Area Studies: Summaries of Consultants' Final Reports,* HMSO, London (1977)
5. Farrell, T. 'Buildings as a Resource', *Architecture: Opportunities, Achievements,* (Edited by B. Goldstein), RIBA Publications, London (1977)
6. Gans, H. *The Urban Villagers,* The Free Press, Chicago (1962)
7. Goldstein, B. (Editor) *Architecture; Opportunities, Achievements,* RIBA Publications, London (1977)
8. Goodman, P. *People or Personnel?,* Vintage Books, New York (1968)
9. Habraken, N. J. *Supports: an alternative to mass housing,* (original Dutch edition 1961), Architectural Press, London (1972)
10. Habraken, N. J. 'The limits of professionalism', *A. A. Quarterly,* London (1976)
11. Harms, H. 'User and community involvement in housing and its effect on professionalism', *Freedom to Build,* (Edited by J. Turner and R. Fichter), MacMillan, New York (1972)
12. Hillier, W. Private Communication (1977)
13. Jacobs, J. *The Death & Life of the Great American Cities,* Jonathan Cape, London (1962)
14. Knevitt, C., 'Community Architect Mk 1 — Rod Hackney', *Building Design,* 258 (July 1975)
15. Lipman, A. 'Professional Ideology', *Journal of Architectural Research,* 5, No. 2 (1976)
16. Malpass, P. 'Professionalism and the role of architects in Local Authority housing', *Journal of the Royal Institute of British Architects* (June 1975)
17. Ministry of Public Building & Works 'Report on Public Participation in Planning', *(Skeffington Report),* HMSO, London (1969)
18. Schumacher, E. *Small is Beautiful,* Blond & Briggs, London (1973)
19. Turner, J. and Fichter, R. (Editors) *Freedom to Build,* MacMillan, New York (1972)
20. Ward, C. *Tenants Take Over,* Architectural Press, London (1974)
21. Webb, S. 'The functions of an Architectural Society', *RIBA Journal,* 71, No. 4 (1964)
22. Williams, R. *Culture & Society 1780–1950,* Chatto & Windus, London (1958)
23. Wilmot, P. and Young, M. *Family & Kinship in East London,* Routledge & Kegan Paul, London (1957)

CHAPTER
FIVE

A Designer's Approach to Rehabilitation

Three inner-London cases

Terry Farrell

As a long established developed nation, with virtually static population and economic growth, do we need any new buildings other than replacement ones? The answer is probably a cautious 'yes'. In particular, new types of building are needed to meet changes in how we do things (e.g. as the airport succeeds the railway station). Newly located buildings are needed to meet internal social and economic re-structuring (e.g. as in the drift from the north to the south and inner city to suburbs) and new buildings will always be needed as the presentation of image of a user to express, say, his self-esteem and taste.

Compared with the rest of the world, however, we do have enough buildings. Our existing buildings have become a resource like coal in the ground or oil under the sea; they represent a considerable expenditure of man hours, energy, materials and equipment; money has been borrowed and spent on them in land acquisition and fees, subsequent care and maintenance; society has expended time and energy 'bedding down' new buildings into the environment — establishing relationships with buildings around and within a growing framework of constraints from light angles to planning precedents, communications and services infrastructures. Society itself is in part created by the environment; our concept of law, politics, family, etc is interwoven and inextricably linked to the environment we have made — to paraphrase Churchill's statement 'we mould our buildings and our buildings mould us'.

In addition to the investment made, there is also the consideration of savings on future expenditure by keeping existing buildings by extending their lives and, when change is necessary, of finding new ways to use them. The actual cost of building new when compared with rehabilitation is always far greater than the mere difference in building cost.

Given the above situation, the role that can be played by the architect who values his design skills as important tools to be utilised in rehabilitating buildings should be examined. The most important aspects of these skills are an advanced ability to conceptualise three dimensionally, a knowledge and feeling for a particularly wide field of building technology (new and old), ingenuity — to overcome the many problems invariably not of the designer's own making, and a developed interest in

the resource (invariably expressed financially) raison d'etre of each and every project.

Now that we have such a large and useful building stock, two approaches exist to its re-use, both equally relevant. Individual projects often require a combination of both approaches: invariably a matching and adaptation process of the user's brief and the buildings themselves takes place, unlike a new building where a user/client feels his relatively static needs can be met by a tailor-made solution. The designer, therefore, can be as creatively involved in re-examining the user's potential for change as well as that of any building in which he wishes to be accommodated. Three projects in London are examined to show how this matching process of adaptation of user and building takes place. In the first case, the predominance of attention is on the user's potential to re-design his own functions (the Student's Hostel, Paddington); in the second case an approach by an owner, and his buildings and the uses to which they lend themselves became the starting point (Comyn Ching, Covent Garden) and, in the third case a project is described where there is a fair balance of both aspects as starting points (The Colonnades, Westminster).

These three projects cover a wide range of rehabilitation work, and are generally concerned with large groups of buildings. Experience over the last twelve years with a considerable number of one-off conversions to domestic buildings has been responsible for the development of many ideas about design, not merely in relation to old buildings. As an example, the inherent flexibility of many of the Georgian and Victorian domestic buildings in London (which is a direct result of their simple cellular structure) has been very influential in the development of ideas of adaptability in new work, especially housing and industrial buildings. Particular design solutions which represent the optimum integration of all these problems will emerge only after the designer has fully understood the way that the building works and what specific physical characteristic holds the key to solving the problem. It is strongly felt that a detailed resource survey ought to be a responsibility of building owners and that this survey work should involve applying a designer's skill in appraisal of potential future uses.

59

Anticipating future requirements

Virtually no organisation is static; anticipating future requirements for changes in process or organisation, space or servicing requirements will ensure that the best possible match of users to buildings will result. An example of this would be the study of all buildings in the ownership of one particular organisation – such as a university, local authority or large manufacturing organisation – which could result in a suitable rationalisation of patterns of occupation or servicing thus obviating the need for redevelopment or expansion which had previously been anticipated.

Whichever of the two starting points finally predominate in any particular problem it is clear that flexibility, (in the sense of allowing for the maximum adaptation by building owner or user, at a level appropriate to the particular building or element of a building under consideration), will ensure that the building will continue to offer a valuable contribution to the economic and organisational requirements of its users for the full term of its extended life. Provided, therefore, that adequate initial investment is made to ensure that the basic structural and constructional fabric of the building is put into a very good state (and the current allocation of money within cost ceilings, applicable to residential rehabilitation intended to have a life of thirty years, needs to be very carefully considered in this respect), there is no reason to suppose that a building which is rehabilitated, with due regard to safeguarding and extending its existing flexibility, should not outlast many recent buildings which have been designed to a tight 'form follows function' design philosophy.

Given, then, the above two ways of approaching the problem which will, hopefully with the full involvement of the real users of the building, result in the emergence of a particular design approach, a second important topic for consideration is the strategy that is adopted to implement this design concept. The most significant aspect of all the schemes illustrated is that they either entail 'addition' or 'subtraction' processes. There are, of course, instances where little physical alteration needs to be made to a building; this process can be called 'restoration' in its non-historical sense. Where true rehabilitation is necessary there is a fundamental requirement to restructure the organisation of the building; in such cases this can be achieved either by the addition or by the subtraction of specific parts of the building. A good example of this is a scheme for a boys' home at Wellbury House, near Hitchen, Herts; it was only with the greatest of difficulty that the client, who had just bought a large, rambling country house which he thought was only just big enough for his requirements, was persuaded to actually pull down all the outbuildings – which represented nearly a third of his current investment – so that his strictly limited budget would be sufficient to put the rest of the building in good order. The resultant 'hard core' of the building was then studied and, by careful use of existing

60

features such as the large central staircase, it was possible to reorganise the remaining space to completely satisfy the original brief.

An example of the opposite technique, where addition provides the solution to a problem, is the Paddington Student Hostel in London; in this instance the new service tower to the rear of the building allowed all small service rooms to be concentrated in one location, where they functioned efficiently and, at the same time, released all the space within the existing houses for their optimum reorganisation as residential accommodation.

Basic criteria for consideration

When faced with an existing building, and a brief for major rehabilitation or the incorporation of new uses, the designer should therefore consider the following criteria before any fundamental design decisions are taken:

1. What is the building like at the moment; how is it constructed and in what manner is it divided into compartments, and why was it built that way in the first place?

2. What is the current state of the building fabric, and will it realistically achieve a life which is consistent with the use required and the likely expenditure? It does not follow that, because, a building has stood for one hundred years, it will continue to stand without considerable effort.

3. What is the relationship between the money which must be expended to ensure a good life expectancy and the money which is necessary to allow for the new use of the building? It is often worthwhile spending a larger proportion of the available money on putting the fabric into good order than in allowing for the specific requirements of the new use – provided that the new services, etc, that are installed are organised in such a way that they do not inhibit future requirement and are a contribution to the potential flexibility of the building.

4. What are the particular characteristics of the building which can be exploited to achieve an optimum solution to the new requirements?

5. What are the respective financial implications of rehabilitation or redevelopment? The factors which are often omitted from this equation are that a building in use is a valuable resource, and that rehabilitation is fundamentally a quicker process than redevelopment; it is also a process which is labour intensive and not material and energy intensive, which should now be of particular significance in the wider economic sense.

These criteria are set down in design guide check list form in *Figure 5.1*. In essence, this means taking a good look at what you have and what you are being asked to do to it, and ensuring that your proposals have a sound economic and physical basis. The particular arrangement of the building, or certain aspects of the brief, will often suggest an answer which at first sight is in contradiction with the client's requirements but which is in fact a rational solution to the whole problem.

Just as buildings of the 1950s and 1960s may well prove to be low in resource value, so might our over-articulated urban design projects, with their exaggerated emphasis on physical complexity. How will we be able to simply adapt our concrete underground garages, under-passes, over-passes, and raised pedestrian decks? Planners have over-specialised land use, causing investment in different functions to be over-structured. Industry, living spaces and educational centres are too limited and fixed in location and dimensions.

In any building resources log, we should seriously examine many large schemes less than twenty-five years old, exploring the potential for heavy infill in places like the wide-open university campuses of Sheffield and Brunel. Spatially and architecturally, they would benefit from increased intensity of use with a wider variety of building types — use introduced so that existing services would become more economic.

A particularly exciting project for example would be to convert the London South Bank 'culture estate' by adding say, one thousand dwellings, a shopping complex and pubs onto the same land presently occupied by the National Theatre, the Hayward buildings and the Festival Hall. The terraces and riverside could be exploited as amenities and leisure resources would then be valued to a fuller extent twenty-four hours a day! Density in itself is neither a 'good' or a 'bad' thing. It is how the experience of high density is handled environmentally that is critical. During the Westminster rehabilitation study it was considered that some estates of over 200 persons per acre (500 per hectare) would benefit from the addition of low rise housing alongside pedestrian routes.

Looking at some recent schemes for vast, very expensive leisure centres in the Middle East, one is struck by how much leisure amenity resources are built-in in Britain, waiting to be better used. The canal system, for example, if re-built today would cost more than Concorde, yet for only a few million pounds (or just more of the current voluntary energy) a network of valuable leisure routes could be opened up, more widely than at present, combining countryside, industrial archaeology, a bit of travel and some physical exercise at the locks.

The nature of change

Certain American architects represent the extreme positions in the architectural philosophical debate about the nature of change in our built environment. Louis Kahn epitomises the search for static values. To him the perfect school was a school for all time that answered all school needs. He told his students to say to themselves, in effect, 'what is the true nature of a school? Is a school a man under a tree talking to a group of people or is it a building? Somewhere in the realm of all building form throughout history and over all societies is a thing that is unchanging called school.'

Buckminster Fuller, by contrast, concentrated his attentions on the fluidity of form and was followed by architects who sought, through technology, a means of creating individual spaces that could be anything the user required, from school to house to hospital, indefinitely.

Both approaches are extremes and the apparent dichotomy is already resolved in the ultimate concentration of building form which is the city. The city is the place where change is most possible and where social activity is at its peak. Yet, by definition, a city exists because of its place; its situation gives it its whole existence and its ability to be defined as being distinct from any other place. Preoccupations then range in type from rehabilitation to new work and in concept from change to non-change. The identifying phrase is that the appropriate level of flexibility (i.e. anticipation of change) achieves the most lasting value (i.e. a resource).

Architectural solutions that epitomise total flexibility fail because they are just like Gertrude Stein's definition of Los Angeles, 'There is no there there'. Such extreme buildings as Beaubourg in Paris are over-serviced, over-structured, and generally over-designed to accommodate all potential changes in an unrealistic and uneconomical way. Equally, the totally static extreme is irrelevant because it is useless in a very short period of time; one would categorise here more than just the obvious architectural monuments and include the more recent and less obvious 'monuments' such as car park buildings (which have environmental standards fit only for machines that are specifically of this moment), motorways, specialised hospitals, and the like.

A strategic view of rehabilitation allows new technology to be used where appropriate. There does not need to be a choice between high technology or conservation; they both have their place. For example, in the Student Hostel both approaches were developed simultaneously. Rehabilitation can be an entirely strategic exercise with very little architectural input on building work. The Westminster study for example concentrates on modernising properties with tenants in situ with the least possible disturbance to them.

At the other end of the scale, new building forms using new technologies have been developed to enable housing and factories for example, to change and meet future needs, i.e. to facilitate future rehabilitation. There can be, in other words, a consistent approach that should be applied by the architect designer in rehabilitation and new work.

Case Study 1: Student Hostel, Paddington

Most of our institutions have experienced an increasing rate of change in their outlook and aspirations and therefore their accommodation expectations. Education in particular has been going through a rapid democratisation process requiring radical re-structuring of existing buildings, as well as new thinking in the briefs given to architects.

An excellent example can be quoted of a Scottish school's expansion programme, where it was possible for the architect to demonstrate that if the client's concept of his own organisation and spatial pre-disposition was altered, the need for new buildings could be virtually eliminated. This demonstration centred around changing the supposed need for 'specialist' classrooms (chemistry, art, physics, biology, etc) to a general pool of standardised, non-specialised classrooms, with specialised equipment trolleys which could be wheeled from any one classroom to another. The idea foundered on the educationalist's inability to change i.e. the 'specialist' teacher's need to maintain territorial rights was considered insurmountable and so new classrooms and new buildings had to be built.

The residential accommodation of students has changed radically from post-war attempts to imitate the older universities' formal, on campus, residences which were direct extensions of the tradition-based academic institutions themselves. Increasingly today students are being seen as just another aspect of society's total housing problem, albeit slightly specialised as to uniformity of occupation/age groups and as to periods of tenure and times of occupation. When this climate of change was at its most rapid, in the late 1960s, an approach was made by a private, church-based body endeavouring to fill a gap not met by the state system – the accommodation of foreign students in London, particularly those from Africa and Asia who were experiencing some difficulty in obtaining accommodation in a city where, unfortunately, there was prejudice coupled with acute shortage. The traditional university structure at that time had funds, or access to funds, to continue buying land and developing hostels under their direct control, as extensions of the universities themselves. As a result students accommodation was tailor-made to be a very formalised self-contained arrangement, often out-of-town, with minimal self-catering and centralised recreation, administration and dining facilities.

Being outside this structure of relatively privileged power and finance, the client had to modify his concept of the 'student hostel' as much as was necessary to get his scheme off the ground, and a joint architect/client re-appraisal of user needs was required to make this possible.

From the first discussion, a rehabilitation project was considered the only likely solution. A low capital cost would be incurred in purchasing large Victorian houses in central London, the time period before occupation would be much shorter with savings in interest and an earlier contribution being made to a pressing housing problem, and, most important, this was virtually the only way a central location could be obtained with resultant savings in students' travelling costs and administration overheads for this rather small organisation.

62

Centralising of services

To accommodate 175 students with 25 in-residence staff, a row of six houses in Bayswater, Paddington, was purchased for a low sum, primarily because of the bad state of the properties. Grant-giving bodies and the University Grants Committee (UGC) wanted the conventional accommodation solution, i.e. single study-bedrooms of $9 m^2$ ($100 ft^2$), a given proportion of communal facilities provided on a unit area per capita basis and certain resident staff quarters (*Figures 5.2, 5.3 and 5.4*).

The six houses had intrinsic qualities and problems of their own which prevented such an obvious solution being adopted. Firstly, the poor condition of the properties meant a minimum of actual building change could take place, so that the existing spaces should wherever possible be left as they were, and that a maximum number of students should be accommodated (irrespective of the communal space and single room requirements) simply to attract enough per-capita grants to raise the total fabric to a state where it was fit to live in. Single study-bedrooms were provided wherever possible, but many sharing-doubles and even 'group' rooms for short stay students were considered appropriate simply because these larger rooms existed and could not be altered within the budget. Communal rooms had to be accommodated in windowless basement areas, again to release all daylit rooms for students' habitable accommodation.

Three main design approaches or solutions were adopted to enable this unusual and challenging brief to work. All bathrooms and other sanitary accommodation (e.g. laundries, tea making, etc.) were located in a 'service tower' outside the buildings to maintain all existing space for maximum student occupation and to reduce interference with the existing structure to a minimum and thus save costs. All existing spaces were retained in the eventual spatial solution and their intrinsic architectural qualities explored and developed rather than a new spatial order imposed. Furniture was specially designed in trolley form to achieve very low cost and a flexible but standardised provision, so that privacy and independence could be obtained in shared rooms and the existing spaces would not be interfered with, at greater expense and loss of character, by fitted furniture.

The idea of providing a 'service tower' structure outside the main buildings but centrally placed in relation to them appealed to the clients, not only on the grounds that this freed space in the buildings to accommodate more students but also because it obviated the need to insert pipework into the old structure (sometimes through walls 750 mm (2 ft 6 in) thick) (*Figures 5.5 and 5.6*). A further technical reason was that none of the existing brickwork of the house could offer sufficient compressive strength to support the 1.6 Ml (3600 gal) water tank needed for the hostel.

Centralising the sanitary facilities meant that plumbing was, in general, cheaper and easier to maintain, and it also appealed to the clients on the grounds that it would inevitably result in

1. *GENERAL:* Think strategically — range from brief-making to building design. Rehab design is essentially a *matching* process — matching *USER*(s) & *BUILDING*(s)

2. *THE USER*

Known user

Understand the user — always build organisation diagram — remember to change users activity pattern and/or make best match with building. Requires a good understanding of how user operated.

Can the user be re-designed? It often costs more to alter buildings than the way we have structured our activities. Consider design input here to be essential.

Users finance resources — strings attached to aid (eg: Improvement grants (etc). Also who will maintain building and staff it: is proposed building rehab capable of being kept up to standard from resources available for maintenance.

Possible future changes that will/could take place in users character/ organisational structure, etc. What in-built allowances should be made for such future change.

Gross space requirements to be assessed against *net* requirements allowing for dual space usage (space invariably costs money from capital and current expenditures).

Unknown user

The *LOCATION* is prime determinant of use.

The buildings are second determinants — what do they lend themselves to best?

What expressed needs are evident, i.e: what activities are chasing space?

Compatibility of newly introduced uses with existing — not only social and economic, also fire escape, building regs, planning.

Is a money earner needed to subsidise improvements/ running costs.

Is there a money surplus which could subsidise a needy user.

When new users selected apply 'known user' checklist on left.

3. *THE BUILDING*

  (a) *Physical condition*

   First priority is repairs and restoration of structure and weather enclosing elements. What life expectation can be anticipated after rehab? How does this match user?

   Materials of construction — what condition; damp proofing, insulation; each building type has its own type and range of defects. What materials can be *salvaged* for re-use?

   Structure: is expert advice needed? Where can alterations be made and where not? What repair work is needed whatever the rehab scheme?

   Services: within the dwelling and outside the dwelling: can drains and other mains services take the load proposed? Again, is salvage and re-use possible?

  (b) *Space gain and space change*

   Within the building envelope; what is the total volume? Floor to floor heights? Is there scope for extra accommodation? Can roof space be used? What structural limitations are there to space re-structuring?

   Outside the building envelope; can spaces between buildings be filled? Can building be extended by annexes, extensions, etc? Can extra storeys be added above rooftops? Can complete new buildings be added to work in conjunction with the existing? What extra space requirements are being generated by new activities, e.g. car parking, servicing, refuse storage and collection, etc.
   Should the area be reduced, or outbuildings demolished in order to achieve overall viable scheme.

  (c) *Architectural character*

   What fabric should be kept? Is there a range of priorities from features 'to be kept at all costs' to 'kept if possible'?

   Does building need restoring in some respects (all respects?) to a previous condition which is much more satisfactory/ attractive than at present?

   What aesthetic rules of existing building — massing, details, angles of roofs, eaves heights, materials: can these/should these be observed?

  (d) *Future change*

   Can spaces be articulated so that they are not over-determined? Can services be zoned and structured to allow for future growth and change?

Figure 5.1 A design check list

Figure 5.2 (above, left) Rear yards – before rehabilitation
Figure 5.3 (above, right) Rear yards – approximately where service tower is now
Figure 5.4 (bottom, left) Front facade before rehabilitation
Figure 5.5 (centre, right) Service tower under construction
Figure 5.6 (bottom, right) Rear view of hostel after rehabilitation

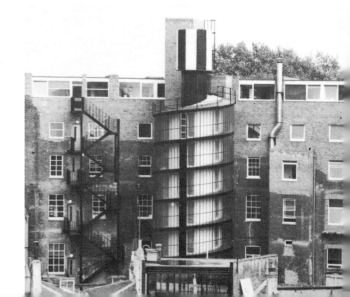

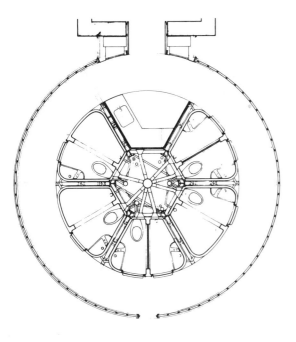

Figure 5.7 Service tower plan

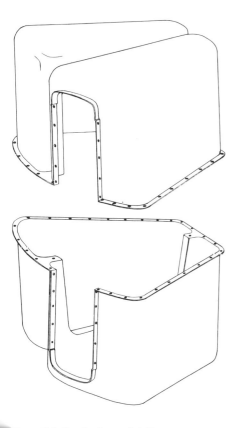

Figure 5.8 Service tower details

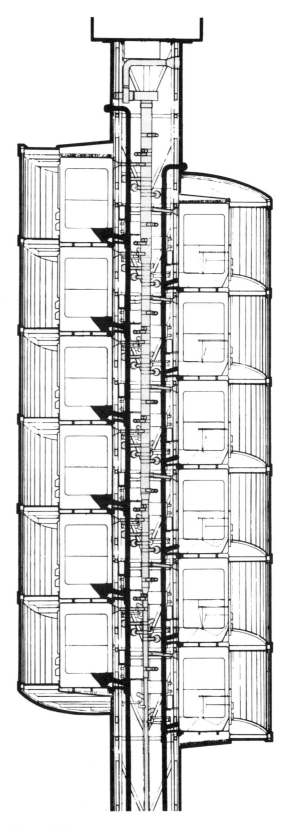

Figure 5.9 Service tower section

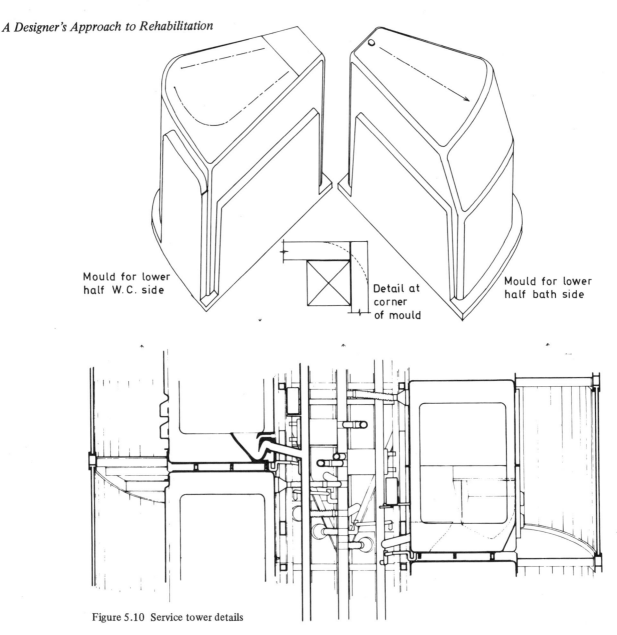

Mould for lower
half W.C. side

Detail at
corner
of mould

Mould for lower
half bath side

Figure 5.10 Service tower details

considerable communal interaction, both between occupants of the same floor and from floor to floor throughout the student-occupied part of the hostel. The aim, therefore, was to provide an arrangement of bathrooms which was easily accessible from all floors of the hostel, even though the floor to ceiling heights varied from 2.6–4 m (8 ft 6 in–13 ft 9 in) (*Figure 5.7*). The brief for the bathrooms themselves was to provide 'hygienic, washable, waterproof boxes with efficient and easily maintainable services'. It was also required that a high proportion of the units should be showers rather than baths (*Figure 5.8 and 5.9*).

The structural limitations were considerable, in that no loads could be imposed on either the mews wall or the back wall of the hostel buildings, and the use of a crane was made quite impossible since the area where the tower was to stand was totally enclosed by buildings (*Figure 5.3*). A further structural consideration was the need to carry the significant

point loading of the water tank down to the ground. The structure used could be described as a sectionalised 'mast' arrangement, similar in fact to a tower crane, with I-section beams hung from the mast by hangers made from angle sections. The sections of the core were made from six vertical 150 mm (6 in) universal column sections which were cross-braced with square section tubes. These core sections were placed one on top of the other by means of a lifting beam which was cantilevered from the roof of the existing houses (*Figure 5.10*).

When the horizontal beams were in place, light tubular sections were bolted between them forming a means of support for the plastic pods, which were then winched into position using a revolving lifting beam fixed to the top of the core. As each pod was bolted into place on its support beams, the ramp unit which was adjacent to it was winched into position and bolted to the respective end portions of the horizontal

I-beam. The ramp units form a steadily rising helix with a gradient of about one in eight (*Figure 5.11*). This means that the helix made a complete revolution every 2.2 m (7 ft 3 in) rise. This enables the spiral to correspond with three out of the five student floors, so that level access to the tower at these three positions was made possible. At the third and fifth floors short flights of stairs had to be incorporated in the conversion in order to make a connection to the helical ramp.

The bathroom unit

The bathroom pods were manufactured from glass reinforced plastic (GRP) and were further reinforced in their bases by chipboard and in their roofs by plywood. The walls of the GRP units were stiffened by 'somic' reinforcement. Each pod was made from four quarter-shells which were joined together in the factory so that the pod could be delivered as a complete unit. By using six moulds to produce these quarter mouldings and by assembling the quarter mouldings in different ways, two types of pod were produced. The basic bathroom unit used shells from four moulds to make a complete pod. The other basic pod consisted of a unit similar in shape and size to the bathroom unit, but divided along the centre line to produce two compartments. This unit was made from only two moulds as it was possible to 'hand' the shells about the centre line of the unit i.e. the floor moulding on the left hand side could be used as the roof moulding on the right hand side and vice versa. The washbasin is not an integral part of the bathroom unit but is planted on to the wall using the horizontal join between the mouldings as its anchorage. The complete pod weighs approximately 113 kg (250 lb) and can easily be handled by three or four men.

There are thirty pods in all, eighteen of the standard bathroom type and twelve divided into two compartments (i.e. shower compartment and w.c. compartment). It is worth noting that, for this limited production run, using normal hand lay up techniques, the mould cost for a unit amounts to about one sixth of its total cost. Materials cost is therefore the significant factor and modifications and variations can be made at relatively little extra cost.

The spatial solution

When considering the spatial solution it should be realised that the six houses were each originally built as grand Victorian town houses in the 'Upstairs, Downstairs' tradition. The ground and particularly the first floors are impressive reception areas and living space, with a grand connecting staircase to each, and on the second and third floors, family bedrooms; basement and fourth floors were small, low-ceilinged, servants quarters and work areas, with hidden side or back stairs connecting to the main vertical circulation. The basic spatial structure then is vertical, hierarchical and depended on servant labour to overcome the considerable height of 20–22 m (65–70 ft) from top floor to basement.

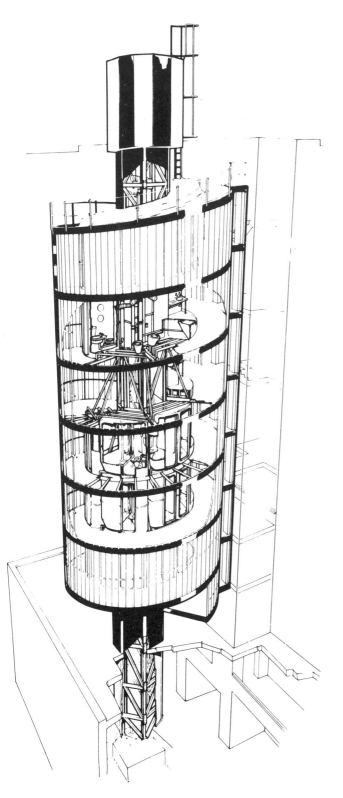

Figure 5.11 Service tower details

67

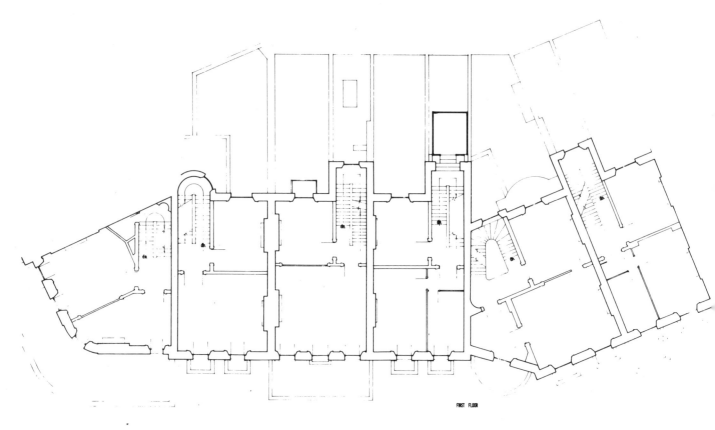

Figure 5.12 Hostel plan before rehabilitation

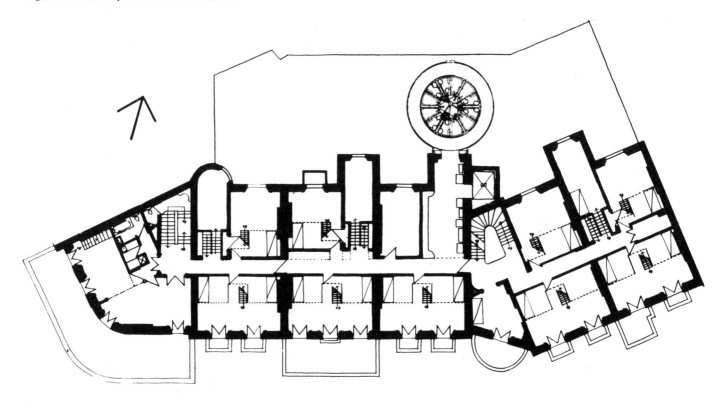

Figure 5.13 Hostel plan after rehabilitation

68

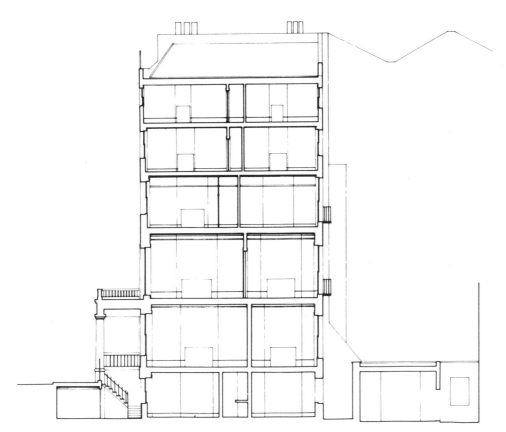

Figure 5.14 Hostel section before rehabilitation

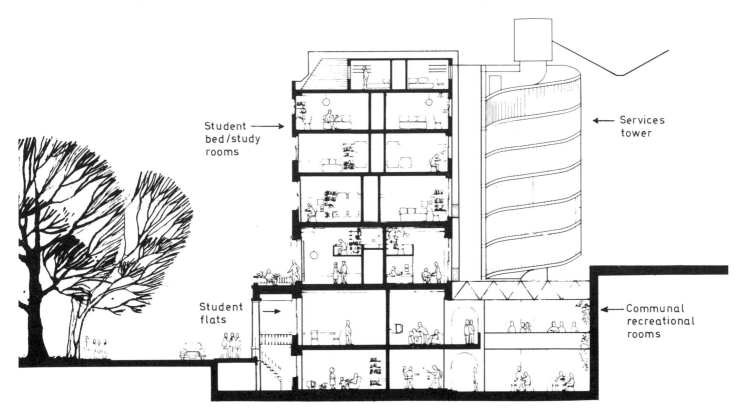

Student
bed/study
rooms

Services
tower

Student
flats

Communal
recreational
rooms

Figure 5.15 Hostel section after rehabilitation

To complicate matters further, the six buildings were on a right angle corner in the street pattern and turned the 90° in two angles making two buildings wedge-shaped, the remaining four being standard terrace plans. At the rear, the yards are very enclosed due to this being a corner site and the rear mews houses no longer belonged to the main houses (*Figures 5.12 and 5.13*).

The client was not prepared at this stage to modify his concept of a hostel sufficiently to leave all six houses independent and thereby side-step the circulation and fire problems ensuing from linking each of the premises. It is interesting to note here that if a block of say six or seven student flats had been formed from each house, or, each house had been made into one 'commune house' with one dining/kitchen area, then the grants structure would have changed from all education-based grants to normal residential mortgage, loans and improvement grants, which might well have been more generous and required a less ambitious construction effort (*Figures 5.14 and 5.15*).

Recently, the hostel having been occupied for nearly ten years, the overseas students' plight has very considerably lessened (they are often wealthier now than UK students and the hostel management body feels that the 1974 Rent Act favours students generally). As a result there is an under-occupation, sometimes as much as 25%, and schemes to sell off parts converted into flats have been mooted by the client. Students generally prefer and indeed expect, today, to live as normal residents of flats or commune houses. So, finally, this hostel did not go far enough in anticipating students' living trends — trends which the original buildings lent themselves to more readily than the hostel to which they were converted.

Even though existing rooms were altered as little as possible, the spatial restructuring necessary to achieve one united building meant inserting a new central corridor at each floor level, eliminating four of the six stairs and installing a lift next to the service tower. Student rooms achieved were in a considerable variety of shapes, sizes and character — this was the main bonus of the scheme.

New single rooms were put at fifth floor in the attic roof spaces and all former bedrooms on the second, third and fourth floors were made into well-proportioned single and double rooms. The high ceilings and large spaces on the first floor created quite a problem, and the solution was to insert new galleries, some of them on top of the new corridor so that two students slept upstairs and two down in one 'group' room for short stays. The smaller rear first-floor spaces provided double rooms with one bedspace at gallery level and one below (*Figure 5.16*).

Finally, single student accommodation was placed in new single rooms in three of the stair wells where the stairs were removed; seven floors at 2.5 m (8 ft) ceiling height were contained in the same vertical space as five floors for the main house, with short stub stairs to and from the central corridor

Figure 5.16 Typical galleried room

Figure 5.17 Rear communal room

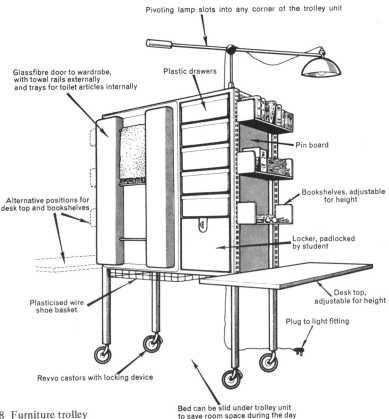

Pivoting lamp slots into any corner of the trolley unit

Glassfibre door to wardrobe, with towel rails externally and trays for toilet articles internally

Plastic drawers

Pin board

Bookshelves, adjustable for height

Alternative positions for desk top and bookshelves

Locker, padlocked by student

Plasticised wire shoe basket

Desk top, adjustable for height

Plug to light fitting

Revvo castors with locking device

Bed can be slid under trolley unit to save room space during the day

Figure 5.18 Furniture trolley

to reconcile the levels — which, together with the windows occurring haphazardly where the old stair landing were lit, made thirty-five very charming and original rooms.

Student family flats with independent street access were produced from the front rooms only at ground and basement levels, and one end, wedge-shaped, house was given over entirely to family flats, providing eleven flats in total for married staff and students.

This organisation within the houses did not provide communal rooms; therefore a light weight roof was erected spanning right across on to the rear wall of the mews houses and enclosing all the rear yards to give a large, continuous, two-storey volume of new space extremely cheaply (*Figure 5.17*). This became the dining and recreation spaces. Small communal rooms (library, chapel, TV room, workshop, etc) were created from the rear ground and basement rooms which, because of the yard's roof enclosure, now looked into this double-height main space; those at rear basement level are entered through the larger space — the communal rooms directly above are served by a simple gallery which overlooks the double-height space. In this way an attractive and abundant provision of communal space was provided from the most difficult parts of the building, which the client originally thought unusable.

The bedroom unit

Cost limitations were extremely rigorous: £72.12½p per student was allotted for fully furnishing each bedroom, which

was more than £50 below the then UGC figure, and expenditure was kept within this figure by the following means. Initially, a fixed unit was planned, but the degree of variation between one room and another made it difficult to arrive at a standard solution. The problem was resolved by designing standard units on wheels which could be placed according to the particular conditions of any room. To meet all conditions several permutations of possible arrangements were built into the units. The main trolley unit measures 1.7 m² (18 ft²) on plan, steel framed in welded square tubes, with the base high enough to allow the bed to be slid underneath it in order to create more floor space when required (*Figure 5.18*).

The wardrobe compartment has an adjustable hanging rail and a robust glass fibre door which is troughed in section, with integral hanging strips at the top and integral pockets at the bottom of the trough, and with a mirror mounted on the inside face, large enough to provide a full image. Small plastic storage trays for toilet gear and glass holder with glass are hung inside the door troughs on each side of the mirror. On the exterior of the door, three rails are provided for towel hanging, etc. A large wire shoe basket is slung beneath the hanging compartment.

Next to the hanging compartment is a bank of drawers of heavy duty polythene and a generous security locker which the student can padlock to secure valuable articles. Bookshelves can be slotted on to the framework at either end of the unit. Ends of units are lined with pin boards so that

71

Figure 5.19 The Comyn Ching triangle

1.7 m² (18 ft²) pin-up space for pictures and other display material is available on each unit. A desk top, adjustable for height, is provided which can be hung from either end of the unit. This is complemented by a pivoting light fitting which slots into the top of any one of the four vertical framing members. The whole assembly is mounted on castor wheels equipped with locking devices, and can pass through a standard door opening.

The bed is a simple structure consisting of a hardboard flush door on bearers, which are mounted on castors, allowing the bed to be moved easily and placed partly under the trolley unit to save space. In addition, the complete 'package' includes a chair, coffee table, wastepaper bin, and all fabrics and pillows and mattress on the bed.

Design considerations

One interesting aspect of the design is the colour arrangement; each of the six old houses is distinguished visually by means of one colour theme per house, which is maintained on doors and window blinds. The trolley unit was produced in permutations of the three primary colours, red, blue and yellow, so that the changes could be rung as needed to match individual student taste, on the framework of the trolley unit, fibreglass door, security locker, bed cover and all the loose items. When a student moved from one house to another all his or her possessions could be transferred with very little trouble by unlocking the wheels and moving the trolley unit and all its contents! Should the student vacate his room temporarily, the locked security locker can be removed as a separate item with all valuables, and put in a safe place.

Assembly of the furniture was carried out by unskilled labour on the spot in a matter of minutes, and the first fifty units which were delivered to the hostel were assembled by two students in a day. Seventeen different manufacturers supplied the components.

There is no doubt that the very flexibility of the client's brief was a creative factor in producing a hostel that is more than just a useful piece of interesting architecture, i.e. it is a good place to stay in and a good place to be in. This project is a good example of how far the traditional user's brief can be successfully re-thought to enable an existing group of buildings to be found and then used to accommodate the client's needs.

Case Study 2: Comyn Ching, Covent Garden

The proposals for an interesting and complex group of buildings in Covent Garden are an example both of a design solution where the buildings themselves were the main determinant, and of an implementation strategy which has as its basis the removal of the existing buildings forming the centre of a triangular shaped city block (*Figure 5.19*). At first sight the problems associated with these buildings might seem insurmountable unless full scale demolition and redevelopment were economically and socially acceptable. However, a detailed appraisal of the existing physical organisation on the site, the legal, economic and emotional factors which were being applied by the owners, their tenants, the local authority, and not least the various local pressure groups at work in the area, has resulted in a strategic solution to this complex problem which has as its basis the original buildings themselves.

The site

The triangular site forms an integral part of Seven Dials, one of the earliest examples in London of formal town planning, and a very important element in the Covent Garden area, both for its streetscape qualities and for the provision of smaller scale domestic buildings in contrast to the larger market buildings of the remainder of the area (*Figure 5.20*). It was laid out in 1692 by Sir Thomas Neale on the then fashionable French baroque pattern. Although the strong geometric street layout remains, Neale's speculative venture soon failed. The majority of the buildings in the area were built later in the eighteenth century, although some evidence of the original development remains. Most of the buildings on this particular site are relatively modest town houses common throughout London, although some contain fine intact examples of internal fittings, and one pair has an interesting double hipped pantile roof which is virtually unique in central London.

The site has been subject to planning blight for over ten years, during which time the future of Covent Garden, following the move of the Market to Nine Elms, has been considered (*Figure 5.21*). Initially it was assumed that substantial redevelopment was an appropriate solution to what at that time was seen as a major opportunity for architectural fun and games close to the centre of London. For instance, the proposal for the majority of the Seven Dials area was a National Sports and Recreation Centre, together with substantial office and some housing redevelopment. At this time the planners also envisaged solving surrounding traffic problems by the technique of through roads and junctions within the Covent Garden Area. These proposals, though generally accepted within the professions at the time, came under increasingly greater attack from those actually living and working within the area (*Figure 5.22*).

As a result, in 1973, the Secretary of State confirmed the Comprehensive Development Area, but at the same time listed 250 buildings, and let it be known that a 'rehabilitation plan' was required which took much greater account of the existing physical and social situation. This has been prepared with a considerable degree of local public participation, and now, after ten years of planning, Covent Garden is about to enter the implementation stage.

Comyn Ching are one of the oldest and most respected firms of metal workers and architectural ironmongers in the country, and have been trading in Covent Garden almost as

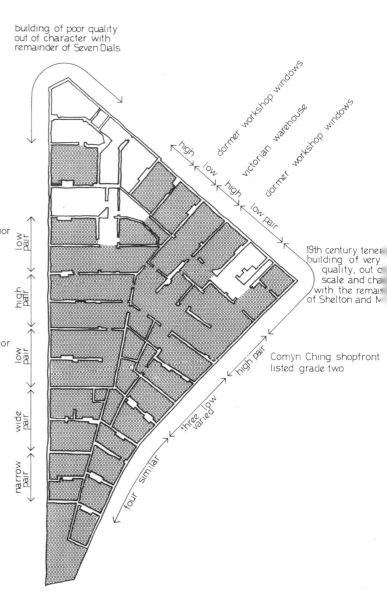

building of poor quality
out of character with
remainder of Seven Dials

dormer workshop windows

victorian warehouse

dormer workshop windows

high
low
high
low pair

fine interior

low
pair

high
pair

fine interior

low
pair

wide
pair

narrow
pair

four similar

three low
varied

high pair

19th century tenem
building of very
quality, out o
scale and cha
with the remai
of Shelton and M

Comyn Ching shopfront
listed grade two

Figure 5.20 (top) The old premises
Figure 5.21 (above, left) Shelton Street
Figure 5.22 (right) Survey and assessment of buildings on
the Comyn Ching triangle

74

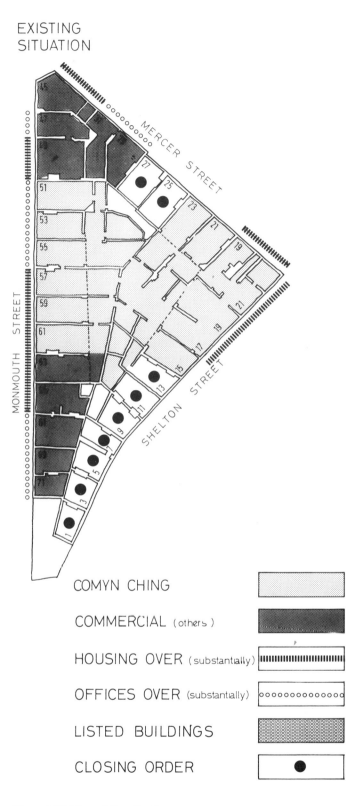

EXISTING
SITUATION

COMYN CHING

COMMERCIAL (others)

HOUSING OVER (substantially)

OFFICES OVER (substantially)

LISTED BUILDINGS

CLOSING ORDER

Figure 5.23 The existing situation

long as the Market itself. They were established on this site in the first half of the eighteenth century, and it is thought that they supplied fittings to Chippendale whose workshop was close by at the top of St Martin's Lane. During the nineteenth century the business expanded: Comyn Ching were pioneers in gas lighting, and in 1835 they installed the gas lighting in Buckingham Palace, together with gates and street lighting in the Mall and St James' Park.

From their initial beginning in one or two buildings, Comyn Ching expanded, acquiring adjoining buildings as the size and range of their stock increased. They now own the freehold of all but two buildings in the triangle. By 1890 the *ad hoc* alteration of existing buildings and random infilling of the centre of the triangle no longer fulfilled their requirements, and Comyn Ching therefore carried out redevelopment to provide purpose-designed warehouse accommodation at 23 Mercer Street. This lofty building, crammed in between the two very small scale domestic buildings with early 'industrial' sliding sashes in the attic, is now a much admired element in the street scene. It is extremely unlikely that a similarly uncompromising design solution would meet with the same approval today. The pattern of use within the triangle is complicated. Essentially Comyn Ching use most of the floors of the houses in Monmouth Street and some in Shelton and Mercer Street, and use exclusively the shamble of back additions and extensions at the centre of the triangle (*Figure 5.23*).

The other tenants are eight commercial users in Monmouth Street and around the corner into Shelton Street, and nine residential tenants in the upper parts of Monmouth Street and at the corner of Shelton and Mercer Street. Many of the leases have long since expired, and existing tenants have remained on a temporary basis pending decisions on the future of the whole site. On the other hand most of them have long associations with the site and Covent Garden, and are anxious to stay on the site, if not the identical location, when changes are complete.

A major objective of the scheme was therefore to allow for the necessary flexibility in dealing with commercial leases, and to ensure that the works could be phased around particular buildings or users. Comyn Ching employ about ninety people; they are therefore one of the major sources of employment in the area now that the Market and other employers have left. Businesses on the remainder of the triangle employ approximately a further twenty people in a variety of shop, gallery, professional and light industrial categories which are so much part of the character of the area.

The buildings themselves are in varied condition, those with closing orders (especially in Mercer Street) being smaller and in the worst structural condition; they are also the least straightforward to bring up to modern standards since many of them are built back to back. The buildings in Monmouth Street are generally larger, and some are in a reasonable state of repair. It is also only in this street that the buildings have any

75

inherent architectural value over and above their contribution to the street scene. However, all the buildings require considerable attention, and the current use as warehouses for quantities of heavy items is totally inappropriate for listed buildings of this type.

A number of 'first aid' measures have been carried out to forestall additional Dangerous Structures Notices, and to improve the fire separation and means of escape for those who live and work in the triangle. More than 80 per cent of the buildings are listed, with the exception of the interesting shop front to Comyn Ching's trade counter, and these all date from the mass listing which indicated the beginning of the change in planning policy. With only three exceptions, these listings are for 'group value' only. The particularly attractive aspects of this group of buildings is that each street elevation has an individual characteristic — the curve of Shelton Street, the variety and steep slope of Mercer Street, and the pairing of tall, short, narrow and wide buildings on Monmouth Street — some of which also contain fine interiors. The listing was therefore 'emotional' rather than strictly historical.

The problems
This situation therefore presented an inter-relating set of problems, which can be summarised as follows:

a complex group of buildings which, for good reason, had been allowed to run to seed for a number of years;

rapidly changing local and official attitudes as to the acceptable methods of dealing with the problem, and political overtones to the context in which any proposals would be judged;

a complex financial and real estate background of existing leases and historical property aspirations, and an uncertain economic situation within which any solution would have to be assessed as viable; and

very strong pressure (backed by a number of sets of legislation concerning the repair of listed buildings, the structural safety of buildings, and the health and safety of employees) that some action be taken very soon to deal with a rapidly deteriorating situation.

These circumstances are common to a great deal of property within the inner areas of our older cities; in this instance they were considerably complicated by their important position within Covent Garden (and indeed represent in microcosm most of the problems and opportunities of the whole area). At the same time it must be understood that the clients were ironmongers and not property developers or financiers. This had the advantage that they were not necessarily looking for a large financial return, but merely to sort out all the problems pertaining to their site and buildings. However, it also had the disadvantage that they could not contemplate any solution

76

which would in any way jeopardise their trading company, and that they would be subject to all the 'fail safe' financial requirements which any financing institution would necessarily look for in a scheme of this kind. The objectives that were therefore set out were basically:

1. To arrest the decay of this potentially fine group of buildings, and thereby to allow Comyn Ching, together with other traditional Covent Carden users, to carry on their business efficiently and safely;

2. To achieve full benefit from the site's housing potential to produce the maximum residential gain;

3. To rehabilitate all buildings worthy of retention, and to restore individual items of architectural interest;

4. To restructure the pattern of existing uses in order to achieve these objectives, and to obtain a small increase in office space in order to create sufficient value to finance them;

5. To reinforce the visual significance of this group of buildings as part of the Shelton Street/Mercer Street scene, and

6. To revitalise the whole triangle so that it can again make an important social, economic and architectural contribution to the life and variety of Covent Garden.

The solution to this problem would also need to allow for the necessary flexibility of phasing and physical organisation to enable the scheme to be implemented without undue disturbance to existing tenants. It should also avoid the necessity for massive finance which would be required by one large building operation, to enable specific parts of the scheme to be carried out by specific contractors, and to allow the residential element to be carried out by an independent housing agency if appropriate. At the same time, it was clear that the success of any solution would depend to a large extent upon the involvement of the many local groups in the planning application and approval process.

The spatial solution
The determinants of the design approach which was applied to this complex set of problems were therefore necessarily based upon a thorough understanding of the current physical organisation of the buildings and the various legal and financial constraints which applied to them. In comparison, solving the spatial requirements of the current and future users was a relatively simple matter — bearing in mind the inherent flexibility of this building type mentioned earlier. However, the pattern of occupation within the buildings was also of considerable significance in arriving at a strategic solution; the central section of the triangle was used solely by Comyn Ching themselves and, since they were the majority occupier and also the instigator of the scheme, it seemed likely that they would in any case have to occupy alternative premises for the major part of the building operation.

At the time this decision was taken this presented little cause for concern, for there was a considerable quantity of empty warehouse space in the immediate vicinity. In addition, the actual process of removal (though traumatic) would clearly entail an excellent educational process in terms of space utilisation, and enable them to operate more efficiently on their return. In the event, the actual planning process has been so drawn out due to political considerations quite outside the scope of the Planning Acts, and the increasing interest in Covent Garden (caused in part by the actual planning process itself) has been so great, that there is now some doubt as to whether alternative premises will be so readily available as had at first been thought.

The final design

The final solution adopted, and approved, is based upon the concept of completely clearing the inside of the triangle and cutting back to the basic structure of the original houses. The space thereby created is filled by a new purpose-designed warehouse at semi-basement level, the roof of which forms a new landscaped courtyard with access from the surrounding pavement (*Figure 5.24*). This new courtyard provides access to the upper floors of all the surrounding listed buildings which are to be rehabilitated. The ground floors of these buildings are thus released for the complete reinstatement of shopping and other commercial users on the main street frontages (*Figure 5.25*).

In order to carry out this complex piece of 'urban surgery' it was necessary to plan for builder access and site space. The only reasonable way this could be achieved is from the Seven Dials corner, since this would involve the loss of only one listed building. It would also avoid the destruction of any of the three important street elevations and create the opportunity for a new replacement building on this corner which could make a significant contribution to the Seven Dials junction, and it would produce some value in the scheme to finance the remainder of the very costly rehabilitation.

The other new building proposed is on the corner of Shelton and Mercer Street, and will form the administrative and organisational hub of Comyn Ching's operations (*Figure 5.26*). It links their new basement warehouse with their trade counter retained behind the famous shop front in Shelton Street, and allows for improved goods handling and loading arrangements. It will replace the present tall late-nineteenth century tenement building on this corner, which, though listed and relatively sound, has such a shallow plan as to be virtually unconvertible for any useful purpose, and is also clearly out of character with the remainder of the two street frontages which it terminates.

This strategic solution, besides achieving a scheme which was entirely acceptable to the various planning and historic building bodies concerned, also has the advantage of being capable of implementation in a variety of phasing alternatives. Once the basic demolition and initial structural work at the centre of the triangle has been carried out, the remainder of the different phases of the total concept can be carried out independently. The rehabilitation of each pair or group of houses can be carried out separately, or in parallel, by a number of smaller specialist constractors working directly off the street frontage in the normal way. This flexibility not only permits the varying existing leases to be respected, but also allows the scheme to be financed in small packages which are not necessarily dependent upon each other.

The scheme involves the loss of only two listed buildings, one of very little significance. The Greater London Council (GLC) Historic Buildings Board were readily convinced of the acceptability of the loss of the other one, partly because they appreciated the care with which the overall concept had been considered, and partly due to the proposal to remove the fine internal stair and panelling from the house which was due to be demolished and re-use it in one of the pair of houses with the important roof structure – thus completing and fully restoring an interesting pair of authentic houses on the site. The proposal was also enthusiastically supported by all the local pressure groups, since they had been kept fully informed throughout the process, and the scheme embodied so many of the aims of the new Local Plan which they were then working out with the GLC in an extensive public participation planning exercise.

The final scheme therefore represents in microcosm the new plan for the whole of Covent Garden. It can solve the financial and operational requirements of Comyn Ching, and will allow them to continue to offer very valuable employment within Covent Garden. It should considerably increase the employment offered by the remainder of the site (total employment potential of the scheme is more than double the existing), and will extend the shopping and other commercial uses at pavement level and introduce four small light industrial units for craftsmen or the small service trades (which are so much part of the character of Covent Garden, but are in danger of being forced out of the area as a consequence of more grandiose 'redevelopment' schemes).

This scheme will bring about a considerable increase in the housing content of the site in a variety of dwelling types and locations, and it revitalises this group of buildings and enables them to make a worthwhile contribution to this part of Covent Garden in terms of streetscape, open space and pedestrian interest. More importantly, perhaps, it demonstrates that the aims of the Local Plan are achievable by private initiative even on the most difficult of Covent Garden sites. It was, however, a process which was directly motivated in design terms by a thorough understanding of the existing physical arrangement of the buildings themselves, and the way that they could be restructured to offer a relevant solution to all the problems posed.

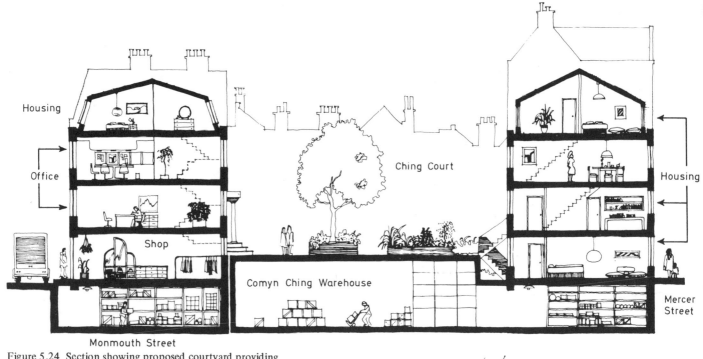

Figure 5.24 Section showing proposed courtyard providing access to upper floors of surrounding listed buildings

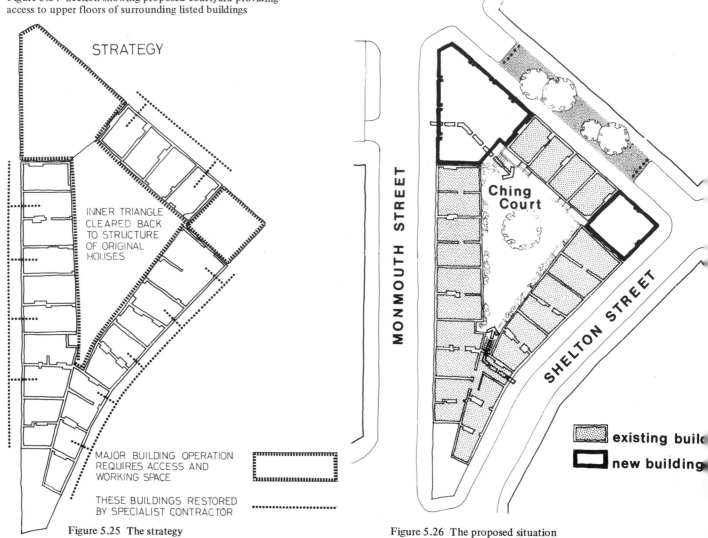

STRATEGY

INNER TRIANGLE CLEARED BACK TO STRUCTURE OF ORIGINAL HOUSES

MAJOR BUILDING OPERATION REQUIRES ACCESS AND WORKING SPACE

THESE BUILDINGS RESTORED BY SPECIALIST CONTRACTOR

Figure 5.25 The strategy

Figure 5.26 The proposed situation

existing building
new building

Figure 5.27 Front elevation before rehabilitation

Case Study 3: The Colonnades, Westminster

The job of urbanising this country is virtually completed; like fields broken in for agricultural use, once the land has been cultivated to support the population, it is time to enjoy and manage it as a resource. With our heightened attitude to resources it should be possible to have agreement on getting more out of our towns which are a vast physical and community resource. Converting bits of towns is like converting buildings; there are existing roads, pavements, sewers and service supply routes surrounding buildings; and there is vegetation to take account of, re-use and exploit. All of these are keys on which to develop our buildings.

In the Colonnades, Westminster, project, a three-acre site containing some existing buildings in a conservation area was being considered by a developer client for a multiplicity of typical inner city uses (houses, flats, shopping, offices, library, carpark, pub, showrooms etc). A terrace of eleven large Victorian houses was considered worthy of retention even though they had declined into use as small commercial hotels, 'bed-sits' and flatlets. Whilst the basic structure was sound, the interiors were in a bad state and years of alterations and repairs had left an appalling confusion of services (*Figure 5.27*).

Several possible alternatives for the development of this part of the site were immediately apparent:

1. Demolition and replacement by a new building was ruled out because it was felt that the retention of these houses would be an important factor in the development.

2. Demolition and rebuilding of a replica facade with a new building behind proved to be too expensive.

3. A traditional conversion of each house into flats did not produce a sufficient density of larger units to make the proposition viable.

Therefore, in order to achieve the high density of large units and still retain the bulk of the houses, it was decided to demolish the conglomeration of rear additions and annexes and to build a completely new reinforced concrete framed extension to the rear. This had the following advantages over the other alternatives:

Firstly, the availability of improvement grants towards the cost of those units or parts of units in the existing houses made the retention of these a viable proposition, provided there were additional new units in the rear extension to maintain the high density required.

Secondly, the existing houses, although in a bad state of repair, were substantially sound and therefore there was a considerable volume of space already built which, with the aid of the improvement grants, allowed the provision of very spacious flats for a price comparable with a much smaller flat in a new building.

Thirdly, one of the major conflicts in the original houses was between the views north over Porchester Square, and the sun from the south. By adding a new rear extension the majority of the units were provided with south facing living rooms and balconies overlooking the proposed residents' square.

Fourthly, although the facades of the existing houses retained their original elegance, the rear had been added piecemeal over the years, and therefore by demolishing these additions and adding a rear extension it was possible to present a new 'face' to the main development.

Fifthly, the standard floor to ceiling heights and thin reinforced concrete floors of the new extension enabled the incorporation of a basement car park at the rear and eight floors of accommodation, in contrast to only six floors in the existing houses, and finally the reinforced concrete frame and minimal party wall requirements of the new extension allowed the planning of a more economic grid for the rear and the incorporation of an extra room within the typical three-house group (*Figures 5.28 and 5.29*).

The existing houses have been combined in groups of three to make maximum use of each lift, thus giving a total of four lift staircases in the block of eleven houses.

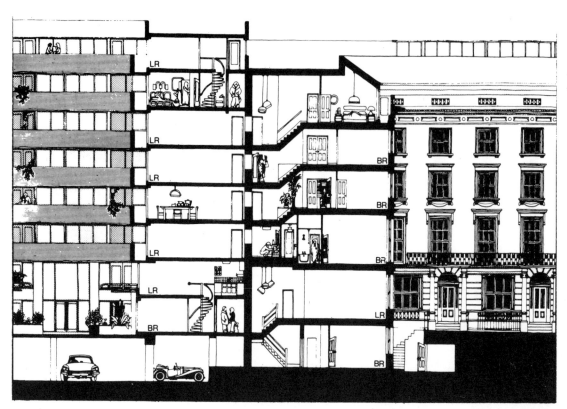

Figure 5.28 Section

Figure 5.29 Old meets new — rear of Porchester Square
during construction

Figure 5.30 Front elevation after rehabilitation

Figure 5.31 Rear elevation of Porchester Square after
removal of annexes and before addition of new block

Figure 5.32 Front elevation after rehabilitation

These were then linked at the ground level to the rest of the scheme by an indoor pedestrian street which bridges over the mews to connect with the main entrance in the adjacent eight-storey block. Along the length of the pedestrian street two double-height conservatory areas give access to and views over the residents' square.

The lower two floors of the existing houses have been combined to provide larger family units at the front, using the existing porticos as their own entrances direct from Porchester Square. At the rear, new maisonettes have been created with living rooms at first floor with views over the new residents' square and a private terrace at ground level (*Figures 5.28 and 5.31*). Above these the four typical floors consist of four units grouped around an internal core of stairs and lift. The top two floors contain penthouse maisonettes entered from a corridor on the lower floor, with a spiral stair to through living rooms on the upper floor with views both north over Porchester Square, and south towards Hyde Park (*Figure 5.30*).

CHAPTER SIX

An Affair of Values, Resources and Investment

The Old Gaol, Abingdon, Sports and Arts Centre

Julian Bicknell

In the world of building the terms 'rehabilitation', 'conversion', 'remodelling', 'restoration', 'reinstatement' and so forth are unhappily confused. At one end of the spectrum of meaning is the historically 'pure', archaeologically accurate reconstruction. The purpose of such restoration work and the special skills and techniques it involves are eloquently illustrated in Warren's case study examples in Chapter 9. At the other end of the spectrum is the fashionable 'conversion' of barns, chapels, and Victorian family houses into modern homes tuned to Sunday Newspaper Colour Supplement eclecticism with spotlights, decorative fireplaces, galley kitchens and patterned bed linen. But though one extreme may be arcane and the other ephemeral, they share an intention to 'conserve'. It is this notion of conservation that gives lasting significance to conversion and rehabilitation.

Conservation itself is also a confusing term, not least because it has become a politically loaded code word in the town planning context. Conservation has come to signify the dogged reaction to comprehensive rebuilding. The very ambiguity of the word is used with great agility by 'conservationists' to press their case. For although conservation involves both historical interest and town planning in a variety of ways, it is essentially an exercise in economics — perhaps not in terms of short term financial expenditure — but economics nevertheless in that it is an affair of values, resources and investment. Aylward has elaborated this conceptual model in Chapter 1 in ways that assist those preparing development strategies. The conversion of the Old Gaol at Abingdon, in Berkshire, may serve as a case history to illustrate this approach (*Figure 6.1*).

Investment in building takes three forms and each form is more or less redeemable. Firstly there are material assets, redeemable both in the sense that raw materials such as stone or timber can be reused in new constructions and in that certain parts of a building fabric may have a longer life than the building as a whole (a coat of paint may only last three years, but a roof should last eighty years; masonry survives three hundred years where foundations can serve after three thousand). Secondly there is labour, redeemable only in part (like energy in thermodynamic conversion). The more radical

the conversion the more inefficient the use of labour assets. And thirdly there is what you might call the 'cultural investment' — the unquantifiable combination of will, philosophy, politics and the accidents of history that bring buildings into existence. This last is the ill-defined 'Historic Value' of the planning jargon. Its redeemability depends — and that very delicately — on the same unquantifiable combination of will, philosophy, politics, etc, that go into the process of conversion.

Looked at in this way the assets of a building like the Old Gaol fall under three headings:

1. The context: most obviously the site and the town planning aspects but also the political and economic circumstances, the demand for certain facilities, the attitudes of neighbours and the public.

2. The fabric: the nature and condition of the structure, the arrangement of parts and the potential for change.

3. The 'cultural assets': including not only the 'official' history but also the academically less respectable agglomeration of memory and myth that makes up the 'folk image' of a building.

Context

The chief asset of the Old Gaol is its site, facing south across the river, to open water meadows immediately next to the mediaeval bridge that carries the London Road into the centre of Abingdon, itself within two hundred metres (650 ft) of the Gaol. A long-term planning strategy provides for parking immediately across the bridge so that shoppers and other visitors pass the entrance to the Gaol on their way to the market square (*Figure 6.1*). The buildings that make up the frontage to Bridge Street leave two narrow openings, one leading to the original front of the building, the other to the north flank or the 'back' of the building. A 5 m (16 ft 9 in) high stone wall used to separate the original prison exercise yards from the neighbouring gardens, one of them belonging to a fine 17th century house in Gt. St. Helen's Street behind.

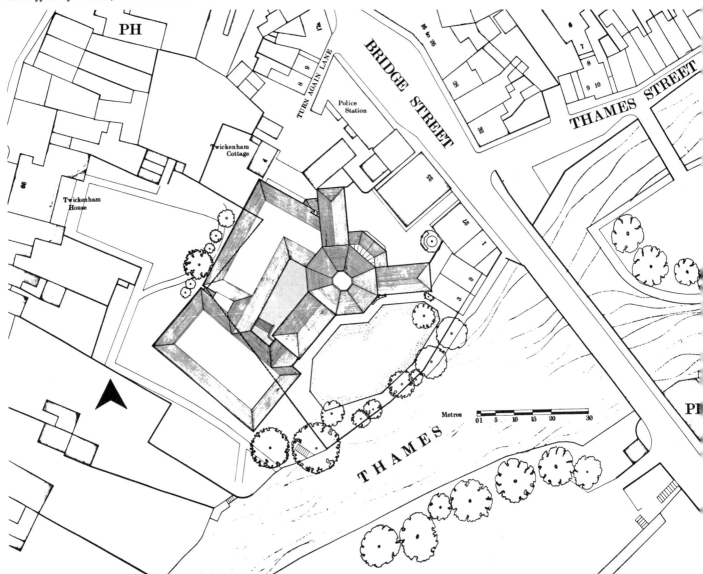

Figure 6.1 Site plan of Abingdon Old Gaol

The cases for and against conservation of the Old Gaol had been aired for some time before Abingdon Borough Council proposed an investigatory student project. At that stage uses had to be tailored to the building as well as vice versa. The students therefore investigated in some depth a variety of uses and a variety of layouts. Alternative schemes were put on public exhibition in Abingdon. They illustrated the severe difficulties of converting and adding to a large existing building, even without the complications of its 'historic' listing. Nevertheless, the schemes did demonstrate the great potential of the site and the building, if imaginatively developed. The site constraints only served to stimulate invention and ingenuity.

The schemes also served to test the feasibility of various combinations of accommodation. A vast list of possibilities had been put forward and one of the problems was to decide which of the many could be appropriately housed. Whether the alternatives could have been displayed and measured more

readily and effectively by the methods Maver points to in Chapter 2 is debatable.

In the event the enthusiastic public response persuaded the Council to commission a design incorporating the best features of the schemes. The brief was further modified by subsequent changes in policy and design response to include:

1. A music school with teaching rooms, an office, rehearsal rooms and storage;

2. Exhibition facilities including a fully equipped space for travelling exhibitions;

3. A hall for films, recitals, lectures and meetings for 150 people;

4. Refreshment and bar facilities;

5. Administrative offices;

6. A swimming pool;

7. A four-court sports hall;

8. A gym for training and combat sports;

9. Comprehensive changing facilities for sportsmen and swimmers and the appropriate servicing and storage space.

The strategy for the disposition of these facilities in and around the old building had to take into account the necessary inter-connections between facilities and patterns of access, the usual statutory regulations particularly those concerning means of escape in case of fire, and the subsoil and other site conditions, particularly the accessibility of various parts of the site during the building operation. A certain reverence to the spirit of the planning legislation was also involved, and this suggested that the inevitably large volumes of the swimming pool and sports hall should not dominate the view from the river. Overall, of course, it was important that the arrangement should be easy to grasp and a pleasure to use.

The octagon at the heart of the Old Gaol houses open foyers at ground and first floor levels, both of them immediately visible from the entrance and connected directly to virtually all the public spaces of the building (*Figure 6.2*). The sports facilities, swimming pool and gym with their heavily serviced changing rooms fill out the ground floor. Filtration and heating equipment were arranged to occupy a semi-basement below the pool deck. The exhibition room, film/recital hall and the bar are on the first floor level which extends via an open courtyard to the viewing galleries overlooking the pool and sports hall. The courtyard is also connected to the riverside garden by an external stair (*Figure 6.3*).

All the ground floor rooms have direct access to the outside for fire escape purposes. Much of the first floor gives onto the raised courtyard for similar reasons. Escape stairs serving the remainder of this floor and the floors above are only required in the north and east wings. The double height of the small recital rooms eliminates the need for further stairs.

The high water table implied a minimum of excavation — hence the raising of the pool deck level above ground. The limited access to the site suggested that the simpler of the new buildings (the sports hall) should be furthest from the street so that the building campaign could retreat in an orderly sequence (*Figure 6.4*). Not only the placing but also the treatment of the bulk of the sports hall serve to reduce it in relation to the Old Gaol itself. It comes as a surprise that the new buildings are greater in volume than the original gaol (*Figure 6.5*).

The brief was adjusted to suit the situation in a number of ways but, wherever possible, a virtue was made of necessity. The foyers are generous but serve effectively as meeting and resting places. They are used for exhibitions (the bar and theatre overflow into them) schoolchildren do their homework there

and so on. The changing rooms are below the recommended sizes but are carefully organised to make them easy to use. However, the flexibility of the brief and the particular disposition of functions makes for a very compact plan with the minimum of unnecessary mystifying passages. The arrangement has a number of unpremeditated benefits such as the outdoor space serving the first floor rooms and the bar overlooking the pool. All in all, the context — the building and the situation — is developed to the maximum.

Fabric

The second category of assets offered by the Old Gaol was the fabric of the building. Although the wings had originally contained a honeycomb of stone vaulted cells, these had been removed when its 'corrective' function was transferred to Reading Gaol in the 1860s. All that survived of the original was the heavy rubble walls with their Bath Stone dressings and the trusses and rafters of the roofs. The surviving floors throughout were of timber, many of them rotten or cut about to accommodate milling machinery. The rubble work outside was roughly coursed, the pointing and stone dressings were badly eroded, the inside was finished with a lime and horsehair plaster finished in limewash.

The major roof timbers were in fair condition except for those bearings that had been exposed to the weather (*Figure 6.6*). They had to be thoroughly cleaned, repaired where necessary and treated against rot and bug infestation. The original metal straps were in good condition and were simply cleaned and painted. The roof coverings were removed and replaced by an asbestos cement slate, almost indistinguishable from the original natural Welsh variety. The same slate was used to cover the slopes of the roofs of the new building.

The timber floors throughout the building were removed irrespective of their age or quality (*Figure 6.7*). Although the great bulk of some of the timbers might have made them adequately fire resistant, the structure was not guaranteed and the floor levels in certain parts of the building had to be altered. The new floors are of precast concrete planks, all of them around 3 m (10 ft) long (the bay dimension of the original building) on a frame system of standard steel sections and in situ reinforced concrete. This provides a light floor of prefabricated elements that simplified the building operation and keeps the load on footings small.

The walls themselves were subjected to a full scale loading test which showed that they were performing as two virtually independent skins. Although the test demonstrated that they might have been able to carry the expected loads, additional structural precautions were taken, firstly to improve the safety factors and secondly to eliminate the risk of eccentric loading. With the exception of the second floor the new floors are supported by a system of reinforced concrete stanchions. In

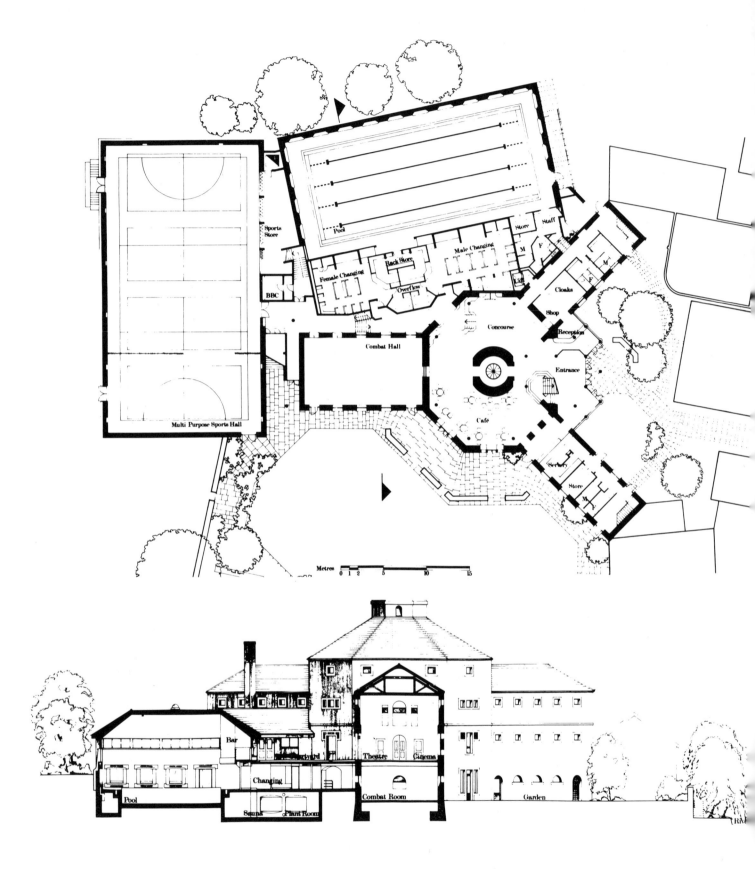

Figure 6.2 Ground floor plan and section

86

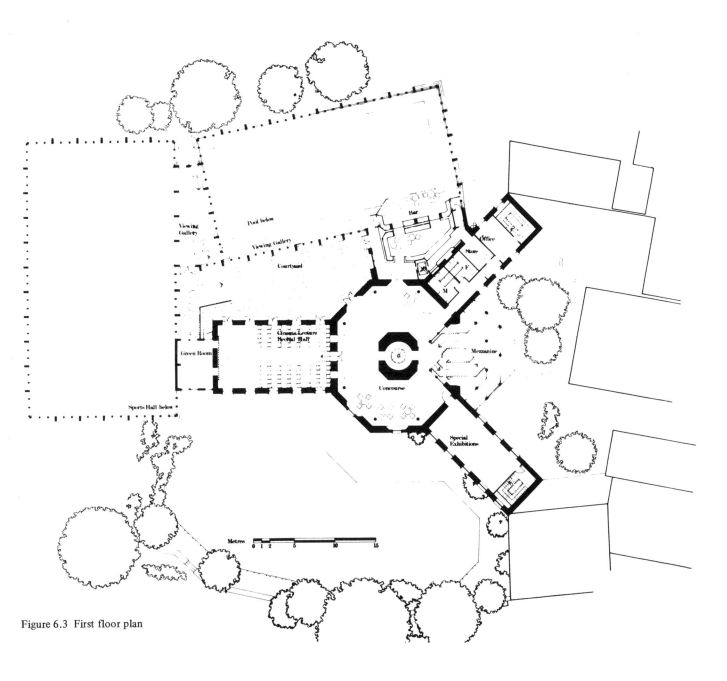

Figure 6.3 First floor plan

Within the plan, the following labels appear:

Viewing Gallery

Pool below

Viewing Gallery

Courtyard

Bar

Office

Store

Green Room

Cinema-Lecture Recital Hall

Mezzanine

Sports Hall below

Concourse

Special Exhibitions

Metres 0 1 2   5   10   15

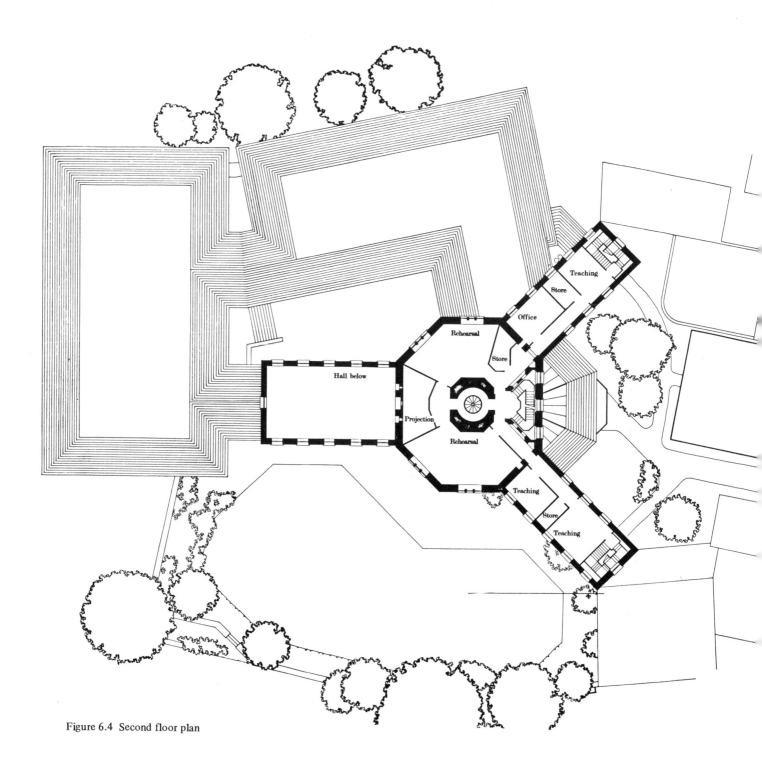

Figure 6.4 Second floor plan

88

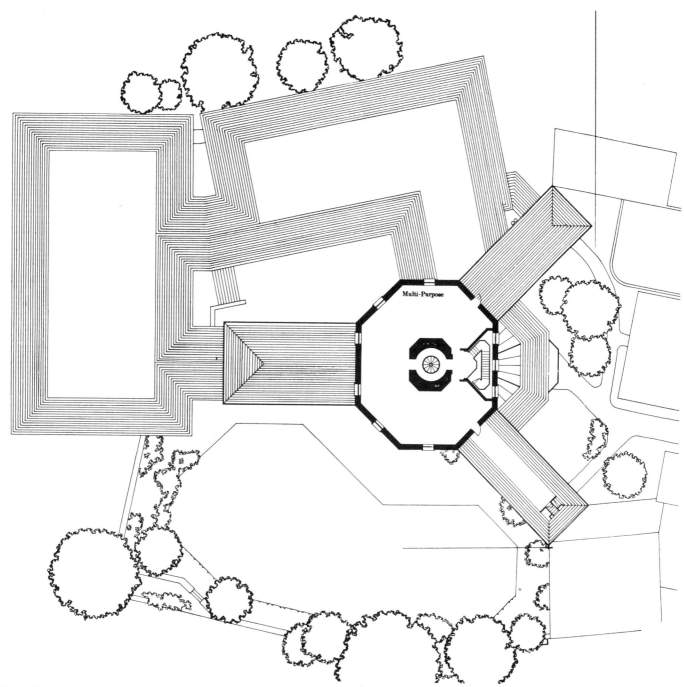

Figure 6.5 Third floor plan

Figure 6.6 (right) The octagonal tower showing the roof and floor structures

Figure 6.7 (below) The floor and ceiling structure of the first floor of the east wing before conversion

Figure 6.8 (left) The great arch
Figure 6.9 (below) The great arch and the main stair at mezzanine level

91

the wings these are formed within the thickness of the walls. In the octagon there are free standing columns in the intrinsically stiff corners. These columns were provided with funnel shaped 'capitals' to ease the pouring which, paradoxically, was done in some cases after the erection of the beams. All the stanchions stand on concrete foundations below the ground floor. In this way the loads of the new floors are independently supported without relying on the existing walls or their foundations. In fact the new structure in the wings serves to stiffen the walls and their footings. The walls were also injected with a PFA grout to fill the spaces within the walls formed by the deterioration of the mortar and the activity of the mice and rats attracted by the milling operations.

The same approach was used to preserve the great arch that had once spanned the Old Gaol's Court Room (*Figure 6.8*). The floors and wall of one side of the octagon (a load of roughly 100 tonnes (98 tons) had been supported by a flat segmental arch of cut stone. The buttressing of the arch had been provided by the abutting wings and the grid of vaults they housed. With the removal of the cells the buttressing was inadequate and the arch was badly flawed at its springing. It is however one of the most dramatic features of the old building and, as such, is important to the atmosphere of the place (*Figure 6.9*). Besides, it permits the unique view of the ground and first floors of the building from the entrance, a valuable introduction to newcomers unfamiliar with the layout of the building.

To make the arch safe the entire load is taken by a reinforced concrete diaphragm between 4 m (13 ft) and 6 m (19 ft 6 in) deep, 200 mm (8 in) thick, to which the arch and the masonry it supports are attached by stainless steel pins. This diaphragm is carried by the original masonry piers and is stiffened by the staircases that climb up the inside face and a pair of 'flying buttresses' that form the roof structure of the new porch. The staircases themselves are 'hung' from the new structure.

The structure of the new buildings though less remarkable is not as simple as it may appear (*figure 6.10*). The concrete substructure including the pool is built as a vast concrete

Figure 6.10 The new swimming pool

raft so as to spread its weight evenly over the gravel substrate. The superstructure of the sports hall is a series of bastardised portal frames encased up to eaves level in concrete; that of the swimming pool, cranked beams on reinforced concrete columns. The difference is due to complications in the building sequence and the limited size of elements brought in by road. Both structures provide the appropriate building profile in a minimum depth.

The walls of the new building are lined with a high density concrete block made from the local gravel and the outside is finished with rubble saved from the dismantling of the original boundary wall — almost 400 tonnes (390 tons) of material that would otherwise have had to be removed from the site. The thickness of these walls, dictated by the depth of the stanchions, is taken up by the air handling system and the seating alcoves in the swimming pool — the old hypocaust arrangement put to a new use in warming the seats by the pool.

Culture

The third category of assets — the 'cultural' or 'historic' value — is a very much more subjective matter. To the scholarly historian the historical facts are essential. But the response of the great majority is a very indeterminate affair combining a smattering of history with a much richer treasury of acquired images, associations and 'gut' reactions. Some of these images, associations and reactions are bred into our culture or are of such a psychologically fundamental nature as to be universal.

As far as the basic history goes, the Gaol was built between 1804, when the Town Clerk put his signature to the design drawings, and 1812 when the master mason carved his initials on the top step of the central spiral stair. It was one of several 'Houses of Correction' built under an Act of 1780 stimulated in part by the reformist philosophies of Jeremy Bentham, John Howard, and others, and also by the atmosphere of social unrest spurred on by the French and American Revolutions.

The plan owes much to the idealised schemes of the period with its separation of the four classes of prisoners (felons, debtors, those awaiting trial, and females) and the almost symbolic arrangement of the court house and other facilities. But it fails in fact to provide the essential characteristic of Bentham's ideal Panopticon, that all the prisoners should be conscious of being observed. In fact the building is more in the tradition (suitably updated by the provision of single cells) of the younger Dance's Newgate Gaol.

The contract was undertaken by the governor at the time of Oxford Gaol who is reputed to have died subsequently in a madhouse, after dramatically over-running his estimates of both time and cost. It is popularly imagined that the work was done by Napoleonic prisoners of war, but already history and legend are inextricably entwined and it is difficult to be sure of the macabre stories of solitary confinement, semi-starvation,

Figure 6.11 The gaol after restoration — Spring 1976

the tread mill, hangings and grim miscarriages of justice. These horror stories are of course unfailingly popular, like Mary Shelley's Frankenstein and much of Dickens' most bitter social criticism.

Certain features of the building that evoke these associations have survived or have been restored (*Figure 6.11*): the cast iron window bars (which also serve to support the over-thin stone lintels), a handful of the original cell doors complete with metal studs and the engraved graffiti of the inmates, and the tortuous spiral stair (a fine piece of stone cutting by any reckoning). The simplicity of the new finishes and a certain generosity in many details are reminiscent of the building's original utilitarian character. These features stimulate the imagination and involve those who use the building in its history. And while the associations are essentially brutal and horrific the involvement with the past is paradoxically calming.

There are other ways, too, in which a building can stimulate the imagination. In the case of conversion there is the universal delight in metamorphosis, a sense of magic in transforming a sow's ear into a silk purse. This type of conjuring is enhanced by surprises and contrasts, for instance, the contrast between the crusty external shell with its tiny windows and the light

93

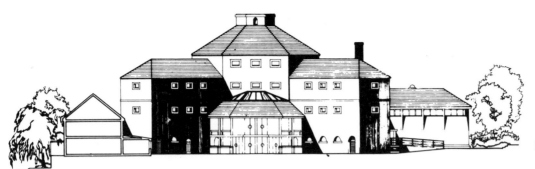

Figure 6.12 North-east elevation

and airy interior with its expansive spaces and generous window reveals. The imagination also reacts to a range of stimuli based in their fundamental form on curiosity and fear. It is these two deep seated mechanisms of animal consciousness that make the age-old architectural tricks work. Most familiar is the arrangement of spaces in a dramatic sequence that offers a succession of clues and discoveries serving to guide and delight those using the building. Certain parts of the building, particularly the entrance and main staircase, exploit other fundamental responses: the fear of falling, the impression of weight and its support, of structure, span and cantilever, firstly for their intrinsic excitement and secondly because they evoke the 'Gothick' atmosphere of the Old Gaol's history. There can be no doubt that a sense of horror, a sense of drama a sense of the unexpected are linked to the images of crumbling masonry, gigantic spans, precipitous voids and fragile bridges that appear in the baroque fantasies of Piranesi.

This business of engaging the imagination at many levels and in ways that are often complex and frequently contradictory is not new. It is as old as building. But the architectural philosophies of the recent past have concentrated on logical consistency and the elimination of extraneous imagery. This architectural puritanism encourages a style which can make buildings that are arid and unengaging. It is no surprise that the 'man in the street' is baffled or resentful and that the most obvious reaction is to mark or mar.

The Old Gaol has been very little vandalised although many of the finishes are vulnerable to penknives or aerosol paint. The materials that have attracted graffiti are the supposedly 'vandalproof' laminate partitions in the WCs and the plasticised surfaces of some of the furniture. This qualified success is probably due to a combination of factors: first the fact that nearly all parts of the building are supervised by a member of the staff in a manner which is effective without being overbearing (there was a conscious effort to devise an economical staff structure that relies on the minimum of mechanical aids); secondly, materials are used in a familiar way often demonstrating the interest and care of the craftsmen over details; and thirdly, there is a world of imagery and dramatic effect, which engages the otherwise listless imagination. It is in this last area that conversion work offers special advantages.

94

The use of pictorial imagery in building has been discredited for so long that it is no longer part of the architectural vocabulary. In re-using existing buildings the designer can draw on established imagery and association. Changes and adaptations however radical will add to an existing pattern of images which comprehensive redevelopment inevitably destroys.

Conclusion

In describing the contextual, material and cultural assets of the 'Old Gaol' their value has been largely hypothetical. But the figures do support the hypothesis. At £1 050 000 the building contract (let in 1974) represents very good value for buildings of this type (*Figure 6.12*). Of course, the same sum might have been allocated in a very different way, in other circumstances but £280/m² (£27 per sq. ft.) is very close to other buildings of this type — many of them lacking some of the good features of the Old Gaol. The 'cultural' value is best confirmed by the attendance figures: during its first year the Old Gaol was visited by nearly 750 000 people. Whether they were sportsmen, art lovers, musicians or sightseers is not recorded but it seems that there is more to the Old Gaol than a catalogue of sports, art and social facilities.

The project as a whole offers insights into a large number of building problems both practical and methodological. Perhaps the most useful lesson is the way in which unexpected conjunctions can be highly productive, how diversity in use, technology, education, finance, style and of course personalities can earn unexpected rewards. For instance, the popularity of the various facilities in the Gaol are inter-related: when the pool is closed, the takings in the bar fall. Equally the unexpected compactions of current building technology and traditional techniques brought the building team together to produce excellent results. Then again, each source of finance for the project, whether private or government grants, existing capital or publicly authorised lending, was dependent on the others. The design method combined the contributions of student and professional designers. Most significant of all the planning strategy combines the revival of a derelict building, the re-energising of a wasted asset with a forward looking social policy for the local community. It is there that one can find a real meaning for the term 'conservation'.

CHAPTER
SEVEN

Limits and Potential

An attitude to rehabilitation, with two case studies

Richard Frewer and Derek Sugden

The situation in relation to rehabilitation is changing so rapidly that there is no question of producing a definitive statement on the subject. However, particularly since the UK Government's White Paper on Inner City Areas was published in June 1977, our concern must be to understand the new direction in which we are travelling, examine our experience in rehabilitation and explore what measures may be adopted to make attitudes to rehabilitation more objective and correctly balanced. Any understanding must stem from a pattern suggested by the factual evidence. In this regard, it is interesting that there are a number of developments with which we are concerned. These can be summed up in one preoccupation — 'Limits and their relation to Potential'. This theme runs parallel with Aylward's thesis and the model analogy presented in Chapter 1. It may be of interest to read these two chapters consecutively.

The background against which rehabilitation is taking place in the UK today is summarised as follows:

1. We have little or no growth in this country in the economic sense.

2. The majority of the vocal public enthuse about conservation.

3. The community is confused and punch-drunk with an excess of complex environmental legislation.

4. Ecologists endorse rehabilitation.

5. The scandal of profligate waste and expenditure extends to the waste and destruction of old but sound buildings.

6. Land prices are down and building prices are up.

7. By world standards, our building costs seem extremely high.

8. There is a growing concern throughout the western world for frugality in the use of all natural resources.

On a different level, it should be stressed that there is no intelligible methodology used by the planners which makes it possible to show that rehabilitation should be a preferred option when redevelopment is mooted. Heroic gestures in favour of rehabilitation have, until very recently been the exception rather than the rule, even in a city of such a size and calibre as Bath.

The limiting factors

There are four main strands which contribute to our preoccupation with 'Limits'. Firstly there is our changing attitude to the use of fuel. In the 1960s, heating and air conditioning systems were used to create an artificial environment. Today there is a move towards the use of mechanical systems to harness ambient energy and to tune it. Secondly, we must pay the real price for materials and realise the full implication of the use of expensively manufactured materials such as aluminium, steel and plastic. There is a move towards the use of such materials with more precision. Thirdly there is our approach to building stock which we still grossly undervalue as an asset. Not only is it capital in terms of man-power and money, it is also environmental art around which people build their lives. Fourthly there are large areas of 'derelict land' in our cities which we can no longer afford. The more focus placed on these areas for building or recreation, the less stress will be placed on the rural areas. Urban and suburban land would be used much more fully for the benefit of the community.

Two other factors contribute to the problem. The standards set within the UK Building Regulations for insulation are written as minima, but are all too often treated as maxima. Thereby the commercial developer who expects to make a return on his money within seven to nine years seldom has any interest in the wider issues of national resources; why should he? If the Government took steps to reward him however, a longer amortisation period for building would show the country real benefits. Small houses are a good example. If more money were spent on energy conservation and building detail, the money saved on the fuel bill would serve the extra mortgage payments required, and in the life of the building would show enormous savings. This attitude taken across the country could make a real difference to our long term prosperity.

At another level, there is still strong resistance within the Building Societies in the UK to the idea of investing in old building stock, and as a majority of the old building is in the inner areas, the outlook is bleak unless there is a complete change of heart. Many Societies strongly resist the idea of converting old houses into flats with the policy that they will only finance those which are purpose-built. One can understand the historical reasons for this attitude but at a time when building is expensive and the quality of the new product has a relatively short life, it is a view that must change.

Ways of encouraging a new approach must be explored or the future for the inner cities is extremely bleak. We can no longer afford this attitude which has been sapping the inner city communities and has allowed the throwing away of building shells with generations of life left in them. It is such a commonly held view as to be near pointless in stating, but it fills one with anger and shame that we should have been sufficiently arrogant and headstrong as to carve up cities with such assurance. The ultimate irony is that the approach that developed as a symbol of a socialist paradise has now changed in peoples minds into a symbol of capitalist consumerism and elephantine beaurocracy. Within this anger lies the new danger, namely that comprehensive development has been a disaster therefore the cure must be conservation. The consequences of such an attitude are similarly politically loaded. Conserving can all too easily slip into preserving and produce an environment which is mummified. This approach can be used by the political 'left' or 'right' in a most sinister way.

A balance must be found that accepts the best of the existing as a 'body' into which new members can be 'grafted'. By this means, the fabric can be renewed to emphasise qualities already present and, as in any good design, can reinforce the variety and richness necessary to form a 'cradle for the inner man'.

There can be little doubt that once we have learnt to differentiate book-keeping from economics, and money from resources, the picture in the UK will be very different from that visible at present. Aided by the present recession and a changing political climate, there are hopeful signs that the building industry is going to have a unique opportunity to change direction and move away from unbridled consumerism. The change of direction does not signal the abandonment of the profit motive. To quote the 31st July 1975 edition of the (American) Engineering News Record:

'The profit motive is combining with urban conservation movement to spur a multi-billion dollar boom in building renovation and a swing from new construction to conversion'.

There are dangers in quoting American experience in a European context, but there are already signs of a parallel movement here. America has an abundance of large-volume, long-life, central-area, redundant buildings. By contrast, Britain's redundant buildings include a myriad of masonry-built residential properties ideal for reinforcing inner city communities.

Looking at Britain, an analysis of the European Architectural Heritage Year 1975 Awards, in the category involving the change-of-use of a building, is most revealing. Approximately one-third of the new uses for old buildings come within the bracket of museum, information/study centre and reception centre, while office and residential categories account for half the new uses. Surprisingly, almost a third of the original uses fall within two categories — namely farms and maltings/grain mills and granaries.

Commercial aspects of rehabilitation

Clearly, the future for rehabilitated buildings cannot depend upon the community endlessly being asked to shoulder the burden of more subsidised uses. Increasingly, our new goal must be to start with the presumption that new urban needs are only permitted in new buildings after the developer has demonstrated that there is no proper scope for using existing redundant buildings.

Nowadays, there is a lot of talk about 'environmental impact analysis', a technique largely reserved for assessing the consequences of building such things as oil refineries, smelters or similar large constructions. This approach frequently involves the evaluation of the environmental cost of opening a new quarry or trundling huge quantities of building materials through the midst of the local community, as well as determining how the visual and ecological impact will be felt. If those techniques had been applied to building proposals such as new Opera Houses in Sydney or Edinburgh, we might soon find that municipal accountants were becoming responsible, not merely for stopping things but for starting different kinds of projects in old buildings and on waste land.

Our attitude to rehabilitation is already changed by a new understanding of how in many instances there is positively no alternative than to 'rehabilitate'. An impact analysis of London Airport flight paths and the consequent noise, plus an appraisal of public transport facilities and road noise and distances, quickly determined the choice of a rehabilitated Holy Trinity Church in Southwark, London as the site for the London Orchestra Rehearsal Hall in 1972, a scheme that is described in the first case study. Without question, the Scottish Opera Company could only have afforded a rehabilitated building — described in the second case-study — as resources were extremely limited. To build a new theatre to the same standard could have cost ten times as much and could have taken four times as long.

In 1965, the composer Benjamin Britten and his colleagues at Aldeburgh in Suffolk decided to look at the possibility of converting the Maltings at Snape for the use of the Aldeburgh Music Festival. The concert hall which resulted is well known, but it is interesting that, at the time, some people regarded it as a fanciful and irrelevant exercise. However, it became the first of a veritable flood of maltings and granary conversions. Today it is often criticised as elitist, but it must be remembered that when it was built, those who supported the festival were teachers, musicians and a very ordinary cross-section of local music fanatics.

As a design, the building illustrates many important points. It combines a directness of construction with a sympathy for its function and surroundings, and has been of very positive didactic value. As always in these cases, a visit to the building does more than any amount of description to illustrate the relevance of its standpoint.

Since the Snape conversion and the attendant publicity, the suitability of other maltings for conversion has rarely escaped attention. In the analysis mentioned earlier, maltings were seen to contribute the space for a museum, study centre, two office projects, five residential schemes, and one shopping complex. In these examples, the decision to rehabilitate arose in a situation where any alternative solution would, for reason of location or cost, be unacceptable. We need now to consider the situations where rehabilitation can be justified on commercial as well as social grounds.

How precisely are we to unscramble fact from fancy in analysing the cost and benefits of rehabilitation? It seems quite certain that nobody can cite a situation where a 'free urban land market' applies without building, zoning or planning restrictions of some description. We must therefore assume that a fair consideration of the global benefits and costs of rehabilitation include an understanding that the acceptance of rehabilitation frequently means that we forfeit the opportunity to transform the road system, parking arrangements, day lighting standards, fire and safety provisions. In the past, the planning machine seems to have been motivated either by a desire to promote 'comprehensive development areas' (CDA's), or more latterly, 'conservation areas' in those districts thought subject to change or too valuable to change. Both of these very different planning measures could become obsolete if the general presumption changed in favour of conservation.

In the Covent Garden area of London a leading property company, holding an option on a street block of extremely decrepit properties, requested a study of the implications of the redevelopment in an area of newly-listed buildings or listed facades. The company were persuaded of the technical viability of preserving a line of facades around a gutted site and the income calculations indicated the commercial viability of the scheme. But the weight of public opinion and the antagonism of the Covent Garden 'activists' prevented the developer from making the decision to 'rehabilitate' this essentially crumbly collection of buildings. Consequently, an area designated for comprehensive redevelopment passed through the phase in which the alternative of piecemeal redevelopment and rehabilitation might have occurred, into a state of unarrested blight and decay. This illustrates how an irrational reaction in favour of the conservation of buildings can be almost as unsatisfactory as the opposing 'bulldozer' syndrome.

What measures then should be taken to achieve a balanced approach to rehabilitation and, in the process, the fullest sensible use of our human and material resources? The reversal of apparently limitless growth trends means the substitution of 'growth in volume' for 'growth in quality' and the more intensive use of labour on fewer projects.

It is our experience that a multi-professional design group working on a rehabilitation project has about the same architect/quantity surveyor bias as a group working on a new building where mechanical, electrical, heating/ventilating/ air conditioning and engineering skills are well represented. Surprisingly, the imbalance between new and old building design is less than one might have imagined, only the structural engineer being perhaps less fully employed. The reversal of growth trends accompanying the changing attitude to energy means that more building and design talent is needed to get comparable standards of comfort and convenience in old buildings as obtains in the new, and for the expenditure of less energy and material.

Current accounting and administrative techniques mean that the system operates relatively straighforwardly for the developers consuming chunks of countryside, and militates against those re-using old fabric. Even with falling land costs and rising building costs, the traditional pattern will not be readily altered without new measures being taken.

Method of planning and organisation

On the basis of the above arguments, new methods of planning and organisation might beneficially be proposed that would include the following:

1. Listed Building Status should be made only very selectively for buildings of quite outstanding historic or architectural interest and might be given a European rating – an elitist device involving perhaps no more than 3 000 buildings.

2. Conservation Area protection should be given to areas on a coherent basis, i.e. the boundaries should be drawn with a broad brush and embrace entire communities and not merely bits and pieces. These Conservation Areas should be a transitional device used initially to tame the excesses of developers and their agents. When and if rehabilitation becomes a presumptive norm they should be abolished, having outlived

97

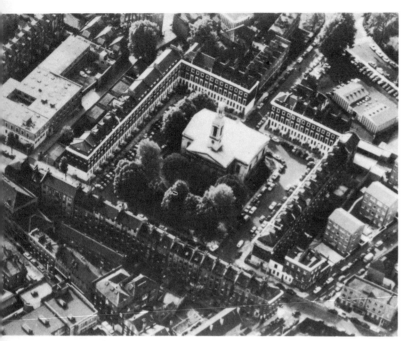

Figure 7.1 Aerial photograph of Trinity Church Square in 1968

their usefulness. Total impact analysis would hasten this process and could speed up planning and implementation procedures.

3. Once listed-building status is made rarer, conservation areas are accepted as transitional devices, and the developers' field becomes less of a minefield full of unfamiliar traps and planners' gadgetry, the emphasis of protection policies must be shifted from a somewhat antiquarian pre-occupation with preserving buildings and areas, to promoting new life for useful fabrics.

These proposals could be largely self-regulating by the straight-forward adoption of policies not dependent upon planners' whims and fancies, but largely upon market forces, as in fact our American friends have already shown. Currently, developers' costs do not approach the true costs of siting, for example, new houses on the outskirts of towns or the cost incurred in building industrial premises in the greenfield sites. New building often means new sewers, gas, electricity and road connections as well as additional school buses, street lights and greater mileage for community workers at times when existing inner urban infrastructure is neglected and underused.

It is suggested that greenfield developers should pay a 'real cost' connection charge and costs reflecting a level of rates that represent their recurrent burden on the community. Before the submission of any planning application for a new development over, say, an acre in extent or employing ten people, the developer should submit a total impact analysis (TIA) report according to a standard format. This would have to clearly demonstrate that there was no other feasible alternative and no existing premises were suitable for his or her needs.

98

It would also have to demonstrate that it was within set, stringent, standards of energy conservation and have acceptable standards of material use.

It is suggested that areas worthy of rehabilitation will be sensibly used if new users find it commercially attractive to move in. Already authorities relax regulations to encourage rehabilitation. Additionally, local authorities might consider 'rate holidays', more penal rating on buildings empty for too long, or those using fuel uneconomically and be more disposed towards granting mortgages on old properties. Accusations that rehabilitation is an elitist device encouraging the gentrification of the Inner City may be excused in a variety of ways but if it is true, perhaps we should take comfort in the statistical fact that elitism is a minority trait that surely disappears once rehabilitation is the norm. 'Is the building suitable for the client?' is a question often asked in designing a new building. Perhaps a more relevant question related to rehabilitation is 'Is the client suitable for the building?'

Case Study 1: Holy Trinity Church, Southwark

In 1970 an assessment of various churches in London was carried out with a view to their conversion into an orchestral rehearsal hall. The possible use of such a hall as a recording studio was also considered as an additional need in their assessment. A summary of the findings of this assessment was presented in 1971, which concluded:

'Holy Trinity Church, Southwark, London, is a redundant church. It is a Classical Revival building, rectangular in plan, standing in the centre of an early nineteenth-century square, now designated a Conservation Area (*Figure 7.1*). The church has been disused for some ten years and the subject of many planning applications for schemes as varied as petrol stations and ornamental gardens. The Disused Churches Committee of the Diocese is required to dispose of the church as soon as possible and there was an indication from the Planning Authority that an application for a change of use would be favourably received. The acoustics are excellent and the church is in one of the most quiet and beautiful squares of south London. Good access to the South Bank, London area, good public transport, limited car parking on the site and car parking allowed within the square, together with the above considerations, made this our selection for preliminary study.'

The following account presents the proposals and details for the conversion of the church into a rehearsal hall and summarizes the various design meetings which have taken place with the client, Southwark Rehearsal Hall Limited.

In 1968, the London Borough of Southwark made proposals under the Town and Country Planning Act to create a series of

Figure 7.2 Test rehearsal in Holy Trinity Church Southwark

Figure 7.3 Holy Trinity Church in 1941, shortly before the railings were removed

conservation areas. Among the twelve areas selected were some of the most delightful streets and squares in the whole of Greater London. Of these, one in particular stands out — the early nineteenth century Trinity Church Square and the adjoining Merrick Square. Both are quite different in size and scale. Merrick Square is intimate in character whilst Trinity Church Square has a grand and formal air. This square is completed by the building of Francis Bedford's Classical Revival Church in 1824. The church is very well situated in relation to the Royal Festival Hall, the new Barbican development and the Fairfield Halls, Croydon, all important 'musical' landmarks.

In 1972, a full scale test rehearsal was held in the church when the two orchestras, all the players wearing protective helmets against the risk of falling plaster, each visited the church with their instruments (*Figure 7.2*). Players sat on the old church chairs, which were last used during war-time air raids, from the crypt below, and played Bach, Stravinsky and Brahms, whilst a team of acoustic and recording engineers listened and made tests. It was a memorable day and helped to convince everyone that this was indeed an ideal place for making music (*Figure 7.2*).

The church and its history
The Act of 1820 authorised the erection of a church on the Trinity Estate and Trustees were appointed. The site for the church was previously a tenter ground which was an open area where cloth merchants stretched their samples on 'tenterhooks' in order to dry them. A public competition was organised for the design and a Francis Octavius Bedford was successful and was commissioned.

Bedford had already designed and built several churches in London and Holy Trinity Church closely resembled his 'Waterloo' Church at St. Luke's, Norwood, with its Corinthian portico, surmounted by a tower and octagonal lantern above. The exterior is faced with Bath stone and the roofs are covered in copper (*Figure 7.3*). It seems, however, that Bedford was not above criticism with his designs, as contemporary articles indicate. It reached a peak in the 'Gentleman's Magazine' for November 1825 with '. . . but who would set up a Doric steeple above a Corinthian portico?' More critical still the reviewer comments 'Did he (Bedford) never hear that it was inconsistent not only with the laws of architecture, but the laws of taste, to elevate a heavier order above a lighter one?' The criticism summarises thus: 'Painful as it is to every admirer of tasteful buildings . . . it is more so to see obvious and well-recognised rules departed from without any cause but mere caprice.'

The interior of the church is austere, with a roof of unbroken span. The bareness of the walls is relieved by a frieze of honeysuckle ornament and by shallow pilasters, with honeysuckle ornament to the heads, ranging from floor to ceiling. The pilasters support corbels on which rest the panelled beams dividing the plaster ceiling into fifteen coffered bays, each with a ceiling rosette in the centre.

99

There are galleries to the north, south and west sides borne on Greek Doric columns. Two staircases in the portico give access to the gallery, muniment room and to two small gallery recesses above with open balustrades and which were intended for charity children. A second stair exists in the south lobby up to the gallery. The only crypt entrance is provided by an external staircase on the east side. Lighting was originally by oil and later by gas lights. Two boilers in the crypt provided heating via large grilles in the nave floor. In 1898 the chancel was altered and the galleries cut back and a large area of steps and masonry were added to the altar which still remains. The underpinning beneath the altar was carried out at this time. The wooden reredos and decorated window surround on the east side were added in 1930. The original stone gate piers and the old stone kerbs still remain but most of the fine cast iron railings were removed during the 1939–1945 war.

The building is constructed principally of massive brick construction with large timber trusses supporting the roof. The main nave and tower walls are 750 mm (30 in) thick and constructed of brick with a light yellow Bath stone facing on the outer side (*Figure 7.4*). The four stout timber roof trusses span the width of the church and the roof is covered in copper. The ground floor, comprising timber and flagstones laid on a rubble fill, is supported on brick vaults, one brick in thickness, and filled with a lime mortar filler. These vaults form a large crypt which extends over the whole area of the church.

The main gallery is constructed with timber joists and trusses and supported on the nave walls and columns along the perimeter. These columns are slightly offset from the crypt vault piers and secondary piers have been built out from the main piers in the crypt area (*Figure 7.5*). The walls and piers are founded on timber sleepers and timber piles. Good quality sand and gravel ballast exists from crypt floor level downwards, approximately ten metres, to the underlying London clay. The water table level is at present two metres below the underside of the brick footings. Following the cutting back of the gallery and the installation of the raised chancel, the crypt piers beneath were underpinned with mass concrete (*Figure 7.6*). Two brick air raid shelters have also been constructed at the east end of the crypt.

The main structure

The main structure of Holy Trinity Church was in a stable condition. There were, however, large cracks in the north and south walls at a position some ten metres from the east end in the centre of the second bay. The cracks ran down through the entire height of the walls and show on the soffit of the brick arches forming the structure of the ground floor.

The brick foundations of the church were originally built on large timber sleepers and timber piles. Trial holes were excavated within the crypt adjacent to the footings to a level below the soffit of the foundations. It became apparent that

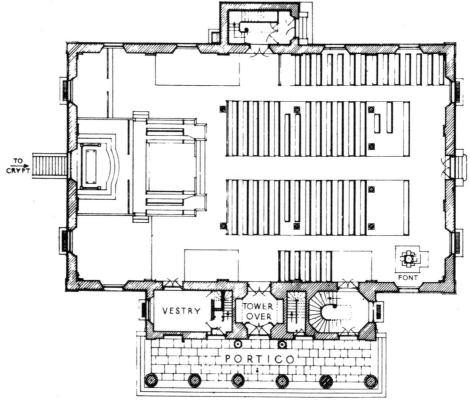

TO CRYPT

VESTRY   TOWER OVER   PORTICO   FONT

Figure 7.4 Ground floor plan, taken from a survey of London, Vol. XXV, St. George's Fields, 1951

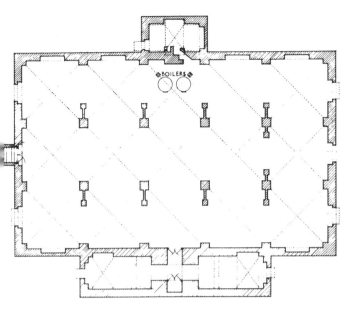

Figure 7.5 Crypt floor plan, taken from above

Figure 7.7 Existing condition of ceiling

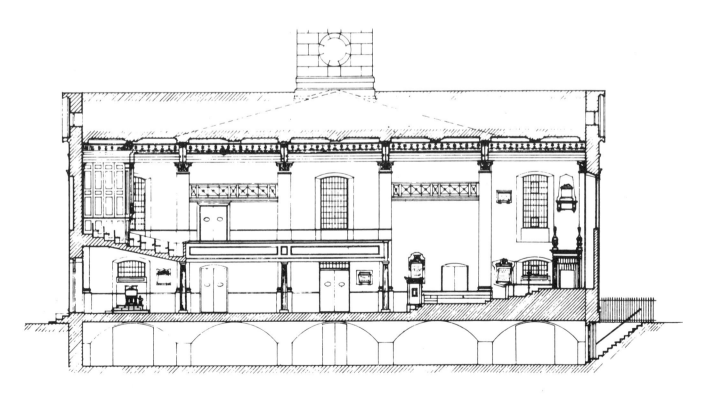

Figure 7.6 Long section

the timber sleepers were in a decayed condition due to the fact that over the years the water table level has dropped. This has caused the timber to rot and the foundation to settle despite the fact that the foundations appear to sit on good, dry, hard, well compacted ballast. Following the installation of the raised chancel, the two crypt piers beneath were underpinned with mass concrete. Two brick air raid shelters were constructed at the east end of the crypt. This caused differential settlement of the adjacent areas and hence cracks appeared. Small cracks also existed in parts of the portico structure.

In 1967, some thirty glass tell-tales were placed across various cracks in the walls at ground and crypt levels. These telltales are very sensitive and, as the majority of them remained unbroken, this indicated that movement had virtually ceased within the structure.

A detailed survey of the building was carried out and measured and the remainder of the fabric was in very sound condition, notably the roof structure. The copper roof was wholly replaced after the 1939—45 war under the authority of the War Damage Commission. However, some flashings had been displaced and seams opened up causing water to penetrate the building and damage much of the internal plasterwork.

The entire church was in a filthy condition and has provided a refuge for wild cats, kestrels and pigeons for long enough to

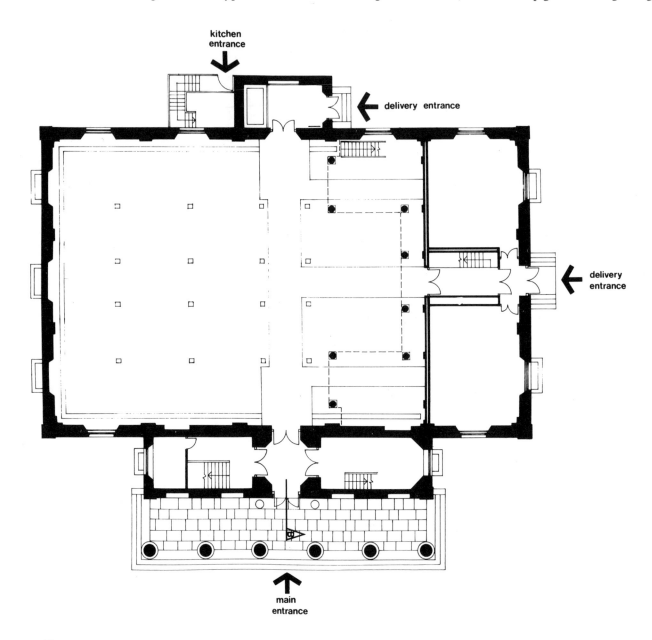

Figure 7.8 Proposed ground floor plan

have made it imperative for the building to be thoroughly dried and cleaned before remedial work to the plaster could be carried out (*Figure 7.7*). A sprayed disinfectant was applied along with superficial cleaning of the nave floor at the time of the test concert.

It can be seen from the above description that the opportunity of creating a permanent rehearsal hall for London's two oldest self-governing orchestras and of restoring a fine old church created a unique conversion project. Holy Trinity Church was well located; it possessed an excellent acoustic; it was the ideal size and in very good condition. But more than all this, the conversion was a fitting new purpose which utilised the best aspects of the building. A minimum of new or alien features were required to carry out the successful adaptation and the aim was for the church to look as though no changes had been made within it. In this way, a beautiful building was restored to its former spendour and given a new lease of life.

Accommodation for the new use

A schedule of spaces was discussed and agreed with representatives from both orchestras, which is as follows:

Rehearsal area
Two recording/tape rooms
Caretaker's office
Cafeteria
Kitchen/servery/preparation/store areas
Two music libraries
Ventilation plant room
Conductor's room with shower room
Male lavatories
Female lavatories
Shower room
Hall Manager's office
Secretary's office
All-purpose areas (upper galleries)
Boiler room
Unloading/delivery area and temporary parking

The principal design decision was to provide a large rehearsal space within the old nave of the church. The existing floor surface was taken up and replaced with a level timber finish leaving small areas of original flagstones under the gallery and adjacent to the entrance doors (*Figure 7.8*). The floor level was raised 200 mm (6 in approximately) to accommodate new

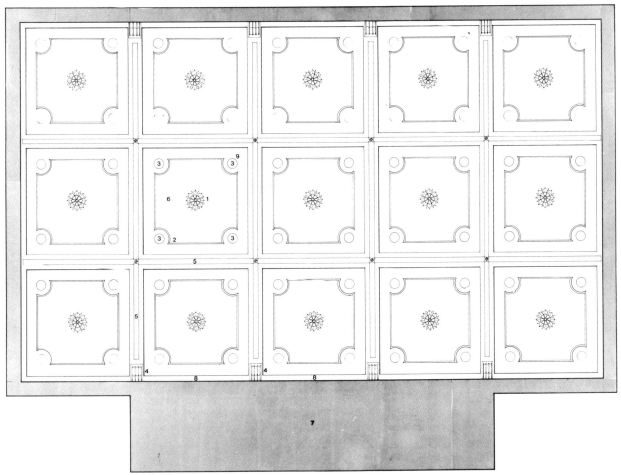

Figure 7.9 Reflected ceiling plan

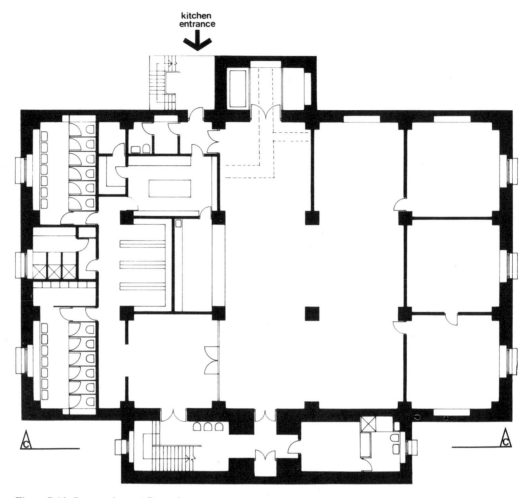

Figure 7.10 Proposed crypt floor plan

ductwork for the mechanical ventilation of the hall. The gallery was reduced in size by one bay to increase the usable floor area to a clear 351 m² (3 777 ft²). The gallery soffit was levelled and the ends of each side gallery remodelled. Two new staircases, with handrails made to match those in the existing upper galleries, were installed to connect the main hall with the gallery. The gallery front was extended approximately 1 m (3 ft 3 in) and the existing columns repositioned to enable a new cavity wall to be built across the rear of the hall beneath the gallery. The gallery can now accommodate a choir of up to 200 people. Two new recording rooms were accommodated below with a separate entrance which also provides a loading platform and delivery entrance to the hall.

The nave was completely restored during the conversion. The decorated and moulded ceiling was renovated in fibrous plaster and the walls repaired where necessary and replastered with lime plaster. The window frames were de-rusted and doubleglazed, and the doors were rebuilt to open outwards and provided with acoustic seals. All existing monuments and plaques were retained on the walls and the pews removed, cleaned and reused in the crypt.

Lighting of the hall provides an overall level to suit rehearsals and recordings. A reflected ceiling plan is reproduced in *Figure 7.9* showing how four light fittings are recessed into each of the fifteen coffered bays with a simple relief moulding.

In the portico, the existing staircases were removed and new concrete staircases built down to the crypt and up to the new floors above. A new floor provides rooms for the hall manager and his secretary, and a lobby gives direct access on to the main gallery. A second stair leads up to another new floor where the two open galleries have been converted to provide multi-purpose spaces for general use, and are double glazed to insulate them from the main hall whilst retaining the fine view of the hall.

The crypt has been adapted to provide a large cafeteria, a servery, kitchen, preparation area, lavatory and store room (*Figure 7.10*). Due to the restricted headroom in the crypt, the existing floor level has been lowered 500 mm (20 in). A new external and separate entrance to the kitchen is provided by reopening the external area adjacent to the south lobby. A music library for each orchestra is included in the crypt and also lavatories for men and women, and a shower room. A

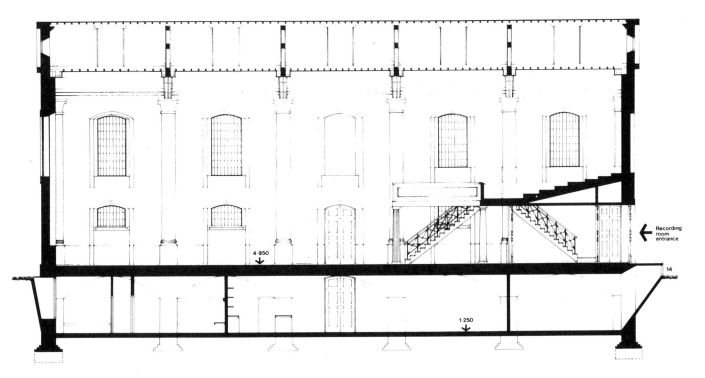

Figure 7.11 Proposed long section

passenger and goods lift connect the ground and crypt levels within the south lobby. A separate room for visiting conductors is provided with its own shower and bathroom.

Refectory-type wooden tables and the existing pews are used in the cafeteria with low level lighting placed on the tables and on the new walls. The crypt brick arches are wire-brushed and left unpainted to help create a warm atmosphere. One wall division is shown on the crypt plan to provide a quiet sitting area away from the main circulation areas. Finishes in the crypt are minimal with a concrete floor covered with matting. Quarry tiles are laid in the lavatories and kitchen. The existing fresh air inlets to the crypt are retained and new openable windows installed (*Figure 7.11*). This is supplemented by separate mechanical extract systems to the cafeteria, lavatories and kitchen. Heating is provided underfloor with radiators in ancillary areas.

Several additional items were discussed and agreed to be desirable features in the conversion. The original organ had been removed and stored but was not considered worth reinstalling. A good new organ of a similar period, has been installed, with casework in the original style.

The building suffered from wartime shell-blast, copper staining, pigeons and general London grime and dirt. The cleaning of the whole exterior was carefully supervised to ensure the building retained its mellow character. Aluminium recastings of the very fine cast iron railings which used to surround the church were leaded into the existing kerbstones. The four tower clocks and the gallery clock have been reinstated. The whole area within the site bounded by the existing kerbstones has been tarred and covered with pea-shingle. Some new trees and shrubs have been planted on the east and west boundaries to help conceal the parked vehicles. The well-maintained garden in front of the portico has been retained.

Although the building was structurally sound and stable certain repairs were carried out during the conversion and restoration. The whole of the foundations were underpinned using a traditional method. Trenches were dug in short lengths alongside the existing footings which enabled the decayed timber sleepers to be removed and replaced with mass concrete. The cracks in the vaulted brick arches of the crypt and walls were pointed and filled with an epoxy-based sand cement grout

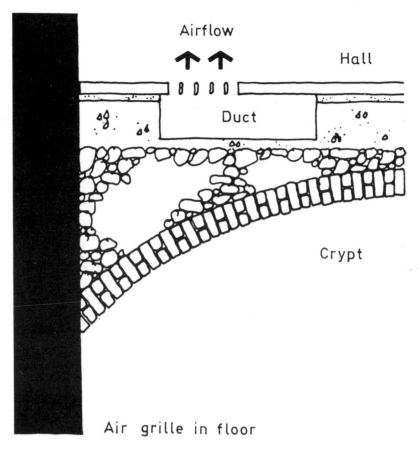

Figure 7.12 Air grille in floor

injected under a little pressure. In the portico, the existing stone floors and stairs were removed and new reinforced concrete floors and stairs cast in situ. New openings were cut through the tower walls to provide access at each level.

Due to the cutting back and provision of new staircases to the gallery, it was necessary to reconstruct part of the gallery. The rear part of the gallery was rebuilt but was supported on a new cavity blockwork wall enclosing the new recording rooms. The existing column supports were brought forward to support an extension to the gallery front. The nave floor was raised to accommodate new ductwork. The weight of the existing construction, consisting of 225 mm (9 in) brickwork, 175 mm (6 in) lime mortar based fill and 75 mm (2.5 in) flagstones was maintained.

Lighting and services

The lighting within the rehearsal hall is designed to provide a minimum level of 300 lux at music stand height. This is achieved by positioning four large fully recessed 250 watt high-pressure sodium lamps in each of the fifteen ceiling bays with 400 watt fittings around the perimeter. The perimeter ceiling light fittings adjacent to the walls are controlled independently to provide a lower level of lighting for the hall should it ever be used for an activity other than rehearsals

or recording. The lights are maintained from the roof void and are modified to enable air from the main hall to be extracted through the fittings. Within the crypt, more subdued lighting is provided by installing simple tungsten wall mounted fittings to highlight the bricked vaulted crypt ceilings. In the main rehearsal area, power supplies are obtainable from a grid of floor outlet boxes in the timber floor. A 1 200 kg (2 600 lb approximately) indirect hydraulic lift provides goods and passenger traffic between the crypt and ground levels.

Two recording rooms are provided beneath the gallery. Provision has been made for an underfloor grid system of trunking to cover the main area in order to provide microphone outlets and keep trailing wires to a minimum.

A low pressure hot water comfort heating installation was provided, served from a gas-fired boiler situated at first floor level in the south lobby. An asbestos boiler smoke pipe is connected into the existing chimney which discharges at roof level. A pumped, temperature compensated, circuit serves cast iron radiators in the main hall and ancillary rooms, and underfloor heating in the cafeteria and library rooms. Mechanical warm air supply ventilation is provided to the main hall, cafeteria and library rooms. Air is introduced into the main hall at a rate of three air changes per hour, through perimeter floor grilles connected by underfloor ducts to a

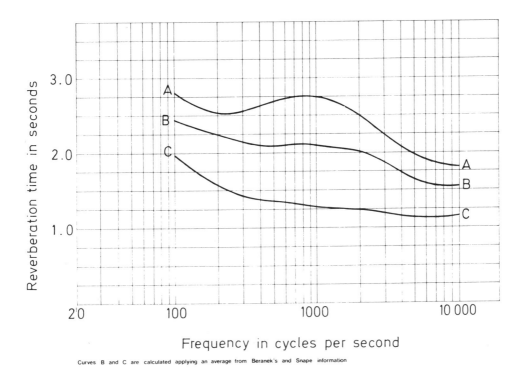

Curves B and C are calculated applying an average from Beranek's and Snape information

Figure 7.13 Graph of reverberating curves. Curve A: Experimental result. Curve B: Orchestra only. Curve C: Audience

plant room at crypt level (*Figure 7.12*). The supply air for the cafeteria and libraries comprises a constant fresh air system to give six air changes per hour, balanced by extract ventilation through the kitchen and lavatory areas. Ductwork connections run between the plant room and distribution grilles at high level into the cafeteria and libraries.

Acoustics

Obviously one of the major features of the rehabilitation was the detailed consideration that had to be given to the acoustics. The body of the church is 31.40 m long × 18.60 m wide and with a height of 10.70 m (103 ft × 62 ft × 36 ft approx). This gives a volume of some 6 343 m³ (730 000 ft³ approx).

Early in 1971, four maroons were exploded within the church and the results were recorded. These were analysed to give the reverberation times in the octave band centre frequencies shown in the table below.

	Hz				kHz			
	63	125	250	500	1	2	4	8
I	5.0?	3.0		2.6	2.8	2.6	2.2	2.0
II	3.5?	2.9	2.7	2.8	2.8	2.7	2.0	?
III	?	2.5	2.5	2.9	2.7	2.4	2.0	1.7
IV	?	2.7	2.6	2.5	2.7	2.6	2.0	2.0
mean		2.7	2.6	2.7	2.75	2.6	2.05	1.9

From these figures, graphs were produced showing the reverberation time in seconds plotted against frequency in cycles per second (*Figure 7.13*). Reverberation times based on the occupation of the church by a full orchestra and audience were also calculated; one set of curves were calculated based on Beranek's postulate for audience absorption and another set of curves were calculated for an audience absorption based on tests carried out at The Maltings Concert Hall, Snape in Suffolk. If an average is taken of these two absorbency coefficients, with a full orchestra of 120 spaced for rehearsal, the middle frequency reverberation time is 2.2 seconds. This was found to be ideal for both rehearsal and recording conditions.

In December 1972 further tests were carried out with both orchestras present and acoustic measurements were taken. With the hall empty, a further maroon was exploded and one third octave analysis of the maroon recording was carried out. Again with the hall empty, live measurements were made of one third octave noise. With the orchestra and a few observers present, one third octave analysis of a maroon recording was made.

A few interested observers, including musicians, members of the BBC and of leading gramophone companies, were present whilst both orchestras played music which included works by Bach, Haydn, Brahms, Elgar, Ravel and Stravinsky. All the measurements of reverberation times in the hall empty and with orchestras present and the recordings made at this

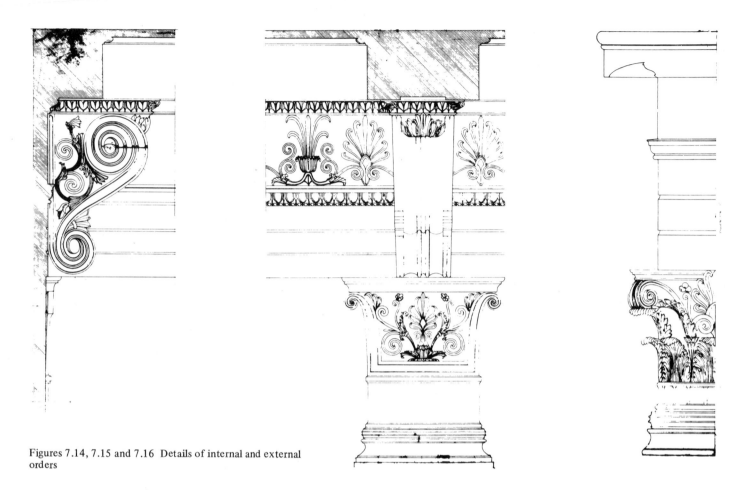

Figures 7.14, 7.15 and 7.16 Details of internal and external orders

test concert, indicated a superb acoustic for both rehearsal and recording.

The church lies between the 35 and 30 NNI aircraft sound contour line for London Heathrow Airport. The average and peak ambient noise levels were measured both inside and outside the church. These have been plotted against the traditional NC curves and, as a result, for both rehearsal and recording conditions, a sound level of NR20 was the aim for the design of the acoustic insulation of the church and for the sound levels of the mechanical installations. Noise level readings taken at the test concert confirm the sound insulation of the church at an average of about 25 dbA. The maximum sound level recorded in the church during the test concert was 95–100 dB measured on the B scale.

During the reconstruction, the sound insulation of the church was significantly increased to a value of 60 dbA. This was achieved by ensuring that all windows were repaired, sealed and the glass thickness increased to 6 mm. Double glazing in 6 mm clear glass was also provided to all windows in the main hall. All external doors were rebuilt incorporating acoustic seals at the junction of doors with frame. All cracks and openings in walls were also completely sealed. No further special techniques were required, mainly due to the massive construction of the building.

Choosing the contractor

From the outset, a new ninety-nine year lease was agreed and signed between South London Church Funds and Southwark Diocesan Board of Finance and Southwark Rehearsal Hall Limited. Various approvals were sought from the relevant authorities concerning the conversion and restoration of the church, which had been declared a building of architectural merit and is protected as a Grade Two Listed Building by the Greater London Council (*Figures 7.14* to *7.16*). Informal discussions were also held with the Greater London Council Historic Buildings Division and the Greater London Council Means of Escape Division. A presentation of the scheme was made to the local residents of the neighbourhood and general approval of the proposals obtained.

The most common method for obtaining a main contractor was on a competitive tendering basis, but because of difficulties in the boom conditions in the building industry at the time of calling for tenders, it was proposed that this contract should be negotiated, a method which offers several advantages as follows:

1. Lengthy tender documents are not essential and time may be saved on the usual tendering procedure.

2. The contractor can be consulted at an earlier time enabling him to plan his resources and construction activities more accurately.

3. The unusual nature of the works may be more accurately assessed and paid for on an actual cost plus basis.

4. A high degree of management expertise can be assured to organise successfully the specialist subcontract operations.

On the day before work was due to start on site towards the end of 1973, a fire was started by vandals and the church completely gutted. The existing timber roof and gallery were both destroyed.

The original programme for the work on site was twelve months. When agreement had been reached to continue the project, it was decided to extend the period to eighteen months. This allowed time for the construction of a new steel framed roof and concrete gallery. Where possible, all the existing features were retained, the copper roof, the fibrous plaster moulded ceiling and the same gallery format were all replaced. The opportunity was taken to remove the original divided arrangement of gallery seating, and the new roof design allowed easier access to the light fittings. The only other significant change from the original plans was the closing in of the open-fronted galleries on the second floor to form the offices.

Case Study 2: Theatre Royal, Glasgow

The first 'Theatre Royal' was designed by the Glasgow architect, George Bell. It was called Bayliss's Coliseum Theatre and Opera House and was opened in November 1867. The name was changed to the Theatre Royal in May 1869 when Messrs Glover and Francis acquired the lease.

On 2 February 1879, the theatre was totally destroyed by fire and was rebuilt to the design of the London architect, Charles John Phipps, who was responsible for the design of more than thirty well-known London theatres and provincial opera houses, including Her Majesty's in the Haymarket, London, the Theatre Royal, Brighton, and the Lyceum, Edinburgh. He was consultant architect to the Drury Lane Theatre and was consulted by committees of the House of Commons and colonial governments on questions of theatre construction and acoustics.

The new theatre was opened on 26 October 1880 under the management of Miss Marie Litton. There were different managers from 1881 and it was closed for some long periods until Messrs Howard & Wyndham Ltd took possession in July 1888. The theatre was reopened on 10 September 1888 with Mr Henry Irving and the Lyceum Company in *Faust*.

On 1 March 1895, the Theatre Royal was again destroyed by fire. The architect for the reconstruction was again Charles John Phipps and the theatre was reopened on 9 September 1895. In 1924, the directors of Messrs Howard & Wyndham Ltd carried out improvements to the Theatre Royal. The theatre was sold to Scottish Television in October 1956.

In August 1972, Scottish Opera, through their General Administrator Peter Hemmings opened up enquiries about the possibility of renovating the theatre which, at that stage, was a makeshift studio and administration building for Scottish Television. An inspection of the building showed that the possibilities were worth pursuing, that the cost, which was much greater than they had expected, could be met and that the money was worth spending.

After further studies and early design work on the stage, pit and seating, designs were prepared in January 1974 with a view to opening the opera house in October 1975. Full design work started in April 1974 and a scheme design report was presented in August. The contract was to start on 1 October 1974 with completion on 30 September 1975.

The design brief

Scottish Opera had asked to be provided with a home; a fully equipped opera house which was also suitable for ballet and theatre. It was to house one hundred artists and to have a pit big enough to hold a Wagner orchestra. It was hoped that at a later date the whole company, including its administration, could be housed in the opera house. The auditorium was to seat between 1 500 and 1 600 people.

For design work on the Theatre Royal, the major references were not books and plans, but the existing theatres at Brighton, Edinburgh and, of course, Her Majesty's in the Haymarket. From the study of these buildings, the atmosphere of the Theatre Royal and the Phipps' design approach were reconstructed. At no stage was it considered that a faithful reconstruction of his design was being made.

The layout of the Theatre Royal, Glasgow, separated strongly the social classes and the different entrances were clearly segregated. What was astonishing was the discovery that although the top tier in the theatre is very sheer, it is said that originally there was yet another one on top. The theatre is now only able to accommodate just over 1 500 people – in the 1890s, 4 000 were crowded in. The theatre was not over-endowed with lavatories and the ventilation was very primitive. Conditions must have been appalling by present-day standards.

By the second half of the 19th century Glasgow had become one of the major trading centres of Europe, and as

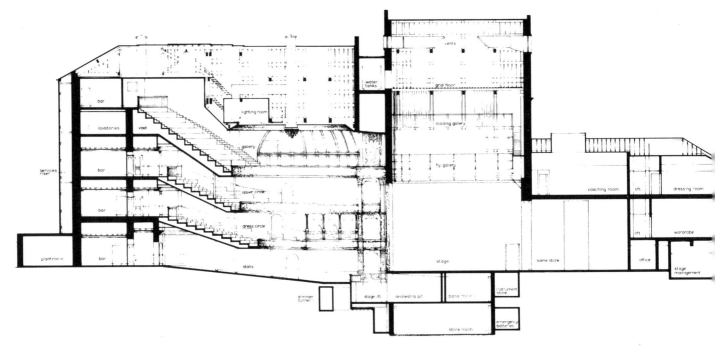

Figure 7.17. Section through auditorium

such it developed a great theatrical tradition. The music hall, theatre and opera were enormously popular. The style of the period was paper-thin, theatrical for its own sake, a style in which classical forms were misused to satisfy self-indulgent flights of fancy. The late Victorian eclectic style was a contemporary 'pop' style; an age of glamour, glitter and frippery, which of course had its most vulgar and debased aspects as well as some of the finest.

The greatest single influence on Victorian theatre decoration was the Paris Opera, designed by 25 year-old Charles Garnier and the introduction by him of the red interior. In those days, this was considered the ultimate in plushyness. However, any style was used and on theatre buildings the decoration tended to be added as an aesthetic veneer on a 'sound' structure. Shall we have instant Tudorbethan, Chinoise or French Renaissance; you name it, they had it. It was 'a creative pastiche'. Their use of the classic idiom would have made Vitruvius turn in his grave, but the buildings had spirit.

As far as the mechanics of performance are concerned,

to produce the spectacular, the Victorians developed highly sophisticated mechanical devices for the stage. Revolves, traps, flying mechanisms all existed and, although machinery has become more sophisticated, most devices now used were existing in the 1880s. The only major developments since then have been electrical.

To keep the right historical perspective on the Theatre Royal, this type of theatre, never highly ornate, has as great an affinity to the Odeon style as to 'French late baroque' which was its stylish label. 1895 is only some twelve years before the establishment of the Werkbund in 1907 and only 14 years before Peter Behrens designed the AEG Turbine Factory in 1909 with both Mies van de Rohe and Gropius in his office. Charles Rennie Mackintosh (Glasgow Art School 1898–99) was practising in Glasgow.

The challenge then was to provide a home for the Scottish Opera Company from a shell which had been used for the previous 15 years as a studio and offices and fitted with a conglomeration of spaces, totally unrelated to its original use.

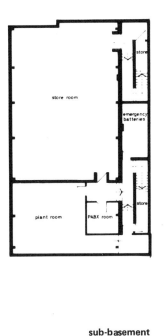

sub-basement

basement

Figure 7.18 Sub-basement and basement plans

The only area which had survived with any of its former splendour was the auditorium where the fibrous plaster, by some miracle, was left more or less intact and had sufficient of its original style to be the basis of a restoration or rather a design in style. When design work started, there was only eighteen months to complete, with the finishing date fixed as 15 October 1975. To have any chance of completing on time a year on site was essential. The work was to be done with a tight buget in the worst inflationary conditions in our history.

Two possible design approaches were examined. The first was to restore the auditorium and redesign the adjacent areas to be in style so that the whole place had a unity and clarity related to the original. The second approach was to restore the auditorium, but to design all the other areas as a modern building so that the centre was held like a rich jewel in a highly disciplined contrasting framework. *Figures 7.17* to *7.23* show plans and sections of the building.

It was decided that the first approach was the only one in the short time that was allowed. It was impossible to know what the construction would reveal when everything was opened up (as the building was fully in use by Scottish Television until after a start was made on site). To produce a modern design with any clarity needs a framework with a clear structure. It was known that as the theatre had been changed so much over the years, it would be impossible to achieve this without a greater time scale and much more money than was available.

Using the existing framework, it was possible to give back to the theatre a sense of style by the way in which the existing structure was remodelled, and the way in which the finishes were matched. Having made this decision and tested it with pilot schemes for the services and space planning, it had to be trusted that the rest would follow.

From the start a number of tactical design decisions were made. The auditorium design was studied and expanded in style. The front of house areas (i.e. bars, foyers, staircases) were to be realized as an extension of the auditorium aesthetic. The dressing room and working areas were to be designed in a simple way which would make them consistent with the rest.

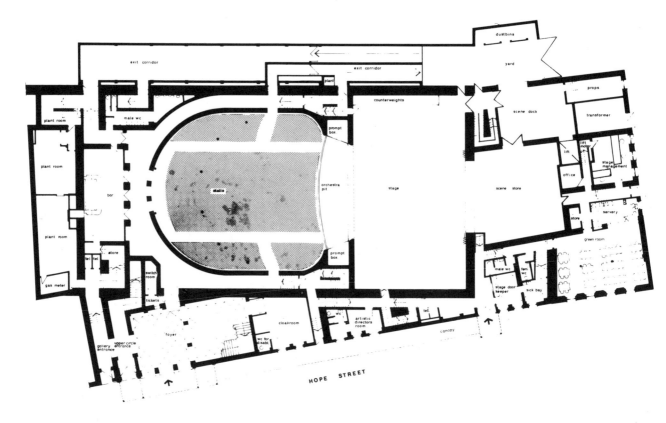

N

Figure 7.19 Ground floor plan

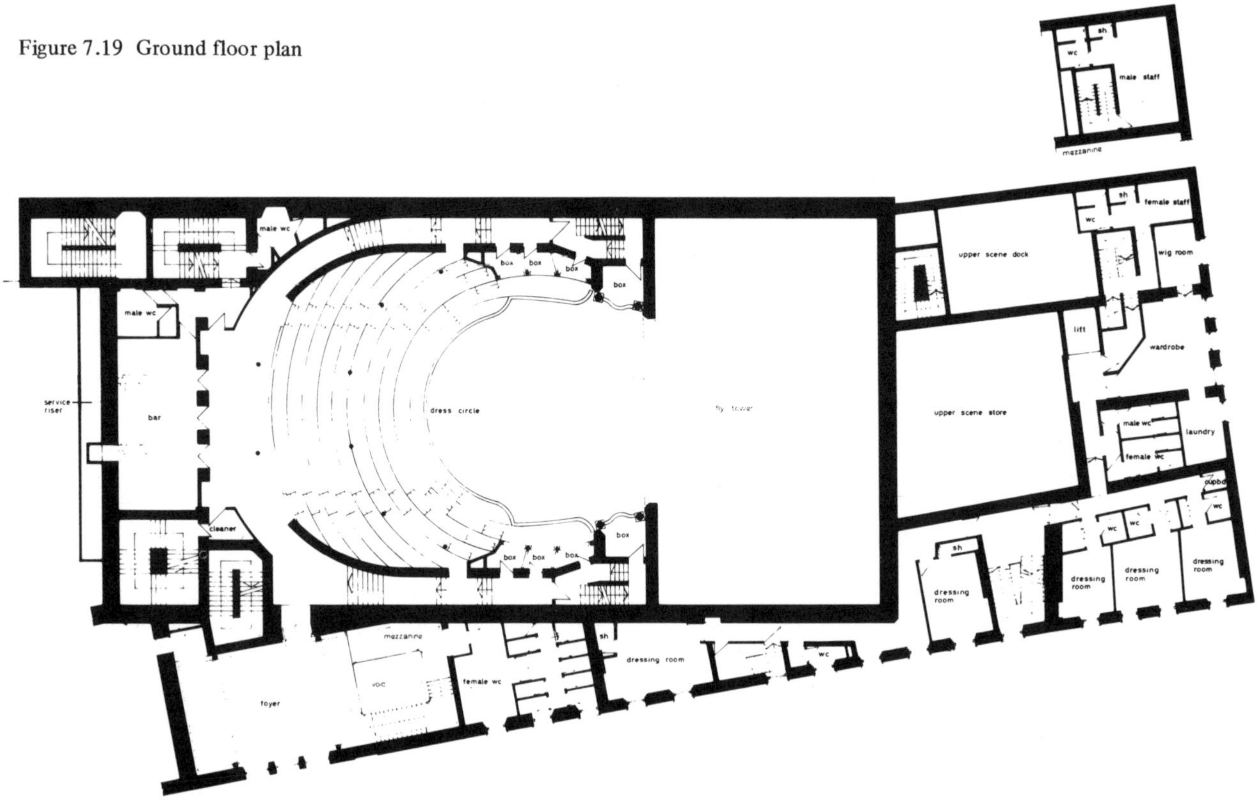

Figure 7.20 First tier plan

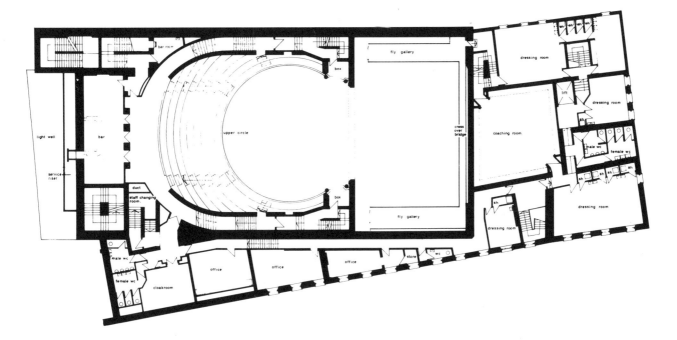

Figure 7.21 Second tier plan

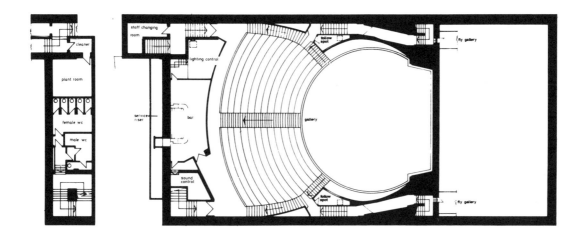

Figure 7.22 Third tier plan

Figure 7.23 The new foyer

Figure 7.24 Detail of joinery in the foyer

Figure 7.25 Balustrade detail from the foyer staircase

Figure 7.26 Auditorium interior, showing follow spots

114

This approach provided a design fix somewhat similar in principle to Greenslade's proposals for a 'kit of parts' for the Liverpool Polytechnic scheme described in Chapter 12. Having produced a vision of what was to be achieved, the greatest problem was to hold that picture intact while making quite radical changes at a late date in the building programme. The problem was once described as 'trying to hold a half-set jelly in one piece through a year of very bad weather'. However, the original design by Phipps proved to be rigorous enough to set out a very logical set of design decisions which were followed right through to the colour schemes.

Much of the work, which was involved, relied on traditional crafts. In 1895 much of the fibrous plaster work, joinery, metalwork and wallpaper could be factory-produced and the architects would have been able to choose their patterns directly from the book. Of course, most of their tradition has now ceased and so the designers were obliged to revert to earlier craft methods to produce their effect. Fibrous plaster moulds had to be specially made, by one of the few master plasterers left in Scotland. Joinery, which was all in mahogany for the front of house, was redesigned using the old pattern books of mouldings and the colour carefully matched to achieve the Victorian French-polished richness (*Figure 7.24*). A consistent use of brass ironmongery required specials to be made. Cast-iron rails were modified and redesigned to be recast in aluminium, and the wallpapers were modified from existing ranges to get nearer to the reality. These details are the ones which 'make' the place and give the tactile quality so much a part of a Victorian interior (*Figure 7,25*).

Spatial requirements

The aspect of design which has most destroyed the atmosphere of the Victorian theatre is the insensitive intrusion of modern techniques into stylish public areas. In many Victorian theatres, modern 'peppermint' light fittings or even neon tubes now fight with cluster lights on the tier fronts. Outsized 'biscuit tins' house gigantic spotlights over the decorated balcony fronts and miles of wiring, ducting and piping festoon the ceilings. We were determined that these services would be installed within the disciplines of the interior.

Four specific solutions are pointed out to illustrate the approach:
1. All lighting for the stage, which is usually hung from tier fronts, was placed in the dome or in the slips. This dome was modified to be a plaster-covered trap door which, during the intervals, is closed, giving the illusion of an undisturbed Victorian painted ceiling.
2. The follow spots, which are large, cumbersome and unsightly, are built into the springing of the dome. This has the effect of improving, rather than detracting from, the interior (*Figure 7.26*).
3. All air vents, which relate to ducts behind plastered and

moulded false ceilings, are hidden behind the old device of a large cornice used in its correct classical context. This device also improves rather than detracts from the interior.
4. All soffit lights in the auditorium are recessed in a dark ceiling giving not a sense of disturbance but adding to the intimacy of the space.

Theatre is an art of illusion and when a theatre is visited a sense of excitement is expected. The Victorians also expected the illusion of grandeur from the building. The sequence of space which is experienced as a theatre is entered should prepare and acclimatise patrons to the idea of watching the stage. The pavement outside the theatre entrance should be welcoming, give a sense of arrival, and be the first semi-formal space for meeting friends. The north end of Hope Street, where the theatre stands, has little charm. A traditional canopy is being provided and will add enormously to the presence of the theatre and prepare for an entrance to the foyer.

Few people who visit the Theatre Royal realise that the foyer is totally new. It is remoulded with its staircases and mezzanines within the envelope of the building and is much smaller than originally planned. The Opera Company tried to purchase the adjacent public house but failed to do so and the scheme was without a foyer two weeks before starting work on site. The total usable area for the foyer and staircase was only approximately 7 m × 15 m (23 ft × 49 ft), very small and, when first considered, thought to be quite unacceptable.

As the problem was examined more closely it was realised that the Victorians often gave themselves an identical problem. By the use of grand architectural devices in a small space, a strange mix can be achieved which is particularly Victorian. A formal, classical space was constructed with a large chandelier in the centre using mirrors at high level. These give the impression of space and continuity. The staircase with its mezzanine gives views at high level of the foyer below and the dress circle foyer above. The fact that there is a crush in the space and people are seen moving up and down the staircase acts to heighten the excitement and feeling of occasion as the theatre is entered. There is a feeling of grandeur. In reality, the space is only about one-third of its apparent size. The colour is neutral and the lighting is crisp and bright (given by three chandeliers which were found in Glasgow and whose owners were persuaded to give them to Scottish Opera).

The hardness of materials, the neutrality of the colour and the formal mood were chosen to give the audience a clean and neutral reference point, after the streets of Glasgow, before entering the richness of the interior.

On leaving the foyer, a contrast is experienced. The staircases which lead from foyer to the top two tiers are carpeted, papered and lit in the same way as the auditorium. Consequently, they are quiet, warm and inviting. When entering the horseshoe corridors of the auditorium from the stalls or dress circle foyer, the experience, it is hoped, is one of expectancy,

Figure 7.27 (right) Stage pulley systems seen from the fly gallery
Figure 7.28 (centre) View of auditorium interior
Figure 7.29 (bottom) View of auditorium interior from third tier

mystery and to some extent nostalgia. The colour is dark leather brown, offset with gold on the wallpaper which varies in effect according to the way it is lit. The tactile quality is soft and the people, pictures and mirrors, become the only focus in the area.

As the velvet seating is passed, one becomes aware of the only bright focus in the auditorium — the front of the tiers. When the centre is reached, the inner crust is entered; this is like a roofed arena. The tier fronts, boxes and proscenium arch, which form the crust, are decorated plaster, painted in a range of creams, touched with gold and lit with brackets set onto the fronts; a deep orange velvet finishes the top. The dome is set as a contrast in a blue with the decoration picked up like strap work floating in a sky.

As the lights are dimmed and the audience quietens, the eye is focused on the thick dark brown velvet curtain, lightened with gold decoration and lit from the auditorium with a red colour which is picked up in the depth of the pile. The curtain opens, and all being well, the illusion is complete (*Figures 7.28 and 7.29*).

Although the floor area of the building was only slightly changed by small infill additions, the circulation backstage had to be completely redefined and the rooms rebuilt. Levels had to be tied together in a logical way and the whole area had to be provided with washing facilities for one hundred artists. The idea of hiding all the services was out of the question, so simple rules were made which would allow services to be put in. A cornice was applied about 600 mm (2 ft) below the ceiling. The exposed services were run above the cornice and the ceiling and services were painted a dark colour. Below the cornice everything possible was done to eliminate evidence of these services.

Lavatories were given another set of simple rules and furniture was made to fit the visual grammar that resulted. By this means, the subcontractors who started in this area of the building could proceed with little information — not an ideal situation but one forced by the speed with which the work was carried out.

Heating and ventilation

Modern standards of heating and ventilating were required without unsightly intrusion on the Victorian interior of the theatre. An inspection of both the Theatre Royal in Glasgow and in Brighton showed that Phipps incorporated natural ventilation in his auditorium design and the theatres were heated by coal fires. His method of ventilation for the auditorium was to have openable windows at stalls level to let fresh air in, and openable windows at the back of all bars with 'chimneys' at the top of the gallery and dome to draw the hot air out (the ventilation took with it any heat gains from lighting); this idea was taken in the new design and adapted. Outside air is brought in free of cold draughts and traffic noise, through low pressure nozzles at the levels of the auditorium as

close as possible to the occupants. This provides steady air movement without noise generation. Mechanical refrigeration cooling was not considered necessary as opera has a winter season when free, cool, outside air is available.

In the planning, it was essential to ensure that the location of plant prevented any noise problems in the auditorium as this had to be very quiet (noise rating of 20). The boiler plant and auditorium supply fan were located on rock at stalls level behind the stalls bar. The exhaust from the auditorium was achieved naturally by stack effect without the use of fans. The timber roof trusses had an unknown natural frequency with the possibility of sympathetic vibration from any fans. This could have caused unpredictable noise. The design of these exhausts was complicated as they had to satisfy all the requirements of acoustic separation, smoke release and volume control. Interlocks with the smoke detection system ensured that if smoke were produced anywhere in the auditorium, stage or orchestra pit, it would not be circulated by the ventilation plant to other areas.

Gas was selected as the primary fuel as it is quiet in operation and requires minimum space. The boilers chosen have atmospheric burners and as the boiler plant room was long and thin, an 11-module plant was selected. This plant had the added advantage of low thermal capacity to respond rapidly to the peaky load profile of the main auditorium supply plant and the hot water supply. The hot water supply had special gauges for monitoring of flow rate and consumption of hot water, as the HWS load may peak at 120 showers in 20 minutes. As this peaks occurs infrequently, the boilers were not oversized. However, when the flow rate approaches this peak demand, unnecessary plant is switched off to dedicate the whole boiler plant to hot water supply.

To handle the special problems of heating a stage, radiant panels were provided under the fly galleries and fan convectors were fixed on the rear wall of the fly tower to warm up the large volume of cold air so that cold down draughts are minimised when the curtain first rises.

Electrical installation

The electrical installation in an opera house is extremely sophisticated and covers every aspect of modern practice. There was an added problem at the Theatre Royal as the system had to be fitted unobtrusively into a Victorian interior. The building has all the electrical systems associated with a public building. Lighting, emergency lighting, power, fire alarms, lifts, telephones, etc, are all needed, as well as those services associated with a fully equipped opera house stage. There is a 1200A supply to the building, of which some 800 A are taken by the stage lighting.

The equipment includes: a total of approximately 700 lighting outlets throughout the building linked to the stage from the dome and the flies, a bank of 240 controlled dimmer channels with the equipment sited under the stalls level, power for stage equipment, including two stage lifts, a lighting bridge and a 4.5 tonne (4.4 tons) safety curtain, a theatre sound system (sound effects and amplification), together with wiring for outside radio broadcasting and a stage manager's sound system.

It is this latter which controls the whole 'operation'. Artists can be paged from any part of the rear of the house to the stage and they can be cued both visually and verbally, and public announcements can be made. In addition to this, special effects, scene changes, off-stage musicians are all monitored from the one mobile stage manager's desk in the corner of the stage.

Acoustics

Before studying the feasibility of structural renovation, the potential sound qualities of the auditorium were examined. Tests were made difficult by the fact that the volume had been reduced substantially and absorbent material had been applied to create studio conditions in a large space. Seven explosions were made in the area of the pit and stage. These were recorded in the auditorium and the tapes were analysed to determine reverberation times across the full spectrum of sound frequencies. The analysis indicated that the final acoustic might have a shorter reverberation time than had been hoped, but with the possibility of varying the surfaces, the even balance of sound throughout the space, and the even decay, it was thought to be a good starting point for an Opera House. For this reason it was decided to cover the floors with linoleum rather than carpet and wherever plaster was required, the harder plasters were used.

Experience with other orchestra pits, taking the geometrical shape of the auditorium into consideration, and the requirement to house an audience of fifteen hundred people, resulted in a decision to build the pit partly under the stage. This has the very real advantage of giving more prominence to the stage sound, though it caused some murmuring from the orchestra musicians.

On completion of the renovation, it was found that the reverberation time was still shorter than that hoped. But, because of the small nature of the space and the intimate quality of the sound, the overall effect is considered by the music fraternity to be excellent. Even a stage whisper registers at the rear of the gallery. From the singers point of view, it is easy on the voice.

The completed Theatre Royal auditorium has, as a basic guide, a volume to audience ratio approaching half the normally accepted value which indicates the degree to which the success of the sound stems from its good direct sound quality (a tribute to the original architect) and the balance between stage and orchestral sound which fully justified the decision to set the pit under the stage.

Conclusion

It was clear from the beginning of this project that to meet the very tight programme (even without the delays that occurred later) the early appointment of the contractor was essential. The most difficult part of the work to assess was the change needed to the structure and fabric of the building. Any contract which attempted to define these in detail would have been impracticable. The 'inspired' guess of a year on site needed to be proven and related to the work content. The contract needed to be flexible to reflect the inevitable changes in a project of this type, as there was no time for haggling in mid-contract. A contractor who was experienced in this kind of work, had initiative and was forward-looking, was needed.

A management contract seemed the obvious way to deal with the early appointment and flexibility. But there were reservations about whether this kind of work could be approached from the 'distance' of a management contractor. In the event a project management firm was appointed four months before site operations began.

Everything except the most tricky structural operation was sub-contracted under the control of the management contract. The execution of the work in the first three months disproved all the principles of programming and the cash flow predictions, and the term 'out of sequence working' became a familiar phrase at site meetings in the scramble at the end.

The standard of programme information is critical to the success of a project of this kind. This requires a high level of expertise from both the contractor and the architect. In addition the standard of cost control and its monitoring related to the programme cannot be over-stressed. Any weakness in these aspects has to be quickly and vigorously remedied.

The fact that the job was finished on time was largely due to the tremendous commitment of all the parties involved and the excitement generated on site. The conditions under which people were prepared to work speaks for their enthusiasm, and the fact that some traders were working around the clock at the end of the job shows the pride that everyone had for the new Scottish Opera House.

Scottish Opera have already formulated plans to add to the building. A canopy, previously described, is to be added to the outside along Hope Street. A dome is to be added to the existing entrance tower to give a larger gallery bar, and a large bar which was once part of the theatre is to be re-used. There are problems with each of these but even longer-term projects are being discussed. All of them are possible but at present must wait.

Meanwhile Scottish Opera's first winter season has now finished and the ticket office had handled a 90% average capacity of the 1500-seat audience to add even more to the very high reputation of Scottish Opera (*Figure 7.30*).

Figure 7.30 Ticket office

Conservation or Renewal

A study of the Library at Blackburn

Keith Scott

The alternatives of conservation or renewal always present difficulties and arguments for and against must be kept carefully in balance. It is easy to confuse conservation with 'preservation at all costs'. Dedication to preservation begs the further questions of cost and longevity. How much money is it worth pouring into a building which may have out-lived its useful function, or whose location is now wholly inappropriate, or whose fabric is decayed beyond repair? For how long should the building fabric be preserved?

These questions are easy to answer at the extreme. Few would argue other than that, say, Durham Cathedral should be kept in good order virtually for ever. Some conservationists are surely on thinner ice, however, when they seem prepared to go to the same length with some minor, late-Victorian, building in a decaying town centre.

Such champions of our cultural heritage are apt to condemn 'comprehensive redevelopment' as though the very term described a leprous concept. Admittedly some avaricious developers have, over the past twenty years, raped our town centres but a materialist, get-rich-quick, discount-orientated society gets what it deserves. Society sets the standards: the constructors of its requirements provide its physical expression. There are now enough European examples of sensitive and commercially successful redevelopments to demonstrate that the notion is not intrinsically evil.

Moreover we often forget that thousands of acres of our Dickensian town centres, especially those in the textile belt of Lancashire and Yorkshire were 'comprehensively developed' in one astonishing burst of activity in the third quarter of the nineteenth century. The only thing that kept the new centres recognisable as a continuity from the old was that, since the internal combustion engine had not been invented, pedestrians and carriages moved much as they had done since the middle ages. New communication routes and concepts of vehicle and pedestrian segregation did not have to be considered as became necessary with our twentieth century redevelopments. Any objective view taken in 1950 of the quality of environment and fitness for purpose in the twentieth century of town centres in Lancashire such as Bury, Colne or Blackburn, must

conclude that they were worn out and wholly unsuited to the aspirations of their citizens.

Earlier in this book there is evidence of the development of theoretical methodologies for evaluating the benefits and potential for a building's conversion. Most studies present currently practising architects with what seems to many of them a bewildering array of mathematical formula, computer jargonese and abstract analysis. This is so far quite foreign to the mixture of deep practical knowledge, intuitive 'feel' for a building's potential and sheer intuitive brilliance which is the hallmark of all good conversion work. Thus, in the following example of the choice between conservation or renewal, a series of decisions are described that had much more to do with aesthetic value judgements than with mathematical equations.

Case Study

For well over a decade the County Borough of Blackburn has been transforming the heart of the town from that of an ageing Victorian Lancashire cotton manufacturing centre into a lively community for widely diversified industry. The market and shopping area is now unrecognisable to those who only knew the town from a few years ago, but in addition to commerce, the cultural, recreational and administrative needs of the towns-people have been kept constantly in view. Hence, Blackburn has now acquired an extension to its fine, neo-classical town hall, and a greatly embellished Victorian cathedral.

In 1971 the Council called for a feasibility study for a cultural complex based on the magnificent Edwardian group of halls just north of the commercial area. The task was a challenge, for it involved not only the rehabilitation of King George's Hall and Windsor Hall, but also an indication of how the old Co-operative emporium could be adapted, or the site redeveloped, to rehouse the library, linked with a future Art Gallery (*Figure 8.1*).

The feasibility study envisaged a first floor 'street' joining all the cultural buildings. It was suggested that, in the long

Figure 8.1 Blackburn Co-operative Society before conversion to library. View from Northgate

Figure 8.2 The reference library

term, this highway could provide a pedestrian way from a new multi-storey car park west of the civic halls, through them across Northgate, bisecting the library, crossing a pedestrianised Town Hall Street into a new Art Gallery, then into a newly modernised cinema complex in the old, neo-Gothic Corn Exchange, before descending to street level in a piazza in front of the Old Town Hall.

The idea of converting a group of existing buildings into a new cultural centre as early as 1971 indicates how far ahead of fashionable thinking was the Blackburn Corporation. In the early 1970s most local councils were thinking in terms of sweeping demolitions and re-building rather than of capitalising on existing building stock. Blackburn, however, had already spent ten years converting their town centre into a completely new pedestrian precinct and had come to the view that further redevelopment should take the form of a careful merging of the new centre into the existing fabric of the town. Early grandiose plans for the fourth phase of the town centre were therefore scrapped in favour of this more sensitive conversion approach.

Figure 8.3 Blackburn Co-operative Society before conversion.
Town Hall Street elevation

The interior

At Blackburn the fine neo-classical Town Hall provides a focal point and the public hall complex, while architecturally undistinguished, presents a substantial and well-built counterpoint to new buildings of the commercial precinct. Between them, and forming a vital link in the cultural complex, stood the old Co-operative emporium. It was built for the Co-operative Wholesale Society in 1932 and was its home in Blackburn until 1972. For two years the building had lain empty and it was already a classic example of the danger of leaving buildings unoccupied and unattended for long periods of time. This example of what Aylward in Chapter 1 terms 'energy withdrawal' is confirmed by a growing body of experience which enables us to quantify the cost of leaving a building unattended. Wet and dry rot eradication in this building cost about £8000 whereas a quarter of that spent on minimal heating, regular inspection and running repairs and maintenance to gutters, windows, flashings and the like would have shown great

122

benefit. As it was, rain had begun to penetrate the roof and walls, and rot had got a strong hold on the fabric.

The external elevations were excellent examples of that most depressing period in British architecture, the nineteen thirties (*Figure 8.3*). It was a mixture of half digested classic stone trim and spandrel panels divided by piers of harsh red Accrington brick, all stained and grimy with the soot of fifty years. The rear elevations were of second class bricks and white glazed bricks, to give a little extra light into the adjacent 'Blackburn Times' offices across a narrow alley. The roof was an obstacle course of various protruberances such as lift motor rooms, ad hoc stores, vent shafts and even a charming little stone columned cupola which was located so far back in the flat roof that it was visible from practically nowhere.

That at least was our view of the building's aesthetic merit. A challenge to think more deeply on the problem was made by local preservationists and North West Arts, who claimed it had a unique character expressive of its time and worth keeping in its entirety. Disagreement was narrowed by our ready agreement not to recommend demolition. The most cursory cost plan comparison showed that conversion was far cheaper than total renewal and more detailed studies confirmed this.

Internally, as befits a department store, there were some large open areas. On the second floor there was a big room with a high ornamental ceiling which had done duty in earlier days as a ballroom (*Figure 8.2*), a meeting place for wedding receptions and for tea dances. A small corner room had a similarly ornate ceiling, but elsewhere there were no spaces of great merit. The two lifts immediately plucked at the heart strings of the architects, because they were in open shafts surrounded by wrought iron cagework with quite distinctive and charming fascia designs on the lift doors. The structure of the building was a composite of riveted steel columns and beams spanning on to masonry and brick perimeter walls. The concrete floors were of the Truscon T-beam type, and from the original drawings all seemed to be plain sailing. A complete photographic survey was made of both the interior and the exterior. The photographs proved invaluable to both the quantity surveyor and the builder when reproduced on standard drawing sheets because they could be readily annotated with instructions (*Figures 8.4 to 8.7*).

In retrospect the mistake was made of assuming the correctness of the working drawings, and this led to a good deal of rapid on-site surveying at the request of the contractor when things did not turn out as expected. In fact, it was discovered over a period of time that virtually nothing on the working drawings was built as shown, and it is clear that no conversion should be attempted without previously undertaking a detailed physical survey. The building envelope was not in fact accurately portrayed, nothing was at right angles, the Truscon floor beams frequently spanned the 'wrong' way and many walls which we assumed to be non load-bearing were essential to structural stability.

Figure 8.4 Working photograph

Figure 8.5 Working photograph

Figure 8.6 Working photograph

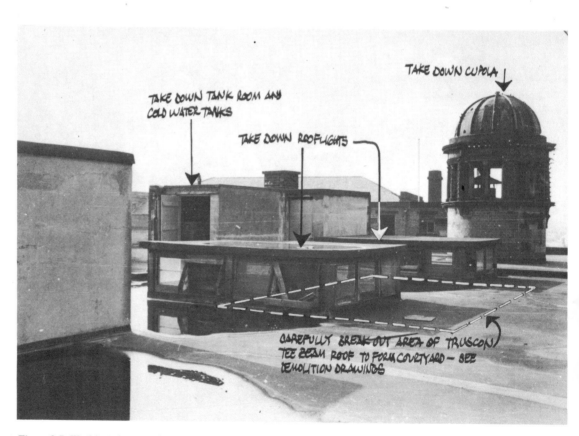

Figure 8.7 Working photograph

Figure 8.8 The Children's Library

Spatial requirements

The planning problems centred around the need to satisfy the requirements of large space users — principally the lending library, the music and drama library, the children's library (*Figure 8.8*) and the reference library. Apart from the fact that the lending library had to be on the ground floor, there was considerable flexibility in the location of other departments. Given that the 'street' linking the town's concert halls to the future art gallery had to be on the first floor to ensure pedestrian/vehicular segregation, this effectively split that level into two. In turn this restricted the size of spaces on either side of this main pedestrian link. It was therefore easy to suggest that the children's library and the music library be located at this level, with elements such as a coffee bar, small meeting rooms and a modest lecture theatre filling in the remaining spaces (*Figures 8.9 to 8.11*). For a large uninterrupted floor area such as required by the reference library and the closed book stacks, the second floor seemed ideal. Various studies were done to ensure the correct disposition of the spaces, and the preferred solution aims to make maximum use of the greatest floor to ceiling height under the ornamental ceiling, so making a large and airy room suitable for prolonged study.

The two staircases wrapped round the original lifts and they were conventionally located at either end of the building. The

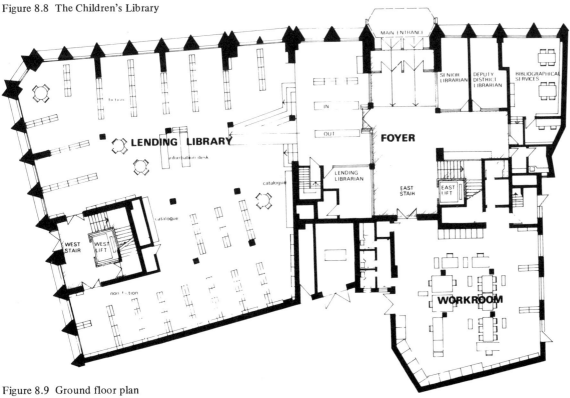

Figure 8.9 Ground floor plan

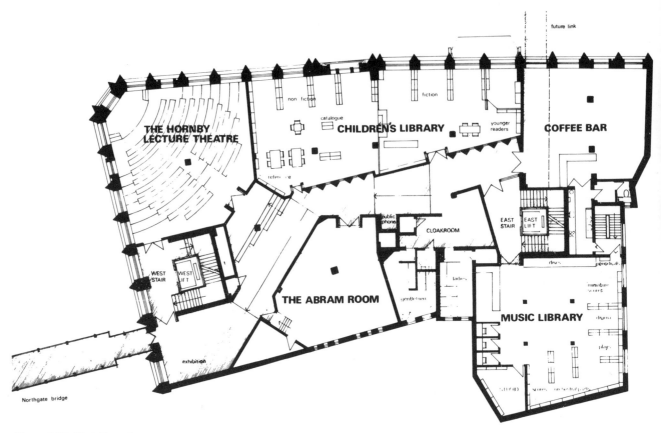

Figure 8.10 First floor plan

Figure 8.11 Second floor plan

lift shafts were obviously re-usable and after prolonged negotiations with the Fire Officer, the Factory Inspector and the Insurance Companies, it was eventually possible to achieve an open lift shaft protected only by glazing inside the ornamental enclosure, and completely new lift cars were installed. The aim was to make these as fully glazed as possible, highlighting the moving car and the counter-balance weights. Any architect who has seen and envied the glazed Hyatt Regency elevators in big city hotels in the USA and tried to emulate them in England will understand the impossible odds against achieving anything so dramatic and exciting.

One of the greatest benefits to be obtained from conversion rather than building anew, is that old buildings tend to have large, easy fitting envelopes within which there are often hundreds — sometimes thousands — of square metres of unused, ill-lit, unventilated spaces. In conversion one can often remedy the worst ills, and the client acquires a considerable amount of usable space which is cheaply obtained and could certainly not be contemplated in a new building. This was amply true of the old Co-op emporium. There were literally dozens of such spaces, especially in the basement and on the mezzanine floors between the first and second, and the second and third floors. One wonders indeed whether some of the rooms and odd-shaped spaces had ever been used (*Figures 8.12 to 8.15*).

A further space bonus came when the decision was taken to throw a lightweight roof over the whole of the various excrescences at roof level. This took the form of a mansard pitch raked steeply back from behind the parapet and clad in slate. A flat roof was laid over the topmost outhouse, broken only by the two lift motor rooms which had to be raised appreciably to house the new equipment. This gesture not only gave the building a double roof in terms of weatherproofing, but created huge roof spaces which will do duty for many years as expansion to storage, closed stacks and so on. So great in fact was the volume enclosed that it permitted the sinking of light wells into the flat roof to give small enclosed courts for rooms such as that of the Chief Librarian and the staff rest areas.

The first recorded library in Blackburn was a subscription library set up in 1787 by the vicar of the parish church. Members were required to pay an initial subscription of 7½ guineas followed by monthly payments of 15 shillings. Understandably only the rich could afford to use the facility, but others followed the lead, and by the beginning of the nineteenth century there were several competitors in the town. By the eighteen forties working men needed reference books to amplify their knowledge, and this led to the many Mechanics' Institutes up and down the country, and Blackburn's Institute opened in 1844. In 1850 the Public Libraries Act provided for free libraries, paid for by the municipality, and although the Act was strongly opposed, Blackburn was amongst the first to adopt it in 1853. In 1860 an official Library Committee was formed and in 1874 the new Free Library and Museum was opened to house 35 000 lending volumes and 25 000 reference volumes. Extensions took place as pressure grew on space and by 1959 the original capacity had been extended to 200 000 volumes — provided under extremely cramped and difficult conditions. The new library gives comfortable accommodation to 250 000 volumes, and for the first time there is ample space for a children's library (*Figure 8.8*), music library and rare book library, and provision for twenty five private study carrels on the mezzanine floor.

The exterior

The exterior of the building presented another sort of challenge. Apart from one's view of the historic value of individual decorative details, the many disparate units of the facade needed to be tied together and the principal task was seen to be one of providing a simple, dignified facade befitting one of the main civic buildings in the town. The site was irregular and totally built-up. Only two elevations (north and west) faced public streets, the south elevation was separated from the Blackburn Times building by a small narrow cul-de-sac, and the east elevation was partly built against by a public house and partly exposed to the backs of some shops facing the main part of the town centre. To the south of the building there was an extension which was of poor construction and of little functional use. It was therefore demolished and the land sold to adjacent owners who are now in the process of extending their premises. The 'unseen' elevations were tidied up, windows inserted, other windows blocked up, and many unnecessary excrescences lopped off to provide as clean and straight-forward a solution as possible. The resulting wall was a mixture of Accrington brick, common brick, concrete brick/blocks and white glazed brick. Over the whole of this medley of materials was applied a plastic paint in a dark earth green to unify the elevations.

In the course of the detailed design of elevations on existing buildings, negotiations over rights of light and waivers to building regulations are almost inevitable. Blackburn Library was no exception and in the end waivers had to be obtained from the Department of the Environment to cover several sections of the building.

The problem of the street elevations remained. As indicated earlier, the preservationists' view was that the main elevations were a good example of design, both in general and in detail, of their day, and that they should be allowed to remain as they were and simply cleaned up. The opposing view was that the design was pedestrian even by the debilitated standards of the inter-war years. The mix of brick and stone was unfortunate and only the overall patina of grime gave a sense of unity to the mass of the building. Cleaning would only emphasise its shortcomings. Apart from the unsatisfactory design of the upper storeys, there was a fundamental problem to be solved on the ground floor.

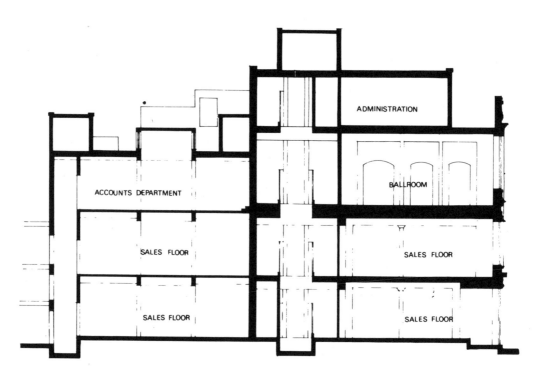

Figure 8.12 Section – 'Before'

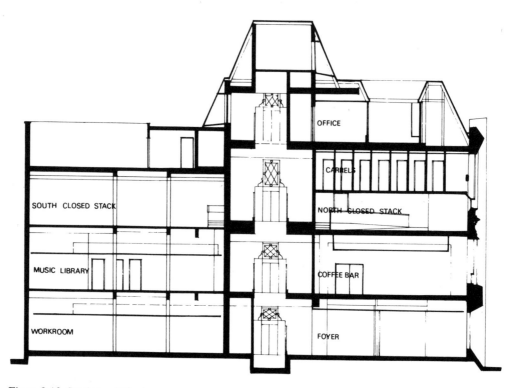

Figure 8.13 Section – 'After'

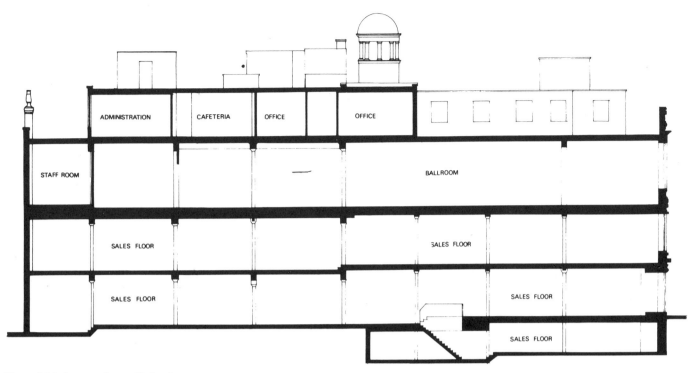

Figure 8.14 Long section – 'Before'

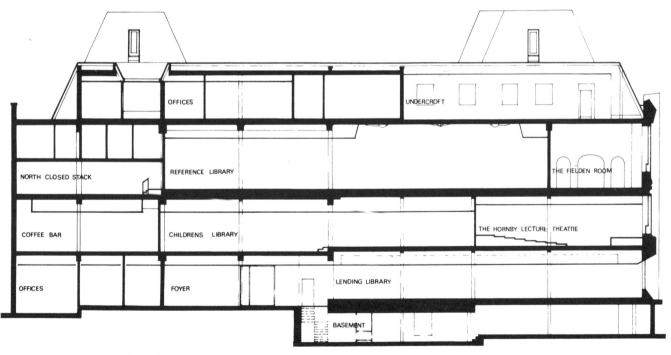

Figure 8.15 Long section – 'After'

The emporium had naturally required large windows with minimum interference and, whilst this gave good showroom conditions, it was inappropriate to the library function and gave the building a top heavy look with an insubstantial ground floor. A further concern was the brick piers separating the window elements and a decision was made to get rid of all brickwork and to try to unify the building material of the elevations. Stone is the ubiquitous material of all Blackburn's civic buildings and the substantial window surrounds and spandrel panels of the old emporium were built of the local sandstone. To solve both these problems in one sweep, mullions or piers were designed to extend from street to roof in such a way as to cloak all exposed brickwork and break down the ground floor into a more powerful module. Natural stone was out of the question on grounds of cost, so artificial stone of matching colour was chosen.

The detailed plan profile resolved itself into large triangular elements and strong (but subsidiary) horizontal units were established at first floor and at roof level to cloak completely the very ungainly cornice. Every job stands or falls architecturally on one or two basic design decisions and the strong, vertical striation imparted by these piers is fundamental to the new library at Blackburn (*Figure 8.16*).

The existing stonework was sand-blasted and to our surprise some of the spandrels proved to be very interesting panels of cast iron rather than stone. These panels are all on the north elevation and have been painted (*Figure 8.17*). Detailed inspection showed the windows to be in a very bad state and in many places almost corroded away. They have all been replaced by timber framed assemblies with all the former intermediate mullions and transoms eliminated, leaving only large but narrow ventilating lights. The west elevation to Northgate proved the easiest to handle since the pavement levels were fairly constant. The Town Hall Street elevation called for much more subtlety in its treatment because the street slopes fairly sharply, demanding great care in the geometry of the splays to the ground floor sills and the triangular stone mullions.

Figure 8.16 Remodelled elevations. New artificial stone mullions, stone spandrels and cast metal spandrels

Figure 8.17 Detail of remodelled elevations

Services

Heating the refurbished building presented a novel problem. It transpired that the local authority had a high capacity heating plant on the far side of King George's Hall in a basement plant room and this equipment had considerable excess capacity. Consideration was therefore given to using heat from these boilers and cost comparisons were made with a conventional heating system in the converted emporium. There was, in fact, very little difference in cost between the alternatives, but it was politically expedient to utilise the town's boiler capacity. It also made good sense in that the system could be extended still further in years to come when the art gallery is built.

Flow and return steam mains had therefore to be routed through King George's Hall, across Northgate and into the new building. The crossing of Northgate could theoretically be done either below ground or above via the bridge link, but in practice the below ground route proved impracticable due to the dense mass of services which would have had to be disturbed. The bridge link therefore had a dual rationale: firstly as a pedestrian link in the first floor 'street' system, and secondly as a carrier of the steam mains providing heat to the new library. Heat exchangers and all the associated plant equipment were established on the third floor and distribution took place from this point.

Full air conditioning was eliminated on cost grounds but the system incorporates mechanical ventilation and heating plus perimeter radiators, and judicious use of ventilating window lights obviates the need for standby fans in case of failure of the mechanical ventilation system. Careful attention was paid to the integration of grilles and other ventilation terminals into the internal design as a whole. In the conversion of so large a building careful thought has to be given to the routing of ducts because it is usually quite impossible to consider going through beams by means of local stiffening and sleeves, as can normally be done in the structural design of a new building.

Design considerations to suit the Fire Officer also proved difficult to achieve. In the end the building had to be almost fully sprinklered and throughout the open spaces there is a smoke detector system, except in the kitchen area where a heat detector was preferred. There is a 'hot line' to the Fire Station and magnetic stays have been fitted to all smoke stop doors. In fact the only areas not protected by sprinklers are the reference and closed book stacks where it was agreed that water would ruin much irreplaceable material far more quickly than fire.

Conclusion

The contract for the conversion was plagued with the kind of misadventures which reduce efficiency and raise tempers. In addition to the influence of the Summerland fire on the thinking of Fire Officers the task of achieving the required standard for precast stonework delayed the job for many weeks. Two sub-contractors went bankrupt and the high-alumina cement scare struck just when the installation of all the new floors had been completed. These promptly had to be ripped out in the over-reaction to the crisis that occurred throughout the country. Most traumatic of all, at the mid-point in the contract local government reorganisation took place and resulted in a 'new' client, because under the provisions of the reorganisation Blackburn handed over libraries, amongst other things, to the Lancashire County Council. Briefing and persuading the many new personalities who had no part in the original concept was time-consuming. Under the new client arrangements, the bridge became the concern of the County Surveyor, and its design standards had to meet up-graded requirements.

The interior fittings were chosen by the client and have clean, simple, lines. Colour schemes throughout were kept cool and muted, firstly to avoid emphasising the irregular angles which appear in most rooms, and secondly to let the gaily coloured book jackets and library publicity speak for themselves. The floor finish throughout is carpet and non-directional acoustic tiles form the ceiling to most of the rooms. In several areas ceilings are used as decorative-cum-functional elements, notably in the lending library with its inverted V-shaped troughs, the lecture theatre with its coffered design, and the reference library and a corner committee room which retain their highly ornate original plaster cornices. The only areas of strong colour are in the lift and stair wells and in the coffee bar. Materials generally are of high quality with ash joinery throughout.

In summary, the people of Blackburn have the lasting satisfaction of knowing that a substantial and well-known building in the town has been retained for posterity, while providing a home for a library of considerable floor area at approximately half the cost of a new library building in an equivalent town centre location. So far as architects are concerned, conservation work can be uniquely satisfying, like giving the 'kiss of life'. Bringing a building back into full vigour and viability seems clearly worth while. One feels that a vital thread of continuity has been rewoven into the environment and the 'cultural assets', as Bicknell described them in Chapter 6, surrounding the old emporium have been retained.

CHAPTER NINE

Integrity in Restoration

The Example of two Mediaeval Halls

John Warren

Out of the heated debates on conservation and restoration a number of conventions, codes and guidelines are emerging, and from these a key thread that can be drawn is integrity. This relates not only to the actual materials of which the building is made but to its spaces and shapes and to the uses and methods of working of all its components. It may be architecturally clever to wrap an old building in some new synthetic guise; it may be economically effective to insert seven floors behind a facade that apparently presents three storeys to the world; it may be convenient to remove an entire structure and replace it with a replica made in new materials; but all these actions raise questions of doubt as to the integrity of handling a structure. The architect who takes any such action must first have honestly and satisfactorily answered such doubts. Once destroyed, an ancient fabric can never be re-created: it may be reproduced, but a reproduction is merely a reproduction.

There is a school of thought which regards old buildings as historic material, valid in their own right and venerable for this reason alone. Thus a villa by Palladio or a fireplace by Adam is an historical document in the same sense as a painting by Lawrence, or a violin by Stradivarius, and a modern facsimile of any one is by equal token a fake or a reproduction. By the values of this present age this is a philosophy which cannot be gainsaid. It therefore follows that any venerable piece of building fabric has an intrinsic worth which depends solely upon its origin, and it equally follows that a simulation of that fabric with intent to deceive is misleading and historically dangerous. A new dimension has entered architecture with this concept — morality based on the intrinsic worth of earlier material which therefore has a priority over added or inserted material.

Conservation morality or, as it is better expressed, integrity in handling older materials, is a vital section of the restorer's decision making. Some further examples may illustrate the point. Christopher Wren, in extending Hampton Court Palace, London, for William and Mary, grafted on to the late Mediaeval and Tudor fabric complete new sections built in a style which was entirely of his own time. Had he chosen to extend the

earlier fabric in false Tudor brickwork he would merely have been making a fake sixteenth century building. In adapting the old for his newer purposes, Wren was working within a principle of architectural honesty which is a familiar artistic motivation. When, however, a repairer takes down from Wren's building a crumbling section of limestone parapet, replacing it with a piece of new but otherwise identical stone, he is simply carrying out a sympathetic repair which is acceptable under a similar logic, although there is then a legitimate argument for the use of some special system of indication of date such as a simple date-mark to ensure that future generations are not deceived as to the origin and date of the actual material used.

The more difficult problem arises when adapting an older building for new uses, where it is necessary to make amendments and adjustments. One cannot date-mark a void and it is difficult to complete a damaged wall, vault or column in dissimilar materials and so identify new work. Problems of this sort tax and reveal the skill of the designer. The qualities perhaps most to be sought in these circumstances are sympathy and honesty: sympathy of response to the existing work and honesty in the handling of the new in relation to the old.

Honesty is, of course, a word which has had much currency in architectural criticism. It was an underlying precept of the functionalist philosophies of the modern movement where the principles of clear expression of the material and of the function it performs became the guidelines to the aesthetic. While honesty is fundamental in work of conservation and re-use, it now takes on another and rather special aspect, suggesting not only honesty in the expression of the material itself but historical honesty in expressing truthfully the period of work.

Where a building is to be retained, it is fundamentally good practice to preserve and enhance every possible part of the structure and to retain, so far as is possible, the original relationship of its component parts. In architectural terms it must always be remembered that the quality of a building derives not only from the physical structure of which it is made, but from the contained and defined space within it and the shapes and aspects of the spaces left between it and other buildings. Thus, to take down a street building, leaving only its facade standing, while grafting a new structure on to the back of the facade, is the antithesis of conservation so far as the building itself is concerned.

The structural integrity of the building and all its internal shapes and spaces will have been destroyed and, so far as the original evidence goes, the building will have been virtually eliminated. However, that very same act of preserving the street facade, regardless of whatever stands behind it, may, in itself, be an important act of conservation in terms of the street and so, in townscape terms, may be entirely justified although the building itself has effectively ceased to exist. The problem is compounded with cross currents of interpretation and understanding, to say nothing of the practical problems introduced by the changing use of buildings.

Even where the type of user remains nominally the same, the structure of society itself introduces changes. In refurbishing great urban terraces of nineteenth-century residential buildings for twentieth-century residential use at approximately the same density, the internal layout may have to be completely restructured. The original arrangement of eighteenth-century and nineteenth-century town housing was typically based on a vertical compartmentation designed for households of ten or twelve persons. Today, under different social conditions, this same number of persons lives in several households and the vertical compartmentation is impractical. Consequently, in restorations faithful to every aspect of the original exterior, the interiors are forced to accommodate entirely new arrangements of spaces which slice through the original vertical walls and in some cases even take away the function of some of the original front doors.

At a very much more modest level, the problems of spatial integrity can be illustrated in the restoration of two Mediaeval halls, both in Suffolk and both restored for the Landmark Trust. Both buildings are historically important and both were restored for residential purposes from conditions of near dereliction. They are structurally similar, having been large open halls of two bays without a chimney, and having, on the common Mediaeval pattern, two-storey bays at each end of the hall.

The two halls in question are Purton Green Farm near Bury St. Edmonds, and the 'New Inn' (The Knowle) at Peasenhall. Purton Green Farm is the earlier and very much rarer of the two buildings. It is an aisled hall in which the central truss of the large open hall is carried upon columns standing within the outer walls, so leaving an aisle on each long side of the building. Being a thirteenth-century building, the trusses are of scissors-braced construction and the timbers are all of a very heavy scantling and generally straight. The 'New Inn' at Peasenhall, on the other hand, is of a later Mediaeval type without aisles and with a crown-post roof construction which is repeated in one end of the building in a 'cross-wing'.

Both buildings had passed through the usual sequence of

modification suffered by Mediaeval halls: that is to say, a floor had been inserted in the large central void and a brick chimney stack had been built in the hall. Subsequently, as timber-framed buildings went out of fashion, both halls had been socially degraded and converted into smaller cottages which were finally abandoned by their inhabitants and condemned as uninhabitable by the local authorities.

No alteration work is undertaken *in vacuo*. The client, the purpose of use, the money and skills available, all affect the work. Both these very remarkable buildings were fortunate in having been rescued from otherwise irretrievable decay by a charitable trust whose purpose is to save and restore small but important buildings and, where possible, to allow the public to enjoy them by visits and by living in them. The Trust is deeply concerned about the quality of its buildings and took advice in these restorations from a distinguished Mediaeval archaeologist.*

In both buildings it was decided that the spatial integrity of the original open Mediaeval hall was of an importance that justified the removal of the inserted sixteenth-century floors and chimneystacks. These objects, venerable in themselves and important indicators of the social and structural histories of the buildings, were dispensed with not only because they were in poor condition but because they entirely negated the original architectural concept which was still retrievable, since so much of the Mediaeval fabric remained in each case.

Though the buildings are archaeologically very different, their architectural similarity will allow a detailed description of the work on one to illustrate the principles of both. For this purpose, the 'New Inn' at Peasenhall will serve, since, unlike Purton Green Farm, its life as an 'open hall' did not involve alterations or conversions and, therefore, its restoration as an open hall was a restoration to a known condition.

* R. T. Mason FSA

Case Study 1: Peasenhall

Peasenhall is a village in eastern Suffolk in a rolling and gentle landscape that was prosperous in Mediaeval times (*Figure 9.1*). The evidence is that the 'New Inn' actually was built as an inn, and we are fortunate in having, from monastic records, a firm late fifteenth-century date for its construction. When ultimately purchased by the Trust the Inn had long ceased to serve a thirsty public and was merely a part of a long row of small cottages purchased comprehensively from the local authority. The Trust restored the entire group, but only the 'New Inn' is dealt with here.

The building bears all the signs of its late fifteenth-century origin and an original brick cellar beneath the low end confirms that it was purpose-built for its public function (*Figure 9.2*). In plan it is a typical 'open hall' structure, with a single cross-wing, and the unusual rearward extension of this cross-wing is perhaps the one other significant indication of the original purpose of the building. The date at which it ceased to function

133

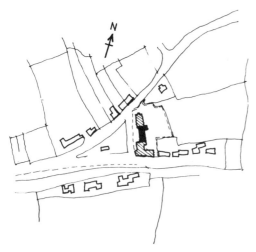

Figure 9.1 'New Inn': location plan (shown solid black)

as an inn is not recorded, but the building suffered the almost universal fate of open halls in being floored over, probably in the seventeenth century. A brick chimneystack was built against the upper end of the open hall and on this stack girders were carried which were, in turn, used to support the floor joists. It may, at this stage, still have been one dwelling.

A timber-framed addition, which appears to have been made in the seventeenth century, provided a false cross-wing to the western end of the original hall house, and extended the low end. At this stage is was obviously still an important building, as the quality of these extensions clearly shows. Later

Figure 9.2 'New Inn': site plan (shown hatched)

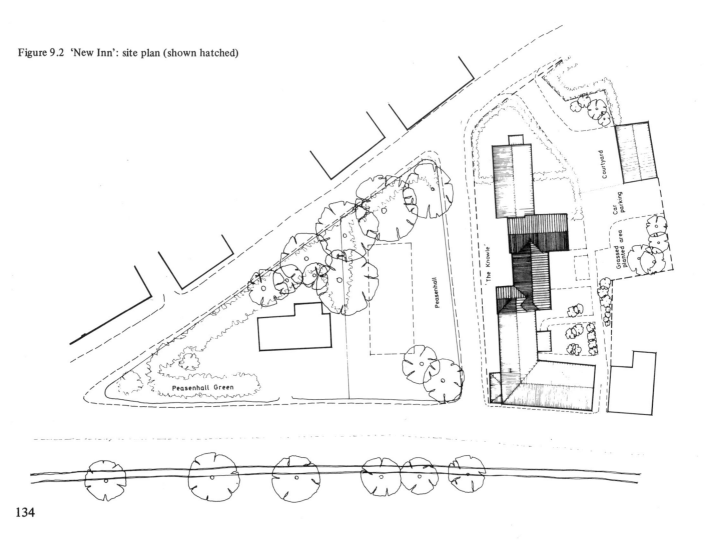

Figure 9.3 'New Inn': before restoration — the front facing the green (cross-wing to left)

it moved down the social scale as the fashion for brick building came in. The hall was divided into cottages and in the process windows were cut into the roof and wall framing. Stairs were inserted and a great many minor alterations took place.

The options before the Trust were to attempt to restore the Mediaeval building to something approaching its original aspect or, alternatively, to restore it to the condition of its first stage of conversion (*Figure 9.3*). There could have been no question of retaining it in any of its later conditions as the arrangement of partitions and the quality of workmanship were inconvenient and poor.

The decision to restore the building to its original state was made on the basis that there are literally thousands of Mediaeval halls surviving with inserted floors and chimneystacks, whereas the public has very little opportunity indeed to enjoy a Mediaeval hall of medium status in its open condition. Added to this argument was the fact that, due to subsequent alteration, there was insufficient evidence to be sure of the state and nature of the building in the seventeenth century after the insertion of the floor. This decision having been made as a matter of principle, it was logical to remove the later additions which had been made at the low end. These included a small secondary cross-wing.

However, as stripping down proceeded, it became apparent that beneath the unprepossessing exterior of this cross-wing there was a fine timber-framed structure, and that the adjacent part of the additional range was of equal quality.

It was also clear that there was insufficient evidence to restore the framing of the gable wall of the lower end and, in consequence, the original decision to restore the Mediaeval hall in

135

Figure 9.4 'New Inn': internal detail prior to restoration – a surviving doorhead in the 'low end'

its entirety was modified to allow the retention of the secondary cross-wing and its contemporary additions. This decision did not modify the principle of the previous intention to return the building to its Mediaeval form so far as the interior was concerned. From within, every visible space is directly relatable to the original rooms, despite the retention of some elements of later construction.

The Great Hall

In the open hall, now restored as one large single open space, a later floor of attractive buff pammets (or floor tiles) has been repaired and extended, and in the wall at the high end, where the first chimney was built, the gap in the framing has been filled with salvaged brick rather than with repaired timbers, to make a visible statement of the insertion.

On the floor itself, the position of the Mediaeval fireplace, ascertained by the area of baked earth, has been marked by a change in the colour of the pammets. In the high end much of the damage to structural timbers caused by later 'improvements' has been left visible and some of the structural timbers used to carry an inserted ceiling have been left in situ as a visible reminder of the changes which have taken place.

The great chamber, or solar, at this high end has been opened up to the roof, as has the hall (*Figure 9.5*) to reveal a fine moulded octagonal crown post, complete with cap and base.

Apart from the structural philosophy, a further fundamental decision which had to be made by the Trust was the way in which the building would be used. The broad decision to restore the hall to its Mediaeval aspect left the Trust as the prospective owners of a house of some twelve rooms, which

Figure 9.5 'New Inn': the open hall after restoration

was obviously inconveniently large for use by one family, particularly as a holiday home, where emphasis must be on convenience and workability (*Figures 9.6 and 9.7*).

The Trust also has a policy of encouraging the general public to view its buildings, and a combination of these requirements led to the decision to leave the great hall itself open, accessible to the public at large, and serving as a great entrance hall to the holiday accommodation built into the solar and service ends. This notion had the advantage of removing the problem of heating the great hall, which stands now open to the rafters and tiles. From within, the roof is seen as it was in Mediaeval times, as a pattern of structural

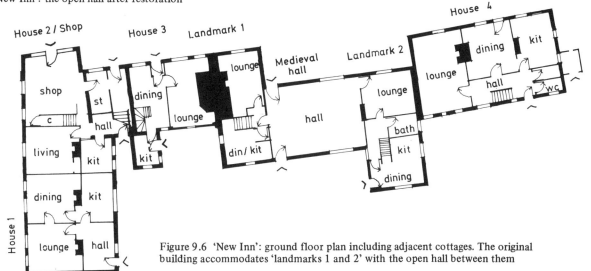

Figure 9.6 'New Inn': ground floor plan including adjacent cottages. The original building accommodates 'landmarks 1 and 2' with the open hall between them

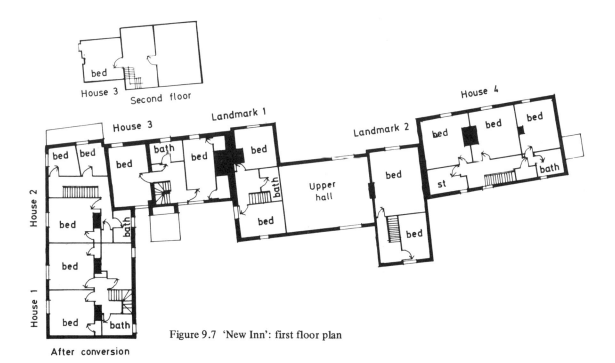

Figure 9.7 'New Inn': first floor plan

timbers, split oak laths and tiles. Had the hall been used for more domestic purposes, it would have been impossible to reveal the soffit of the roof covering in the original way.

The individual rooms

In the high end, the structural partitioning was accepted for what it was and the rooms were adapted to the sizes dictated. A concessionary alteration was made in the case of the stair, which obviously could not be placed in its original outside position; this was, in any case, uncertain. Its present position is determined by a trimmer which is early, if not original. At one stage it was thought possible to retain an outshot to the rearward projection of the cross-wing in which a stair might originally have been housed. The possibility of putting a new stair in this position was rejected for various practical reasons and because its inclusion would have been an apparently firm statement of position, although the evidence for the original stair was inconclusive.

At the low end the original buttery and pantry, with the rooms above and cellar below, were augmented by two small rooms contained in the secondary cross-wing. As occasionally happens, unexpected features of the original design came to light as the building was stripped down to its essential elements. The roof of the low end of the hall proved to have been half-hipped originally, though later adapted to form a gable. The half-hip was, of course, restored.

Various later artefacts were retained in the restored building so that it is now possible to see Victorian fireplaces and recovered Mediaeval windows almost side-by-side. Historically, this attitude to retention demands of the observer some discernment; but although the effect is historically muddled it is aesthetically satisfactory and is better by far than the destruction of one or other of the elements if they can be retained or enhanced by practical use.

In such circumstances occasional awkward adaptations also have to be made. For instance, in the low end a wall dividing a bedroom from a passageway actually contains a Mediaeval window which originally looked out across the position where the secondary cross-wing was added. The window has been opened up again and although it looks directly into a bedroom, curtains provide the privacy required. The same bedroom is entered by a door which, if it were normal height, would penetrate the wallplate. Rather than do this, a very low door has been introduced, so low that even the smallest adult stoops to pass through. The result is a bedroom which is fun for children, though it was something of a strain on the tolerance of the Building Inspector.

'If in doubt, leave out'. This convenient adage encapsulates a vital notion for conservation. There are many occasions when the restorer is tempted to make a decision which reflects his interpretation of doubtful evidence, and at that point the jingle may help him avoid a positive statement which will weight the historical evidence in the eyes of the later beholder.

138

Thus items which cannot be omitted should be replaced with material which is clearly self-dating. This applies not only to modern sanitary or lighting fittings but to doors and even to wall panels. It is also vital that the materials used are sympathetic.

There is a tactile and visual pleasure from older artefacts which the Landmark Trust relishes. Thus doors, where possible, are doors which have been salvaged from the existing building. None of them is mediaeval — these all disappeared long ago — and they are self-dating by their construction. No attempt is made to confine them to their original positions, which in many cases have now disappeared with the loss of inserted partitions or added outshots. The doors are treated simply as valid objects which are pleasurable to handle and which can be retained without confusing the discerning student.

When no suitable door exists a modern door is made in materials which are sympathetic. Broadly, these are normally softwood ledged and battened doors, sometimes braced additionally. In the repair of timber framing it is frequently necessary to insert new material in order to complete a panel or extend a member (*Figure 9.8*), and where new material is used it is selected from a section and grain similar to the original, glued, pegged and scarfed to the existing timber in a workmanlike manner, avoiding special surfacing and retaining a band-sawn finish which will mark the timber down as a product of the twentieth century.

On this basis it becomes possible to complete a building by providing the missing elements in readily-obtainable materials, as may be appropriate to their situation, and at the same time to re-use components of the building while respecting the spatial arrangements and configurations of the period of restoration. Much of the joinery is left finely band-sawn rather than planed, to provide a compatible surface. Where an effect is dependent upon the use of 'replica' materials, these are introduced without qualm, as, for instance, in the roof, where new split oak lath is used to achieve the texture which would otherwise be unobtainable.

If the philosophy of conservation is thus defined in general principle, it is rarely difficult to decide how to treat any individual problem. The overriding consideration must be for retention of the original material and the original space; and throughout the conservationist must feel in his heart a veneration for the genuine.

To use the words 'space' and 'material' in the same context is to emphasise their parallel importance. There is a breed of historian (or building anatomists), which has spent so long peering myopically at the evidence of joints, mortices and mouldings that it has lost sight of the reality of architecture, which is the creation of spaces for human use. To retain multifarious examples of original material, and by so doing to destroy original form and space, is arguably as damaging to the architecture as the destruction of tangible artefacts themselves.

The aim of the restorer must be a blend which retains and respects space, contour, colour, texture and material to

Figure 9.8 'New Inn': first floor bedroom after restoration

produce a balanced truth. This is the basis of the philosophy applied in Peasenhall in repairs and adaptation.

Damage to the structure

The damage suffered by the 'New Inn' during its life can be catalogued as follows:

1. Deliberate mutilation of the upper chamber (solar) of the 'high end' by the hacking off of root stocks and chopping in of fixings for ceiling joists, in order to give a fashionably smooth finish to the walls and ceiling (*Figure 9.8*).

2. Cutting about of the roof and 'high end' partition framing to allow the construction of a brick chimneystack.

3. The removal of framing of the 'low end' outer wall for the insertion of the chimney of an adjacent building.

4. The cutting out of a section of the wallplate on the front of the hall for the insertion of a dormer window, so reducing the effectiveness of a tie and allowing the building to spread by as much as eighteen inches.

5. The settlement, due to rotting, of soleplates on the outer walls of the building, dislocating the joints between posts and plates, causing spread of the walls. This spread was unequal due to the protection of some plates from the weather while others remained exposed. Consequently, rafters at the lower end suffered major deformation, being as much as 760 mm (2 ft 6 in) out of line in a length of little over 4 m (13 ft).

Other damage included the cutting about of walls and partitions to form new window and door openings and allow the enlargement of rooms. This had all been done on a piece-meal basis, frequently in the worst possible way, when the building was in use as four cottages.

The restoration programme

The process of repair and restoration falls into two parts. Having made the decision in principle to restore the hall to its mediaeval condition, it followed that a thorough programme of restoration of the timber frame was the initial basis of the

139

Figure 9.9 'New Inn': detail of roof truss, crown post

Figure 9.10 'New Inn': after restoration (crosswing at left)

work. To achieve this the inserted chimneystack was taken down and the inserted floor was removed. The entire roof covering and wall infilling was taken out, all rafters were taken off and the frame was lifted back into its original level and alignment (*Figure 9.9*). Component timbers were then repaired or replaced, replacement being limited entirely to those that were missing or could not be repaired by the scarfing-in of new material of proportionate section. Like material was used, oak-for-oak, and no special attempt was made to obtain seasoned material.

This entire section of work was undertaken by an independent craftsman.* He was able to take up residence on the site until the timber and structural repairs were finished. At this stage the main contractor's labour and shop facilities were made fully available under the architect's and craftsman's direction. On completion of this stage of the work the frame was left repaired and complete, even to the riven oak laths for the tiling. The 'low end' partition, which had survived almost intact, including the two service doorways, was carefully protected throughout.

In the gap left in the framing of the high end by the removal of the chimneystack, the main contractor built a wall of the brick salvaged from the inserted chimneystack. It had been possible to retain wattle and daub panels in the 'low end' partition and in parts of the external walls. These also were carefully protected throughout. The remainder of the work consisted of inserting new concrete foundations, bringing up a foundation wall to the underside of the inserted sole-plates, replacing missing panels of wattle and daub by panels of rendered wood-wool faced internally with an insulating panel, and the insertion of necessary partitions, doors and equipment.

Fortunately one complete and one part-complete mediaeval ridge tile survived on the roof. These showed that the early tiles had a coxcomb pattern on the crest of the tile, producing a serrated ridge line. Replicas were therefore made by a specialist potter. Now that they are fitted, the ridge has regained its mediaeval aspect.

It is, of course, true that even after all this work the building is, virtually, a compromise. It does not have exactly the aspect it had when it was originally built. Not only is there the later cross-wing: there are inconsistencies in the windows and in the walling. Though much of the external walling has been restored to its original half-timbered condition, the ground floor front wall at the 'high end' had been completely removed. Without any evidence of mortices any replacement in timber would have been suppositious and a straightforward rendered wall was therefore employed (*Figure 9.10*).

Similarly, although the great windows of the hall have been restored to their original condition, the eighteenth-century windows inserted into the ends of the building have been retained, the evidence for mediaeval windows having completely disappeared. To have attempted to replace genuine eighteenth century windows with simulated mediaeval windows would

* Gunholt Greiner

have added to the crime of conjecture the difficulty of meeting current Building Regulation requirements. Despite these deviations, however, it requires little effort of imagination to see the New Inn at Peasenhall as it stood originally.

Case Study 2: Purton Green

Unfortunately the same cannot be said of Purton Green Farm, a thirteenth-century house lying inland in 'high' Suffolk, near Stansfield, south of Bury St Edmunds (*Figure 9.11*). At some time in the seventeenth century the entire 'high' or 'solar' end of Purton Green Farm was destroyed and though its timber-framed replacement is of high quality it is between three and four hundred years younger than the original and is stylistically quite different. In addition a much earlier alteration took place (perhaps in the fifteenth century) when the original outer walls of the building were removed and replaced by new timber-framed walls set a little within the original alignment. But, by virtue of its rarity and quality, Purton Green Farm is of outstanding archaeological importance and the removal of the inserted floor allows the original great hall to be seen as a complete spatial entity so that the building offers the visitor the almost-unique experience of standing in a thirteenth century aisled hall house and seeing the structure in an almost-original state.

In addition to its very remarkable scissors-braced trusses, Purton Green Farm contains the nearly-unique feature of an arcaded partition in the low end. This consisted of a range of blank pointed-arched arcades, repeating the profile of the two service doorways across the whole width of the low end wall and, by their rhythm, establishing the original width of the building — a fact revealed in no other way.

Although the curved head-members of these arcades had been removed in a very early alteration, their visual importance and archaeological significance was such that there was no hesitation over their restoration, particularly since the evidence of mortices and setting-out lines so clearly delineated the original profiles.

Conclusion

The philosophy of conservation followed both at Purton Green and at Peasenhall has been very much the same, and broadly the scope of the work was similar. In each the essence of the project was the restoration of the integrity of the timber frame of the period of first construction and opening up the original hall to re-establish the fundamental space, so to re-define and make immediately comprehensible the shapes of two mediaeval hall houses of two quite different periods of construction.

If there are any general principles to be drawn from such work they may be summarised as a respect for the original

Figure 9.11 Purton Green: 'High' end

Figure 9.12 Purton Green: 'Low' end

nature of the building, for the spaces and volumes it contains, and for the authentic materials of its construction. The principles of the repair and introduction of a new use into these old structures, therefore, involve a clear distinction between new and old materials, a sympathy between the materials used and the techniques employed, and a special sensitivity in the use of space to minimise the distortion of original volumes through adaptation to the new function.

The Management of Change

New working environments from obsolete industrial buildings

John Worthington and Peter Eley

Today's inner urban areas bear little resemblance to the tightly knit urban fabric of fifty years ago. Streets of two storied Victorian housing have been cleared to make way for mixed development housing estates (*Figures 10.1 and 10.2*). The economic base of cities has changed too, as manufacturing firms have moved to green field sites in search of room for expansion, easier access to the transportation networks, and the skilled workforce who moved out to the suburbs, leaving the inner city with large areas of empty, decaying industrial buildings (Gripaiors, 1977)[8]. The plight of our Inner Cities has been further exacerbated by comprehensive redevelopment which has swept away not only the buildings but also the small firms and those marginal social amenities which take time to establish.

It is now apparent that the intricate pattern of urban, social and economic life is destroyed by comprehensive redevelopment. The rich range of different sized, shaped and priced space that was provided by the historical building stock is difficult to recreate instantly in large scale redevelopment schemes. New business communities cannot be generated rapidly in new layouts, and existing buildings and networks of activity have become an essential resource for the birth and growth of new enterprises.

Small firms, particularly in urban areas, rely on highly developed networks and easy face to face contact between customers, suppliers and outlets. They function on the edge of existing economic markets, where new ideas are the operating currency. The small, new firm is flexible in outlook and fluid in organisation. The accommodation they require need not be custom made to fit the activity involved. But it must be cheap and immediately available on short term leases (Falk, 1976)[5].

The stock of empty buildings at present available in inner city areas could provide the perfect incubator for emerging enterprises. The buildings provide a variety of environmental standards, greater room for personal involvement and cheaper accommodation than purpose built space. The range of premises required can be likened to the car market where the consumer can choose between the £150 secondhand jalopy and the £10 000 sports car. The young first-time owner naturally finds

the correct rung on the market ladder according to his means and aspirations. The same degree of sophistication could be achieved in the accommodation market with careful husbandry of the existing building stock, and a sympathetic attitude to standards.

The past experience of comprehensive redevelopment suggests an incremental rather than a 'grand slam' approach to change, continuity rather than disruption. Vandalism and dereliction begin as soon as a building or site are left unattended. Decay spreads rapidly, and planning should aim to keep buildings and sites in use by a variety of measures. This could be done by granting short life building approvals, pinpointing potential buildings that may become redundant and phasing in new uses before the existing uses disappear, and by upgrading property floor by floor or block by block, rather than relocating firms.

Decaying inner city areas are characterised by vacant sites, empty buildings, and unused upper floors. London alone has approximately two million square metres (twenty million square feet) of vacant industrial space. The potential for providing small units of accommodation is available and the demand exists (Falk, 1977)[6]. A sharper perspective is required of the type of space available, the needs of small firms and of the financial and organisational mechanisms that will need to be developed to re-use the empty decaying and vandalised industrial buildings which characterise inner city locations.

The re-use of existing buildings requires effort, ideas and perseverance. Existing regulations may become barriers and statutory requirements can generate crippling conversion costs and delays. Financial institutions are on the whole unprepared to invest in old premises and unproven firms. But attitudes are gradually changing. The sensitivity and experience of architects, planners and designers can provide valuable support in overcoming these hurdles.

Professionals may be involved with three different types of client:

1. Groups of users who are looking for a suitable building to accommodate their needs;

Figure 10.1 The traditional urban fabric provides for multiple uses, integrating living, working, and leisure within the same neighbourhood

Figure 10:2 Comprehensive redevelopment schemes have zoned uses, and provide single use building forms

Figure 10.3(a) External facade and interior, Kingsgate, West Hampstead

Figure 10.3(b) Typical floor, West Kingsgate

2. A pressure group wishing to save a building for its historical or architectural associations, and are looking for a suitable use;

3. Local amenity groups who are concerned to save the existing physical, economic and social fabric of a neighbourhood, which may be threatened by redevelopment or planning blight.

The following case studies provide the basis for a conceptual framework which can match buildings, users and alternative strategies for initiating a project.

Case Study 1: West Hampstead, London

Kingsgate Road in West Hampstead, London, is the focus for a local community situated in a city block set back from the successful retail outlets on the Kilburn High Road. Many of the shops along Kingsgate Road have closed but several of them have been reused for workshops, a neighbourhood cafe and the offices of a short-life housing association, mainly through the efforts of the West Hampstead Community Action Group (*Figure 10.3*).

At one end of the road is a three-storey furniture repository. As the only industrial building in the area, it is a potential asset to the neighbourhood. The building was originally used for light engineering purposes. Then, in an unsuccessful policy to relocate 'non conforming' users it was purchased by the local Council for demolition so the site could be used for housing and open space. The economic climate however meant that money was no longer immediately available for redevelopment, and the

144

Council estimated that the costs of refurbishment were prohibitive. So the building was left vacant and deteriorating.

The local community group supported by the Camden Industrial Action Group, recognising that the building could provide local employment opportunities and bring activity back into the area, approached the local authority with alternative estimates for conversion. Their arguments were that, as no change of use was required the statutory and planning requirements could be met without major expenditure, that a demand existed amongst local craftsmen for small workshop units and artists workspace and that for a five year life no major work would be required on the structure and fabric. As a result of this approach the community have, with the help of the architects, negotiated a short lease with the Council, prepared a budget for raising money, contacted small firms who would be interested in renting space, and prepared a scheme for the subdivision of the factory into small units (*Figure 10.4*). They also studied the financial feasibility of the scheme related to the rents that could be charged.

Grass roots action has succeeded in persuading the local authority that the acceptance of realistic standards and short life uses allows a building to be economically converted that would otherwise have been wasted. Activity in the building should replace blight with new vitality. Space for at least fifty jobs will be created. New ideas and energy will be attracted to the area and the process of initiating and carrying through the project is providing a focus for the community. The project has shown that a local community group together with local political motivation can provide a viable force to initiate development.

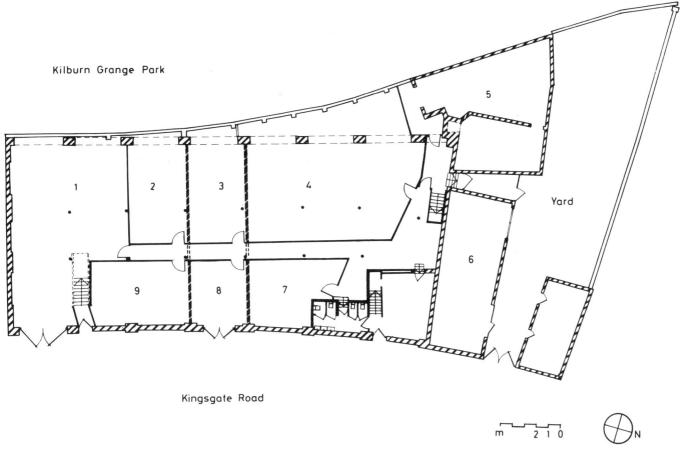

Kilburn Grange Park

Yard

Kingsgate Road

m 2 1 0   N

Figure 10.4(a) Plan, West Hampstead

Figure 10.4(b) Section, West Hampstead

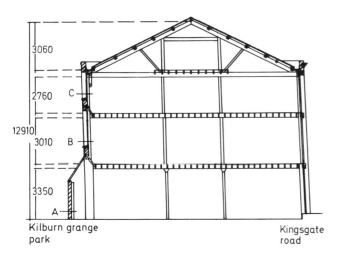

3060

2760   C

12910

3010   B

3350

A

Kilburn grange
park

Kingsgate
road

Case Study 2: Rotherhithe, London

Rotherhithe is one of London's original dockland communities. The area retains much of its origins as a riverside village, with its eighteenth and nineteenth century warehouses that cluster around the Green and the Parish Church of St Mary's (*Figure 10.5*). The neighbourhood has strong historical associations; the Mayflower set sail from the steps where the public house now stands and Brunel's Engine House for the Thames Tunnel is located nearby.

The structure plan of the late sixties proposed a continuation of the riverside walk and park which had already been established to the west, the retention of the church, public house and some selected buildings, but the demolition of most of the old warehouses to provide for new housing and open space. Comprehensive redevelopment of this magnitude would have dramatically changed the equilibrium of the area and destroyed one of the few remaining places of character in the Docklands (Architectural Design, 1975)[2] and (Industrial Building Preservation Trust)[2].

A small group of enthusiasts realising the quality of the

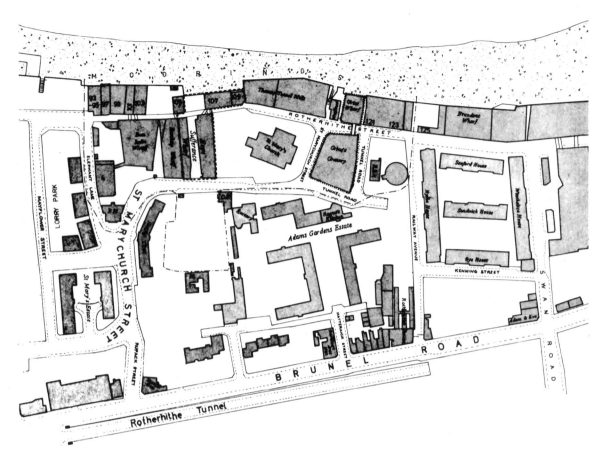

Figure 10.5 Aerial view of St Mary's Rotherhithe Conservation Area

area and its potential as a focal point decided to press for an alternative planning strategy. With the support of the local Bermondsey and Rotherhithe Amenity Society they began a campaign to retain the existing riverside buildings and re-introduce workshop uses.

As a focus for action two groups emerged, namely the Brunel Exhibition Project and the Industrial Buildings Preservation Trust. The first group (Brunel Exhibition Project)[3] proposed that Brunel's original engine house be used as a small museum (*Figure 10.6*) with an exhibition dealing with the history of the Thames Tunnel and the surrounding area. So far the project has succeeded in transforming a junkyard into an attractive brick landscaped area (*Figure 10.7*).

The original proposal was to clean up and weatherproof the Engine House with the main objective of providing accommodation for the Brunel Exhibition. However, due to the rising costs of complying with the requirements of different

authorities, and the derelict condition of the roof, the committee were unable to raise sufficient funds to complete the work. The Industrial Building Preservation Trust (IBPT), the second group that emerged (Woolley, 1976)[11], was set up to organise the conversion of the five buildings of Hope Sufferance Wharf (*Figure 10.8*).

At present 650 m² (7 000 ft²) has been completed out of a total of approx. 195 m² (21 000 ft²) with the aim to provide about fifty units. The trust has charitable status and is limited by guarantee. It is in partnership with the London Borough of Southwark who have a lease on the building. Originally, the centre was to be managed by a company, Rotherhithe Workshops, working as a tenant's co-operative in which each of the individual occupants have shares. The initial tenants include glassblowers, silversmiths, potters, sculptors, an ivory carver and a dance studio. Those who are taking in apprentices and teaching other people their skills are encouraged. A community

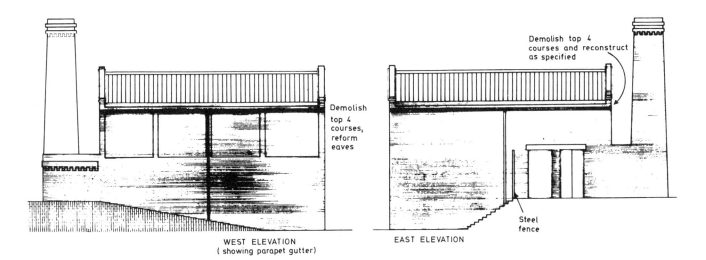

Demolish top 4 courses, reform eaves

WEST ELEVATION
(showing parapet gutter)

Demolish top 4 courses and reconstruct as specified

Steel fence

EAST ELEVATION

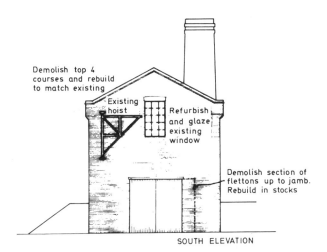

Demolish top 4 courses and rebuild to match existing

Existing hoist

Refurbish and glaze existing window

Demolish section of flettons up to jamb. Rebuild in stocks

SOUTH ELEVATION

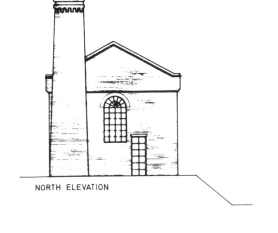

NORTH ELEVATION

Figure 10.6 Proposed restoration to Brunel Engine House

Figure 10.7 (below and right) Surrounding area to Brunel Engine House before and after landscaping contract

147

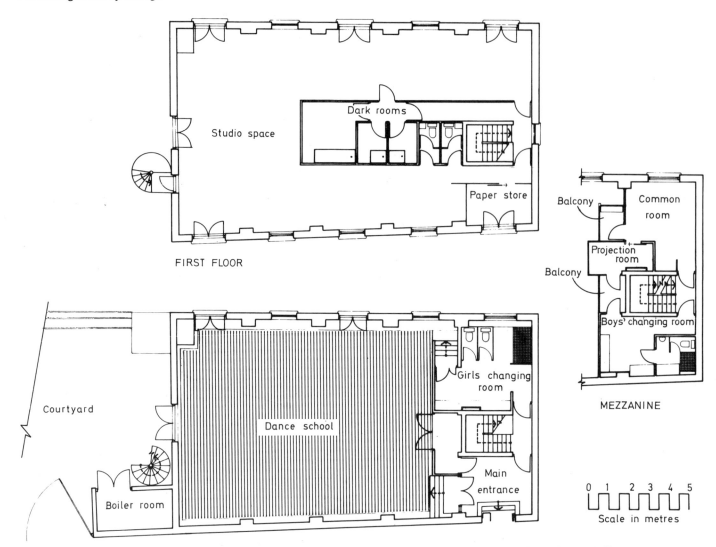

FIRST FLOOR

GROUND FLOOR

Courtyard

Boiler room

Dance school

Girls changing room

Main entrance

Studio space

Dark rooms

Paper store

MEZZANINE

Balcony

Common room

Projection room

Balcony

Boys' changing room

Scale in metres
0 1 2 3 4 5

Figure 10.8(a) (above) Proposed use of Hope Sufferance
Wharf buildings
Figure 10.8(b) (left) View of completed Dance School

workshop, where local people can make or do things is being established.

There are a number of advantages for small enterprises in coming together. It allows possible space for expansion, work can be sub contracted between tenants, and people can help each other. When it is fully developed it will be large enough to afford an administrator, sales and reception facilities and the services of accounting, business or legal advisers might be shared. Finally for the small business there is the feeling of companionship and solidarity that comes from working alongside other like-minded people.

The finance was raised in forms of grants from charities and loans from the local authority and banks. The rental of about £6.00 per week is for a basic space of approx 19 m^2 (200 ft^2). The project was subsequently taken over by the London Borough of Southwark who are completing it as originally conceived.

The Rotherhithe project has been successful on several counts. Firstly, the existing character of a unique part of London has been retained and the potential for over 100 jobs has been created in an area where job opportunities were disappearing. Secondly, other projects such as Grices Granary and the Riverside Workshop have flourished in the area (Architects Journal, 1977[1] and Federation of Working Communities, 1977[7]). Lastly, St Mary's has been established as a conservation area and Rotherhithe has become an attraction.

The impetus for the change in attitude is largely the work of a few individuals with flair, enthusiasm, imagination and vision, supported by local organisations. The architect's role as professional support has been to float proposals for how the area might be developed in the initial stages, and to suggest and evaluate alternative uses for the existing buildings as well as provide plans, some working drawings and a general specification with structural and services support from professional engineers for the conversion work.

The Trust appointed their own full-time project manager who was responsible for site supervision and some design work. The major elements were sub contracted under his direction and some direct labour was used.

Experience has shown that the buildings were expensive to convert due to the relatively high standards of specification required (full heating, sprung dance floor and clear span spaces) and that the use of direct labour and management by committee was costly. The learning process in setting up a contracting organisation and using inexperienced labour can cost, rather than save, money.

However, as a result of the physical improvement, the area now has the Rotherhithe Workshops, a theatre and an emerging picture reference library. A thriving 'Working Community' has been established indicating the considerable economic and social regeneration that has taken place.

Case Study 3: Covent Garden, London

Covent Garden used to be the traditional home of London's Fruit and Vegetable Market. In 1975 the Market moved to a less congested site south of the river leaving vacant a rich stock of warehouse, industrial and commercial space.

The area with its central location and historical and artistic associations provides an environment conducive to the birth and growth of small creative and innovative firms (URBED, 1976)[10]. The business community comprises six flourishing networks of activities (*Figure 10.9*) which cover the full spectrum of employment from office to light industrial uses. These include:

Printing, publishing and bookselling;
Arts, crafts and design trades and professions;
Entertainment, theatres, public houses and restaurants;

Film production, processing and photography;
Business services, banking, import-export, insurance, trade associations;
Professional and educational services and voluntary groups both of the 'establishment' and 'fringe' variety.

Each activity network spans a variety of planning use categories. The theatrical network covers the timber firm which supplies wood for the stage-set carpenter, workrooms for costumiers, workshops and stores for the lighting specialists and the small offices for literary and theatrical agents. The loss or restriction of any one of these uses could well affect the equilibrium of the system. Most of the activities are inter-related and closely linked to Covent Garden itself. Two-thirds of the manufacturing firms trade with other enterprises in the area and half with other West End firms.

A survey of firms in the area showed that out of seventy firms nearly half were 'tiny', consisting of 1—5 employees and were accommodated in premises of under 300 m^2 (3 300 ft^2) (URBED)[10].

The Urban and Economic Development Group (URBED) appointed the architects to undertake a study into the problems and possibilities of providing accommodation for small enterprises in Covent Garden. URBED is a non-profit-making

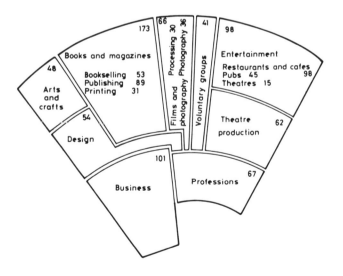

Figure 10.9 Major networks in Covent Garden

research and consultancy organisation financed by the Gatsby Charitable Foundation, whose main work is directed at fostering small enterprises and finding new uses for empty buildings. They believe that the needs of the 27 000 people working in the area had not been represented in the planning strategy with the same force as those of the 3 000 local residents. They also believed that one of Covent Garden's main functions was to provide low cost space for small productive and creative enterprises, and that one way of bringing into use the large empty warehouses was to subdivide them for use by small firms.

The complex networks of activities and services in Covent Garden are attractive to newly forming or expanding small enterprises. However, problems exist for the small firm in finding suitable accommodation. Much of the vacant space is not available for immediate use as it comes in large units imappropriate to small firms and requires upgrading to meet fire regulations and other statutory requirements. In addition it is usually only available on short or medium term lease and suffers from planning uncertainty as a result of changing official attitudes. Generally it is not a good proposition for raising finance for the building work needed to adapt the space to new uses and it requires change-of-use planning applications which take time to acquire. Delays are also likely if the space is in one of the large number of listed buildings where statutory and planning requirements may be incompatible with the users needs. Where space is vacant and could be moved into immediately it tends to be badly located in odd shaped units with short leases.

The firms who do consider the larger vacant units of space available may well be put off by the burden of raising the finance, organising the building work and meeting the statutory regulations, for they lack the time, financial resources and expertise. Most small firms want to run their businesses, not develop property.

The objective of URBED's involvement in Covent Garden was to take stock of the space available in the area, assess the demand for small firms looking for accommodation and explore and foster the agencies who could initiate developments (Duffy, Eley, Giffone and Worthington, 1976)[4].

The central area of Covent Garden was surveyed to establish the types of buildings available (*Figure 10.10*). The buildings were predominantly four to five storeys high, narrow fronted, with a shallow depth and of one or two way aspect (*Figure 10.11*). Contrary to what had been expected, the majority of the buildings were small. Two thirds had a site coverage of

Figure 10.10 Types of Buildings within the Central Area of Covent Garden

		DEPTH OF BUILDING			TOTALS
		SHALLOW 30–40 ft	MEDIUM 40–50 ft	DEEP over 50 ft	
FRONTAGE OF BUILDING	NARROW 12–18 ft	28% Single space type Two way aspect 60% shop front access Load bearing wall construction	19% single/multiple space type One way aspect 46% shop front access Column/load bearing wall construction	3% Single space type Two way aspect 100% shop front access Column construction	50%
	MEDIUM 18–30 ft	9% Single space type Two way aspect 64% shop front access Load bearing wall construction	8% Single/Multiple space type One/two way aspect 58% shop front access Column/Load bearing wall construction	3% Single space type One/Two way aspect 58% Shop front access Column construction	20%
	WIDE over 30 ft	11% Single space type One/Two way aspect 23% shop front access Column construction	14% Multiple/Single space type Two way aspect 36% shop front access Column construction	5% Single/Multiple space type Two way aspect 37% shop front access Column construction	30%
TOTALS		48%	41%	11%	

BUILDING CHARACTERISTICS		PERCENTAGE OF BUILDINGS IN SURVEY AREA
NUMBER OF FLOORS		
Single storied	9%	
Two/three floors	4%	
Four/five floors	78%	
Six floors and above	9%	
BUILDING FRONTAGE		
Narrow 4—8 metres	50%	
Medium 8—10 metres	20%	
Wide over 10 metres	30%	
BUILDING DEPTH		
Shallow	48%	
Medium	41%	
Deep	11%	
CONSTRUCTION		
Load bearing walls	48%	
Columns	62%	
ACCESS		
Front Access	52%	
Off street service access	12%	
ASPECT		
One way	43%	
Two way	49%	
Three way	7%	
Detached	1%	

Figure 10.11 (above) Characteristics of the Buildings in the Central Area of Covent Garden

Figure 10.12 (below) Sectional form of buildings in Covent Garden

BUILDING TYPES	FORM	PERCENT OF BUILDINGS	PERCENT OF BUILDINGS WITH GROUND FLOOR OVER 1400 sq. ft
Simple - (single type of space)		66 %	34 %
Complex - (variety of types of space)		34 %	61 %

151

LOCATION ABOVE GROUND LEVEL				TOTALS
SIZE OF UNIT	**Ground floor/Basement**	**First/Second Floor**	**Third Floor or above**	
up to 1000 ft²	15% – Buildings of shallow depth/ narrow frontage – Medium type spaces – 90% with shop front access – 41% in listed property	16% – Buildings of shallow depth/ narrow frontage – Small type spaces – 43% in listed property	14% – Buildings of shallow depth/ narrow frontage – Medium/small type spaces – 67% in listed property	45%
1000–3000 ft²	16% – Buildings of medium depth/ narrow frontage or shallow depth/medium frontage – Medium/large type spaces – 38% possible open plan shared use – 76% with shop front access – 41% in listed property	14% – Buildings of medium depth/ narrow frontage or shallow depth/medium frontage – Medium type spaces – 47% possible open plan shared use – 10% possible cellular shared use – 16% in listed property	11% – Buildings of medium depth/ narrow frontage or shallow depth/medium frontage – Large type space – 53% possible open plan shared use – 14% possible cellular shared use – 14% in listed property	41%
over 3000 ft²	4% – Buildings of medium depth/ wide frontage – Large type spaces – 50% possible open plan shared use – 50% with shop front access – 33% in listed property	6% – Buildings of medium depth/ wide frontage – Large type spaces – 100% possible open plan shared use – 25% possible cellular use – 28% in listed property	4% – Buildings of medium depth/wide frontage – Large type spaces – 100% possible open plan use – 33% possible cellular shared use – 33% in listed property	14%
TOTALS	35%	36%	29%	

Figure 10.13 Types of vacant space available within the Central Area of Covent Garden

less than 150 m² (1 600 ft²) though the bulk of floor space was in the remaining third of the larger complex buildings.

The character of the larger buildings was that they were complex in form, containing a variety of space types, varying in depth and configuration over each floor (*Figure 10.12*). This variety and character seems impossible to recreate in slab blocks, where each building contains only one space type and the form is constrained by a multitude of statutory requirements.

Using the survey of buildings and spaces within the Central Area, URBED was able to assess the amount and character of the spaces (*Figure 10.13*). From the survey it was apparent that forty per cent of the buildings in the area had vacant space, and of these spaces just under half were smaller than 100 m² (1 070 ft²). Only a small proportion of the buildings were totally empty and these tended to be the larger warehouse units with medium length leases. It was also apparent that the vacant space within buildings that were otherwise largely occupied tended to be inaccessible, small or oddly shaped areas.

152

The conclusions of the survey were that the key resource of Covent Garden – the diversity of its building stock – was being constrained due to a planning policy that tended to disregard this asset (use categories being a product of ideological desires rather than of the most appropriate use for a particular building configuration, construction and physical condition) and a wasteful management of the space. (The desire to lease-off prime space at an attractive rental invariably compromises accessibility to less attractive spaces.)

This key resource was also being affected by building owners postponing action in the hope that planning policy might change, so raising the value of the property, and by there being no available agency prepared to take the initiative to convert and subdivide the larger warehouse units for use by small firms.

Feasibility studies of seven different types of vacant buildings in the area showed that conversion costs varied according to the condition of the building and the existing facilities as follows:

Category	Condition of building	Average conversion costs
A	Structural alterations major reconstruction	Offices : £150-220 m² (2 400 ft²) Workshop: Not applicable
B	Repair to fabric, fire proofing, new services	Office : £100-150 m² (1 600 ft²) Workshop: £ 80-130 m² (1 400 ft²)
C	Non structural partitions, overhaul services, upgrade finishes	Office : £ 50-100 m² (1 100 ft²) Workshop: £ 40- 80 m² (860 ft²)

In the buildings studied, the most common items of building work required were making good the roof and replacing windows and doors. Thirty per cent of the budget in the examples looked at was concerned with statutory requirements: providing for fire protection, means of escape and sanitary accommodation. Further, it was found that, where they existed, mixed uses provided a sound economic platform and allowed for interdependent activities to be located in the same building.

An analysis of the manner in which small firms are presently accommodated showed that Covent Garden already provided prototypes of the way large empty buildings could be organised into small units. Four distinct patterns of tenure were evident:

1. *Sub-leased shared space*. Individual workplaces rented within another firm's work area, with telephone, reception and secretarial services normally being shared.

2. *Sub-leased individual space*. Self-contained within a larger block. The firm's name is typically on a name board in the main reception area, access is from a common corridor.

3. *Communally administered shared space*. Tenants have a say in how the accommodation is managed. Services and facilities are shared. The individual firm's area is defined by screening within an open planned area (Chapter 11, Case Study 1).

4. *Communally administered separate space*. Similar management structure to previous category. Each unit is enclosed and lockable (Case Study 2 in this chapter).

Similarly experience in Covent Garden showed that a wide range of potential agencies exist to develop the vacant properties. These vary from institutions, using a full professional service, to individuals, doing it themselves (*Figure 10.14*). Property companies, local authorities and large landowners have the permanence and security to find large sums of finance, handle long-term projects, and often provide their own in-house professionals. These attributes are best suited to large 'listed' buildings. The locally based developer, association of users, or small firms do not have the same security or professional support but can offer low overheads, flexibility, enthusiasm and contact with potential users, abilities admirably suited to the smaller units, and short life holdings.

Covent Garden is at the present time a political battleground. Shifts in attitudes are the result of many voices, which are creating a commitment to support small enterprises and wherever possible re-use existing buildings.

Under the direction of URBED, the Covent Garden Enterprise Centre was formed to act as a focus for the small firms. One of its primary services is a Space Exchange, set up to take stock of the vacant space, help firms find accommodation, bring together users, and to convert some of the larger buildings still vacant. Covent Garden's rich stock of existing buildings has finally been seen by planners, landowners and occupiers as an asset rather than a liability.

Creating a conceptual framework

The scope of work and professional involvement at Kingsgate, Rotherhithe and Covent Garden was each different, but many of the questions posed are similar. What sorts of uses are most suitable to the buildings available? How much investment may be required and in which areas could it be most usefully spent? How can development be initiated and in what ways can it be implemented? In each case the designer required a simple language of building and user types, and a shorthand of possible strategies to clarify the discussions with client, user and statutory authorities.

In the case of user types, firms may be classified either by the work that they undertake (Standard Industrial Classification – SIC) or by the way that they use space. The way that a firm uses space is dependent upon the amount of space provided for people, the amount of space provided for special equipment and storage, the amount of sub division required, and the demand for natural light and ventilation. *Figure 10.15* represents a means of describing firms by the way they use space. Using the SIC categories typical uses can be assigned to each type of spatial organisation. Uses can be further defined according to their specific demands on access, floor loading, servicing, and floor to ceiling heights.

Building types, on the other hand, may be described by the number of floors, frontage, depth, construction, access and aspect. Each of these variables affects how the building may be used, its ease of subdivision and cost of conversion. The critical attribute of building form in meeting the demands of different user types has been found to be its dimension from front to back (referred to as building depth). Shallow buildings, 10–15 m (35–50 ft) deep, are most suitable for firms requiring small cellular spaces. Medium depth buildings, 15–20 m (50–70 ft), are appropriate for a combination of cellular and more open plan areas, whilst deep buildings, 20 m (70 ft) and above, are more appropriate for organisations which require a great deal of interaction, the minimum separation or have a high proportion of machinery or storage which does not require natural light. *Figure 10.16* relates different user types to buildings of varying frontage and depth.

Figure 10.14 is a matrix chart titled "Alternative approaches to developing vacant space". The rows are attribute categories and the columns are the development agents. A bullet (•) indicates that the attribute applies to that agent.

Category	Attribute	Property company	Local authority	Large landowner	Locally-based developer	Building preservation trust	Association of users	Established small firms	Very small firm
Source of funds	Institutions	•	•	•			•	•	
	Banks	•		•	•	•			•
	Charities					•			
	Government		•			•			
Type of funding	Investment Co's				•		•	•	•
	Mortgages	•	•	•			•	•	
	Loans	•	•	•	•		•	•	
	Short term loans				•		•		•
	Grants					•			
	Personal investment						•	•	•
Tenure	Freehold	•	•	•			•	•	
	Long term	•	•				•	•	
	Medium term lease				•	•	•	•	
	Partial freehold					•		•	•
	Joint tenancy								•
	Short lease				•	•		•	•
	Licence								•
Complexity of building work	A Major structural Alterations & services	•		•					
	B Repairs fire escapes etc	•	•	•		•			
	C Electrical upgrading finishes				•	•	•	•	
	D Fitting & finishes only				•	•	•	•	
Type of unit	Small narrow front bldg (brick & timber constr)	•	•	•	•	•		•	
	Large deep plan bldg (cast iron or timber)		•	•	•	•	•		
	Large deep plan bldg (concrete structure)	•	•	•			•		
	Grd floor unit with shop front access				•	•	•		
Project organisation – Construction	Main contractor	•	•	•			•		
	Sub contractor				•	•	•	•	•
	Direct labour		•		•	•	•		
	Voluntary labour					•		•	
	Do it yourself					•	•		•
Project organisation – Professional advice	Full service	•	•	•			•		
	Partial services				•	•		•	
	Voluntary advice		•			•			
	Do it yourself								•
Project organisation – Project manag'mnt	Contractor & Prop		•	•			•		
	Project manager	•	•	•		•	•		
	Do it yourself				•	•		•	•

Figure 10.14 Alternative approaches to developing vacant space

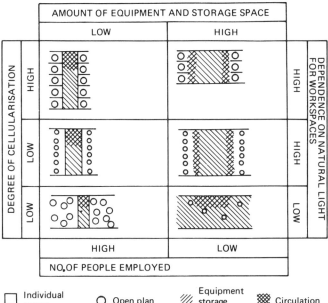

AMOUNT OF EQUIPMENT AND STORAGE SPACE

	LOW	HIGH

DEGREE OF CELLULARISATION

HIGH / LOW / LOW

HIGH / LOW

NO. OF PEOPLE EMPLOYED

DEPENDENCE ON NATURAL LIGHT FOR WORKSPACES

HIGH / HIGH / LOW

☐ Individual rooms   ○ Open plan   ▨ Equipment storage space   ▦ Circulation

Figure 10.15 (above) Typology of firms according to their physical requirements

Figure 10.11 (below) Types of activities related to frontage and depth of Building

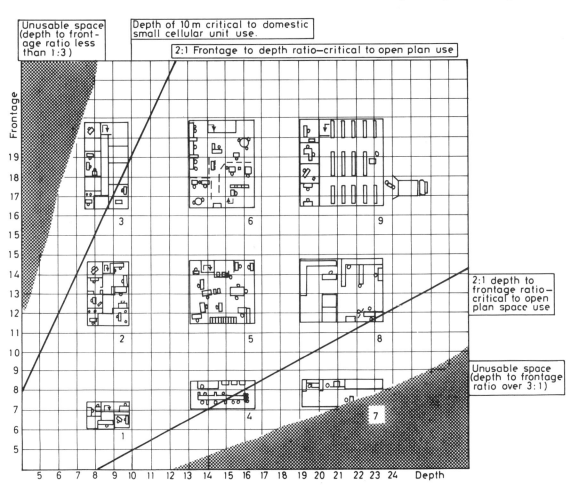

155

Type	Characteristics	Type of management	Type of building	Types of user
1. LEASED SHARED SPACE	Workplaces rented within another firms work area e.g. sublease agreed on a "gentlemans agreement" to be reviewed at 3 monthly intervals	Head lease or owner relinquishes no legal responsibility for space. May provide telephone, secretarial and receptionist on time sharing basis	Any building type	Tiny firms (1–5 persons) newly founded, require low overheads, minimum commitment. Subsidiary of existing firm
2. LEASED INDIVIDUAL SPACE	Self contained space rented in a large building. Access from common corridor	Common receptionist Individual firms name displayed. Individual unit with own services	Shallow or medium depth with central corridor	Small well established firms. Requiring own identity
3. CO-OPERATIVELY ADMINISTERED SHARED SPACE	Individual firms areas defined by screens or storage within open planned area	Tenants participate in management of accommodation shared services and facilities	Deep plan	Small expanding firms. Compatible uses without security requirements
4. CO-OPERATIVELY ADMINISTERED SEPARATE SPACE	Each unit enclosed and lockable with access from common corridor	Same as three	Shallow or medium depth with central corridor	Small firms, requiring security and undertaking conflicting activities

Figure 10.17 Alternative approaches to providing accommodation for very small firms

In each of the case studies described the demand was for accommodation in units of up to 100 m² (1 100 ft²) for the 1–5 person firm, but the floor areas of the buildings available provided much larger units of accommodation.

A number of examples now exist of projects that have been initiated to subdivide large redundant buildings for multiple use by small firms (Federation of Working Communities, 1977)[7]. In analysing existing uses in Covent Garden, the approaches may be broadly classified as, leased shared space, leased individual space, communally administered shared space, and communally administered separate space. *Figure 10.17* describes the characteristics of each approach, the style of management and the types of users and buildings they are best suited.

Certain economic climates have been shown to create an interest in the small firm and a desire to re-use the vast legacy of redundant industrial buildings available in our cities. The potential use for each is dictated according to its location, past use, configuration and condition. Buildings, like individuals, possess a personality and inherent qualities. A designer must understand these and sympathetically match uses to them. Location, availability or political expediency may suggest uses for buildings. If the characteristics of the building are out of sympathy with the proposed use, conversion costs can be high and the organisation may be at variance. The designers role is to understand the personalities of a building and to sympathetically match suitable uses.

156

This chapter argues the case for understanding existing buildings as a resource. It provides a basis for matching buildings to users. The work described is the beginning of a vocabulary which can be refined and enlarged in the light of experience.

References

1. Architects Journal 'Grices Granary', *Architects Journal* 11th May 1977
2. Architectural Design 'Opportunity Docks', Special issue *Architectural Design* February 1975
3. Brunel Exhibition Project *'A battle for conservation in the docklands'* The Project Rotherhithe
4. Duffy, Eley, Giffone, Worthington *'Accommodating small firms in Covent Garden'* URBED Internal Report. The Group. London October 1976
5. Falk, N. 'The future of small firms in the inner city' Employment Seminar. Internal Paper *Centre for Environmental Studies* January 1976
6. Falk, N. 'First steps in regenerating London inner areas' London looks forward conference Background Paper No. 6. *Thames Television Ltd London* July 1977
7. Federation of Working Committees *'The Why's and Wherefore's of Working Communities'* A Manual. The Federation. London. June 1977
8. Gripaiors, P. 'Industrial decline in London – an examination of its causes' *Urban Studies 4*. London 1977
9. Industrial Building Preservation Trust *'Workshops at Rotherhithe'* The Trust London
10. Urban and Economic Development Group *'Ensuring a future for small enterprises in Covent Garden'* URBED Covent Garden Report No. 2, The Group, London. October 1976
11. Woolley, T. 'Building conversion – Use conversion Rotherhithe Workshops' *Architectural Design* December 1976

Building Conversion and Rehabilitation

Re-using buildings — a new art and science

David Rock

The difference between new building and conservation is not one merely of degree but of kind. The significance of this itself is not yet fully grasped, either by members of the public or of the building professions, and hence the variety of ill-defined terms used in describing this work — e.g., 'conservation', 'renovation', 'rehabilitation', 'renewal', 'recycling', and 'conversion'.

Whilst, as yet, many architects do not fully grasp the difference in approach to the two types of design activity, it would appear that other members of the building team, especially quantity surveyors and building service engineers, find it even more difficult to do so. It may be that their educational background fits them less well to a flexible design approach, and they appear also more ready to reject solutions which involve re-use, extension, mixing or modification of existing systems, and more prepared to strip out and start afresh. There is certainly a need for all members of the design team to learn new skills and adopt new attitudes in an area of work which may well become a substantial, if not the major, part of the building industry's output for the next generation or two.

The structure of an existing building together with its character and services systems can, and must, form a base for creative solutions. To understand the full implication of what exists and to use it creatively as a base for something new requires empathy and sympathy with the situation — attitudes which are currently strengthened by the revised interest in architectural history and the study of the vernacular. It is an interesting and perhaps disturbing thought that, when working on the redesign of an existing building, one is, in effect, probably working in partnership with a dead architect or engineer.

The sympathy and empathy referred to should not only prevent gross stylistic incompatibilities — such as that which can occur between the style of a modern insurance office and a High Victorian building — but, even more significantly, such as can occur when the original sequence of spaces is radically altered. The clearing away of internal wall or structural elements, the removal of staircases, lightwells, windows and other features, and the opening up of a series of small spaces into a single large one — processes frequently carried out in conversion work — can also remove the less tangible scale and space character of a building in a way which no amount of adherence to, and re-production of, decorative details can ever restore.

If this thesis is accepted then the justification for building effectively new structures behind empty shells or facades, except in very rare circumstances, is difficult to find. It is an approach which lacks integrity and which seems to create a division between the inside and outside of buildings totally false in relation to any genuine architectural approach.

An appropriate aesthetic

With increasing experience in conversion work a sound 'conversion aesthetic' appears to have developed in which the old and new are contrasted and complementary rather than being mixed up in an ill-defined and ambiguous manner. In the more successful examples the new is openly added to the old with a crisp distinction, and often a loose fit, between the two. For practical reasons, services often have to be separate from the existing structure and therefore become clearly articulated as well as highly adaptable. Lighting solutions also tend to be more specific and different from the general overall solutions found in many new buildings; usually more reliance has to be placed on a low, general level of illumination, with high local illumination from a flexible lighting system.

The two case studies that follow both exemplify some of these approaches. For instance, the multi-purpose ducting which is used over the whole space and houses power, lighting and telephone services in a regular grid, allows telephones, desk lights, electric typewriters and other equipment to be supplied at almost any location by means of exposed plastic flexible tubes, often highly coloured, which can join the fittings to the services grid without the need for heavy, pre-formed service ducts. This type of system also gives a layout with a good deal of general and local flexibility thus allowing for the possibility of rapid changes in organisation, as well as accommodating a number of small firms without limitations as to their kind. These principles seem to apply irrespective

157

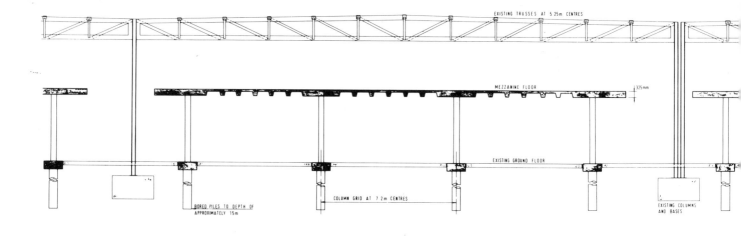

Figure 11.1 Middlesex Polytechnic: factory conversion

of the age of the old building, as is shown by the conversion of a recently-built factory in North London for Middlesex Polytechnic. Services and a concrete mezzanine floor have been added in clearly and obviously as additive features (*Figure 11.1*).

Although general ideas about services are discussed in other chapters, perhaps insufficient emphasis has been placed on the fact that lighting, above all other services, is closest to the central issues of architectural design and especially so in conversion work. The support systems for lighting in many ways define and determine the characteristics of the space, both functionally and aesthetically and, as yet, there are few lighting engineers with experience to work sympathetically with architects and users in this area. The principle of separation discussed above also leads to cost reductions and better value for money. It enables system components to be used with less covering up, building in, and spatial fitting and trimming. These standard systems and components can be more easily priced and obtained by subcontractors and suppliers, and there are less 'unknowns' as the work proceeds.

The most important savings are, however, strategic and depend on the fact that people and organisations are at least as adaptable as the buildings they inhabit. Provided the right decisions are made about the nature of organisations and their location within an existing building, many wasteful and expensive building operations can be omitted. One example of this is the limitation, in the London area, placed upon designers by fire protection requirements. If no change of use is entailed in the conversion then it is not mandatory to upgrade the fire protection — although, of course, this may sometimes be required nevertheless for safety and good practice. Usually the cost of good fire protection of an existing structure is prohibitive and unnecessary, as well as visually unacceptable. In the case of the second case study described (Barley Mow), the conversion

was from a largely industrial building, with some attendant offices and showrooms, to a mixture of studios with offices and workshops. The essential idea was that of a working community; this is what the clients and the designers, as well as the local authority, wanted to see. Provided at least 51% of the space was to continue in use for light industrial and ancillary purposes no change of use would result and hence greater planning flexibility would be available. This in fact was the approach taken and it also required that the space remained in the control of one firm which, in this case, was the service company controlling the lease.

One lesson learnt from this type of exercise is that there is an advantage in having a licence rather than a sub-lease arrangement. In both case-study examples the service company licenses the participating member firms who cannot sub-let and who must offer the space back to the service company when they vacate it. The service company thus maintains control of the space as well as control over the type of firm or person to whom space will be licensed. The licensee is prevented from putting up partitions or drastically changing the appearance of his space, two limitations which again benefit the common interest of all users. Moreover, if they did fully subdivide the space the local authorities could then insist on additional fire protection, which would otherwise be unnecessary. This is a half-way measure between complete open planning and full partitioning which retains a sufficient degree of open layout (including the clearing away of temporary existing partitioning) but which also results in easier and safer fire escape routes.

One approach to cost prediction and working within a budget is to try to devise analytical predictive techniques such as those described by Frey in Chapter 3. It is unlikely, however, that this type of systematisation will be capable of solving most of the varied and complex situations which arise in practice. An alternative approach is a form of lateral thinking which involves the acceptance of the difficulty, or even impossibility, of accurate prediction and a fixed budget. In the first case study, (Dryden Street) the landlord agreed to an alternative method of work in which the final agreed rent was to be determined in relation to the cost of the building conversion. This meant that every pound borrowed by the service company from the landlord over the original budget limit raised the rent over the lease. This arrangement had tax advantages for the landlord, the owner of the capital and for the service company and its licensees. It also meant that the work could proceed more rapidly and that the consultants could concentrate on the minimum it was necessary to spend in the best interest of the client, rather than being concerned primarily with keeping costs as low as possible.

This traditional approach, when used within a fixed budget situation, often results in drastic cuts having to be made at a late stage in the project, when it is frequently fittings and services which are drastically curtailed, simply because their installation is a late operation. In this case-study the result of the more open method was that the landlord had to be approached twice for further loans as the work proceeded, the total cost ultimately being about 72% above the original budget figure.

Conversion broking

This approach to finance, design and use seems to require new architectural skills of a very entrepreneurial kind. Often it requires someone to propose a basic idea and philosophy, after which it can be relatively easy to bring financiers, owners of existing buildings and potential users together in an integrated design activity to produce a new enterprise and environment. The architect/planner is well qualified to work in this way and can use his bridging skills to good effect. Although it is commonly thought that professional rules of conduct constrain architects' freedom to work in this way, in fact these restrictions are often more imagined than real. Johnson's strictures, in Chapter 4, against traditional professional attitudes are really criticisms of the way most professionals interpret the rules rather than criticism of the rules themselves. It may also be that these rules appear to be more restrictive in the provinces than in London, perhaps because of a certain parochial view of professionalism which can develop when the more intense economic pressures and the more cosmopolitan use patterns of a capital city are not present.

The architect is able to express the potential value of a building and suggest potential uses, taking into account that activities can be designed and re-designed as well as buildings. He is free to act as a kind of architectural broker, taking stock and keeping a record of empty or unused buildings; identifying their conversion and use potential; carrying out feasibility studies with regard to financial, planning and legal requirements;

and also possibly eliminating the need for the traditional role played by financier, planner, legal advisor or local authority official. There is little formal training currently available for this kind of entrepreneurial activity although, clearly, it involves a knowledge of finance, planning, architecture, law, organisations and national requirements. Of all the ways into this kind of activity, a good architectural education appears to be as sound and broad a base as any and, although something could be done to teach the principles of this type of work, the essential element is practical experience.

Case Study 1: Dryden Street, London

In this project the design arose from an initial need recognised by the architects that their own professional and space requirements were similar to those of many other similar organisations and, from this, the concept of a general workspace for design and related professions emerged.

The building chosen for this prototype experiment was a five-storey Edwardian warehouse in Dryden Street, Covent Garden, London, totalling 1 670 m^2 (18 000 ft^2) converted in 1972 by a limited service company, formed and owned by thirty-five small firms — involving about one hundred and thirty people — which remain independent while sharing some common facilities (*Figure 11.2*).

The shared facilities are both physical and intangible but give the group mutual support at a level which is often associated only with the larger and wealthier practices or firms. They include conference rooms, a technical library, a company manager, receptionist, telephonist, metred phones and intercom, joint heating, lighting and other building facilities, joint cleaning and maintenance, facilities for coffee and refreshments, a communal centre, an art gallery, public relations services and other features. All this led to the build-up of a strong morale between a large group of related and friendly professionals. These include planners, architects, interior furniture and industrial designers, quantity surveyors, space planners, building surveyors, civil, structural and services engineers, typographic designers, model makers, illustrators' and artists' agents, reprographic printers, drawing equipment and art shop, jewellery designers, dress designers and dress-makers, and a secretarial firm.

The range of professionals involved changes from time to time but an attempt is made to control it and the balance of skills is maintained when a space becomes empty and a new firm has to be selected. There is always a waiting list of new firms and expansion of the accommodation is planned. The aim of the company is to maintain a base for good design and practice, trying to obtain the advantages of a large firm without losing the advantages of smallness and flexibility. At the same time some of the advantages of a multi-disciplinary practice have been obtained without too many of the restrictions of an integrated firm.

Figure 11.2 The Dryden Street building

This idea of a working community is one that, both on social and professional grounds, is increasingly attractive. The response to the idea was initially by private and unaided action in a situation where there were many decaying buildings, whose effective use was otherwise being prevented by bureaucratic and financial institutions which could not easily adjust their rules to embrace ideas of this kind. There are many small firms which feel the need to combine and to look, and to feel, stronger without losing their independence, but there are few developers to cater for such firms because, on the whole, there is little interest in small units in the property market.

At the time when this venture was started there was a good deal of planning fluidity about the future of Covent Garden. It was an area in which there were many buildings with deep plans which seemed an insuperable obstacle to conversion by many potential occupiers. Experience drawn from buroland-schaft planning was needed to adapt these spaces. Moreover, most of these buildings were on five or three year leases and under threat of redevelopment by the ground owners. Under such circumstances no traditional institutions would lend money to convert a building with such an uncertain future, nor would most borrowers be willing to risk borrowing money for such an enterprise, even if they could.

On the other hand it appeared that the Covent Garden Conservation Area had a fairly fluid boundary and was likely to, and in fact did, extend northwards to take in several other buildings, including 5 Dryden Street. At that time there were three listed buildings in one city block of eleven buildings and there was a national and local trend that indicated that such listings would increase. It was also evident that byelaws and ground coverage restrictions would make it uneconomic for the ground owners to redevelop the gaps in the eleven buildings on the site and, even now, the Covent Garden situation in this respect has not hardened. It seemed unlikely that the landlords

160

of the Dryden Street properties would be able to let the building against this background, so they were approached to lend the money to convert it. The landlords appointed the architects and agreed the financing and licensing arrangements through the services company, as has already been explained. All users became voting shareholders of the services company and adequate legal and financial safeguards were built into the organisation.

It was clear by now that the organisational aspects were more important than the actual physical conversion and that the relationship between the two was an intimate one. An important element, too, was the commitment by both individuals and firms to the ideology and philosophy behind the enterprise. The overall building cost was £32 per m^2 (£3.3 ft^2 approx.) including carpeting, light fittings, as well as all electrical and heating services. The resultant rents, which vary for different floors, are fixed at an average of £22 per m^2 (£2.3 ft^2) until 1980.

The interpretation of this general philosophy, in details of the building conversion, is further explained through the illustrations. In *Figure 11.3*, for example, can be seen the renovated third floor area mainly in the roofspace, which gives a more 'romantic' interior. The cast-iron columns at this level had to be restrained horizontally by steel channels to reduce their slenderness ratio.

A large corner window, which can be seen in *Figure 11.1* in place of the original large double timber doors, expresses the character of the interior to the street. The overhead flexible duct system is clearly visible (*Figure 11.4*), as is the vertical flexible conduit taking wiring to fittings in one of the one-man workspaces. The building is painted in the original brown and cream used by the building's earlier designer and occupants and now provides very appropriate accommodation for member tenants.

Case Study 2: Barley Mow, West London

Whereas in the case of Dryden Street half of the people and firms to occupy the buildings were known prior to the conversion taking place, in this second case-study at Barley Mow in West London, the building had to be converted before the ultimate users and their activities were identified. This meant that these activities had to be predicted and that the establishment of a 'user community' who were also going to manage the building, would have to be done in an almost completely artificial manner with the attendant problems of developing an identity and a commitment.

At Barley Mow, in the Borough of Hounslow, there was 3 060 m^2 (33 000 ft^2) of floor space on three floors of several interconnected buildings in what used to be an old Chiswick wallpaper factory. In the conversion the space was divided about 80% for the member firms and 20% for communal and shared space. Within the member firms' space, about half was

Figure 11.3 The third floor workspace

Figure 11.4 The ground floor workspace

for workshops and the other half for studios. The combined services were on a better scale than at Dryden Street because of the increased size and greater available resources. There is a management staff of four to look after all building services, maintenance and cleaning, and some of the member service firms, such as a secretarial firm, a restaurant, a bookkeeper and a reprographic firm with a shop, also provide services direct to the individual member firms if these are needed.

Again, this conversion project involved no change of use. Finance was obtained in the open market, and both the financier and the local authority were enthusiastic about the concept from the beginning. In the situation of unknown future users, various planning models for different kinds of firms of varying sizes were made and then applied to the existing space. Certain elements, such as main corridor runs, fire escapes and services and telephone grids, emerged as constants in each exercise. The various model mixes were also

required to estimate the amount of subsidiary corridor runs to give access to individual firms and this figure in turn was needed to calculate the possible rent return from the letting of actual working space which would be licensed. The brief remained flexible and there was never any formal written agreement in this; rather it grew during discussions between the architects and the manager designate who, in fact, had already worked for two years at Dryden Street.

The work involved a complete internal improvement on the upgrading of details and finishes, new heating and electrical systems, the installation of an internal telephone exchange and phone system, a new internal staircase, new fire escapes and external staircases, a new kitchen and alterations to lavatories, and new lighting, carpeting and redecoration. This project at June 1976 prices, cost an estimated 30% of an equivalent new building.

The detailed services are similar to those described in case study 1 and further specific points are described in the illustrations. For example, *Figure 11.5* shows a close-up of the main facade before it was cleaned and the wiring removed. This facade was part of an 1893 building facing on to Barley Mow Passage, on the other side of which was a C. F. Voysey building, reputedly his only industrial design, to which it was linked by a bridge.

The entrance in *Figure 11.5* now not only leads to the new workspace by way of a small hall with lift and stair, but also to industrial workshops on the ground floor. *Figure 11.6* shows the new reception space with studio space beyond. Member firms are connected through the switchboard, and the whole service, including Telex, is included in the overheads. On the upper floors of the central block a new mezzanine deck was inserted, and this is supported on the new square columns shown in *Figure 11.7*. This illustration also shows the main heating, lighting, power and communications services distribution running at high level, together with the new standard industrial staircases and cross-bracing. Services can be varied easily to suit tenant needs, and the carpet colouring varies to differentiate circulation from tenant space. *Figure 11.8* shows the mezzanine deck before occupation. *Figures 11.9* and *11.10* show two typical uses of the newly converted spaces — a joinery workshop for furniture craftsmen and an exhibition. The 'loose-fit' approach adopted in housing the member-tenants is demonstrated in *Figure 11.11*.

Conclusion

As these two case-studies clearly show, cost savings are one of the main motives for conversion and this aspect is relatively well understood and covered in a number of other chapters. In addition, some less-substantial but nevertheless clear advantages include the character and ambience of older buildings, the conservation of land and of the country's building resources, the conservation of energy, the search for historical and social continuity, an easier vehicle for self-help, less restrictions from

161

Figure 11.7 The third floor after conversion but prior to occupation

Figure 11.5 Barley Mow Building – the main facade before conversion

Figure 11.8 The new mezzanine deck

planners who have a clearer idea at inception of the completed project, a quicker turnover of finance and quicker occupation time for the client. However, there is also a negative side. For many, both layman and professional, conservation helps the retreat from design thinking and appreciation, and also increases the danger that the country could be building up a stock of future structural and maintenance problems. As yet, the extent of these dangers is not clear, but they are probably ones which creative thinking and good practical design should be able to overcome.

Lastly it is worth briefly mentioning the problem of 'temporary' or 'short-term' conservation. This seems to be at least as big a problem as that of permanent re-use, especially as inner urban areas become less inhabited and sometimes less commercially viable. Planning blight usually has an unknown

Figure 11.6 The Reception area with studio space beyond

162

Figure 11.9 Part of a tenant's joinery workshop

Figure 11.10 Multi-use space used for an exhibition

time duration, so there are many buildings capable of short term use ranging from six months to three or four years which, provided economic leasing and planning facilities were available, could, and would, be in continuous occupation. Fringe activities, such as student accommodation, summer camps, legalised squatting, sports facilities, trade markets, urban farming and self-help housing associations suggest themselves. Low cost methods of temporary conversion, including perhaps higher cost re-usable units for heating, sanitation, waterproofing and insulation, offer themselves as possibilities in this temporary conversion work. The same approach of separation between new and old perhaps offers a way of re-using many components and materials.

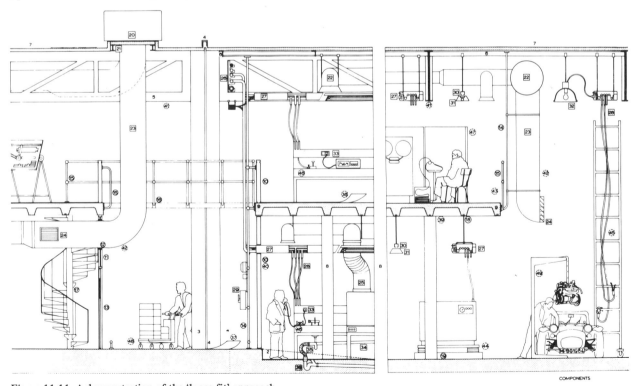

Figure 11.11 A demonstration of the 'loose-fit' approach to tenant unit planning

CHAPTER
TWELVE

Historic Building Re-use

Converting Albert Dock for Liverpool Polytechnic

Robert J. Greenslade and Richard G. Saxon

In the past few years, considerable evolution has occurred in the theory of designing new buildings and the attitude to converting existing ones. This has occurred particularly in design for institutional users with changing, unpredictable needs, but applies to the whole field of accommodation. This evolution can broadly be described as an awakening to the effect of time on the relationship between user and building.

Users' needs change so quickly and radically nowadays that a building too closely tailored to the first user's described functions will be rapidly obsolete. A less tailored, loose-fit building will be more responsive to change, will in the end be more functional and have a longer useful life. Built form does not follow the transient functions of the first user, but the constant functions of the building itself: enclosure of space, modification of climate, circulation of people, goods and services in a rational and also architecturally satisfying way. Thus, an old building with suitably generalised accommodation may be as sound a prospect to house an organisation as any new building.

Victorian industrial and warehouse structures are now frequently converted for commercial use; their wide floors are often more suitable for modern layout ideas than the thin slabs of the 'daylight factor' period of this century. Moreover, as the low comfort, high energy cost implications of the narrow, overglazed, building have become apparent, the smaller-windowed massiveness characteristic of Victorian and Georgian building is returning as a conservation-conscious design requirement. Thus, ironically, there are sometimes found old buildings which are more 'modern' than those much more recently erected.

Albert Dock warehouses are some of these 'modern' buildings. They are of a scale, layout and mass which, by fitting nothing in particular can fit most things reasonably well. Their warehouse history ensures that they can carry floor loads far in excess of modern needs: new partitions and equipment can be added without strengthening and moved later as necessary. Their conversion, therefore, could represent a more rational, economical and lasting investment in the future.

The design process in an historic context follows a different path to that for new buildings. It starts with an intensive study of the buildings, including survey, architectural analysis of the design and tests of the structure. From this, acceptable solutions to the essential needs of the building are developed – repairs, circulation, servicing, sub-division, etcetera. These solutions then form a 'kit of parts' with which to plan for the needs of the users of each part of the building complex.

Conversion of an historic building without detriment to its essential character can only be achieved if the designers are fully conversant with the nature of that character. Judgement of the success of such a design must also be based on knowledge and awareness. In undertaking a conversion to put new life into an old building, extensive and detailed surveys have to be made and researches done of the building's origin and subsequent history; an analysis of its character has to be undertaken. A summary of such an analysis is provided here, so that there can be an understanding of the building and of the approach and judgements of the designers. The analysis and the outline of proposals that follow are largely concerned with the subjective element of the process of designing for conversion.

More objective analyses, including the match between new user needs and existing building capabilities, as referred to by Maver in Chapter 2, are also required to serve the growing movement for the conservation of valued parts of our cities and their conversion for modern use, marking the changing view of the relationship between the form of buildings and their function.

Case Study

In early 1973, Liverpool City Education Committee requested that a study be made of the feasibility of consolidating and expanding the city's growing Polytechnic in the empty historic warehouses at Albert Dock, south of the famous Pierhead. Later in that year recommendations were made that the Polytechnic should use Albert Dock as the most advantageous of the alternatives available and in 1974 and 1975 design work was carried out.

Figure 12.1 View from north east

The building analysis

Albert Dock is a roughly rectangular body of water covering 2.8 hectares (7 acres), about 195 m × 135 m (650 ft × 450 ft) in plan. Openings to adjacent docks lie in the north west corner and mid-east side. Five discrete blocks of warehouses were built in a clockwise sequence from the mid-east side opening. They stand right up to the edge of the quay, with a roadway behind. The blocks, named A to E, were completed over a two year period from 1846 to 1848 (*Figure 12.1*). The dock and warehouses were built on the foreshore with the eastern half of the complex founded on rock with masonry footings. The western half is on timber friction piles in the silt and clay overlying the deep rock. The exact changeover point from rock to pile foundations is unknown, as no cracking is discernable from differential settlement.

From these foundations the colossal granite quayside structure was raised to a height of forty feet from the low tide mark. The quayside wall is 2.4 m (8 ft) thick, with the rest of the quay supported on ponderous iron and brick vaults forming the base of the buildings. The quayside was placed 0.9 m (3 ft) above the ground level around, to provide off-loading height for road vehicles.

From the quayside, the warehouses rise a further 18 m (60 ft) in five storeys. The ground floor is 4.8 m (16 ft) high and was open throughout for freight handling. The first and second floors are 3.6 m (12 ft) high, the third floor 3.3 m (11 ft) and the fourth floor of similar height though with space rising under the curving sheet-iron roof.

The exterior walls are of solid brick, 900 m (3 ft) thick at the ground floor, and diminishing by a brick thickness at each storey to 450 mm (18 in) thick at the cornice. On the quayside the exterior wall is lifted off the base by iron columns: massive cylindrical doric columns, 1.2 m (4 ft) in diameter, at 5.7 m (19 ft) centres, march around the quayside. At intervals a column is omitted and the first floor is cut back to form a two storey, eliptically-arched, space so that cranes can swing goods onto the quayside.

The internal structure is of repetitive cast iron bays, approximately 5.7 m × 3.6 m (19 ft × 12 ft). Slim columns carry inverted Y-shaped beams over the longer span parallel to the dock, with floors of brick jack arches spanning in the twelve foot direction. Wrought iron tie bars are taken through the jack arch to take the tensile stresses.

The warehouses are laid out to a common theme, though with variations. From the quayside they run back four bays, 15 m (50 ft), to a brick spine wall. Running at right angles to

165

the dock are cross walls at intervals from four to eight bays apart forming large compartments. Behind the spine wall there is an alternation of further storage compartments and open courts, defined by the crosswalls. Thus the interior consists of a series of brick walled compartments of varying proportion while the outside is continuous to the quayside and massively articulated on the back or roadside.

The logic of the layout is found in the need to provide secure storage. Access from the roadside is controlled at gates in the wall or tunnels into the courtyards. Goods are hoisted into and out of the various compartments from the courts, and rolled out onto the open quaysides to the ships. The back walls of the buildings could be impenetrable and, in fact, the accessible flanks of blocks D, E, A and B were built with no windows at all, the openings being formed but brick filled. Only the riverside C block, whose security wall stands clear of the buildings, could afford windows on the roadside. All windows are formed with very small pane iron security frames, and doors are solid sheet iron.

Scale and significance

Even by modern standards the buildings are awesomely big. At the time of building, in the mid-1840s, only the railway structures could approach them. Nothing like it had been done since ancient Rome and the Victorians knew it. In four years, thousands of craftsmen and labourers laid 23 500 000 bricks, 47 000 tons of mortar and 1 130 000 clay floor tiles into a structure of 305 000 m² (1 000 000 ft²) partly carried on 73 km (48 miles) aggregate length of Goodwood beech piles. The eponymous prince was suitably impressed when he opened the dock, both with the greatness of the works and the fineness of the detail. A replica of quayside granitework was built at Windsor at his request and a model exhibited in the Crystal Palace in 1851. The sense of grandeur is important to the appreciation of the buildings. They come to us from the period of total self-confidence and innocence of the early industrial Revolution. The buildings have the appeal of the big idea carried successfully through which is so far from being possible, even if thought desirable, today; they command profound respect (*Figure 12.2*).

Naivety and sophistication

Albert Dock warehouses, however, are not just warehouses. There is a higher sensibility to be found in them than in the many contemporary buildings of the functional tradition. For example, a Golden Section proportion system governs the openings, even on the rear. But they are also not Versailles in brick. Far from being a consistent, conscious work of architecture they are a fascinating blend of naive, functional, artisan work and academic sophistication.

The key to understanding their complex personality may lie in the joint authorship of the buildings. They are the work of a brilliant, pragmatic Yorkshire engineer, Jesse Hartley, and of

166

Figure 12.2 Courtyard E Block

an eminent London architect, Philip Hardwick. Hartley was engineer to the Liverpool Docks throughout their ascendant period and almost single-handedly created the enclosed system. His work is highly original and beautifully constructed. Hardwick worked with Telford on the innovatory St. Katherine Docks beside the Tower of London in the 1820s. He was also associated with railway development as well as building many commercial and club buildings in London.

It must be surmised that Hartley sought Hardwick's advice because of his experience at St. Katherine Dock, and then asked him to design the quayside facade to the warehouses. Hartley had already provided the basic layout, plans and section and the structural system. Hardwick influenced the treatment of some general details but, essentially, he was to provide the impressive front to the visiting ships of the world and he overlaid his ideas on the buildings as far as he could. Evidence for this lies in the sharp change of character between the quayside and the rest of the buildings, and in the clumsiness of the layout which defeated the successful application of the facade design to the whole quayside.

The basic layout of the whole complex, and the development of the individual blocks, have the hallmarks of the work of independent master craftsmen. They were working with the iron components Hartley provided for them but were their own masters in stone and brick. Three different plan forms are used. A, D and E blocks, the first and last two built, are of a common plan, asymmetrical but handed to deal with the north east corner and the eastern dock gate. There is some development of ideas from A to D and E, but all have tunnel access to the courtyard through a full depth compartment with no spine wall. B block is far more massive in every way, though using identical iron elements. Total plan symmetry and a courtyard entered directly distinguish it. The eight bay wide interiors are divided by an internal crosswall. C block shows a different hand again. Midway in plan depth between B and the rest, it has four pavillions and three courts, entered freely from a protected road along the rear. It has eight bay wide interiors, but sees no need of sub-dividing crosswalls. Unique to C block are the strongly rounded corners, full height at the southern end, up to first floor on every courtyard. The blocks lie around the dock as if they were tipped from a toybox. They are not square to each other, nor particularly skewed. A birdmouth corner in the north east contrasts with differing lapped corners in the south. The two dock gates are handled entirely differently above the waterline.

Onto this artisan anarchy Hardwick tried to impose grand order. He devised the motif of an elliptical arch across two bays, with a hoist loophole above its centreline up to the cornice. Windows on each side of the hoist were slightly reduced in width, while normal width windows completed the four bay design. This design was surely intended to be repeated in each compartment of the plan, ideally on its centreline. Had the layout of the blocks been developed to receive this motif each compartment would have had an even number of bays, as this is essential to axial location. This is not so however. A column line down the centre of a compartment alternates arbitrarily with a bay down the centre. The arch motif cannot therefore be applied consistently, and the pattern of compartments and courts behind cannot be read at all from the arch locations. This is apparent in long views when the roof is visible, or when light shines through from the courtyards. The most striking proof that this is a *post hoc* concept is in B block, where the totally symmetrical plan cannot permit an arch on its own axis as the central compartment alone has five bays not four.

Hardwick sought a different emphasis for the building than the one emerging on the roadside. Hartley's windows are tall and slim, floor to ceiling, and with frequent hoist loopholes and the re-entrant angles of the courts a vertical emphasis is established. The cornice line is a nominal thing of little weight. The quayside is horizontally emphasised, with the quay wall and arcade allowed to set up sweeping lines. Elaborate roof drainage pipes eliminate downpipes from the front. Hardwick widened the windows and raised the sills to a near square proportion, so that they do not interrupt the horizontal flow of wall. Only the cornice and parapet could not be changed, as it was visibly continuous around front and back. The inadequate weight of this is a point which is returned to in the design proposals.

Finally, Hardwick did not use the slender, arched iron and brick style of the interior. For architectural reasons he inflated the columns to enormous size at the quayside, and used flat, concealed iron lintels to carry the brickwork above. As a transition to the interior he used a lesser column on the second row where the archway caused the set back at first floor. The alternation of Hardwick and Hartley columns on the second row is seen in a few instances. The whole quayside facade is like a stage set. Hardwick's improvisation is not obvious on visiting the dock, any more than is the naive stepping down of the quoin stone sizes to suggest greater height. The tricks are convincing and lend the aura of grand design to basically vernacular buildings.

The richness of this interplay between vernacular and academic, traditional, architecture and rising technology is one of the fascinations of Albert Dock. Repetition in the sense that modern buildings are built of repetitive elements does not exist. No two rooms in the dock are exactly alike. Like the Pont du Gard, the building makes scarcely noticed adjustments as it goes from bay to bay, bringing a life which endlessly repays study.

Perception

Because of their siting and layout the buildings are seen only from a limited range of viewpoints. This is significant when judging what impact changes will have. Albert Dock warehouses are isolated on all sides but the south by bodies of water and on all sides by open space. Distant, elevational views are common. There is then a jump to the road immediately behind the buildings, and to the quaysides. From the roads only oblique views of the rear are possible with the courtyards as shaded clefts. From the quayside it is impossible to see the form of the building when standing underneath and only oblique views across the water are possible, all observation taking place from an elevated viewpoint, between 3 m and 5.8 m (9 and 20 ft) above the 'ground', or water plane, depending on the tide. The arcade becomes the piano nobile.

Photographs of the buildings mislead when telephoto lenses bring the opposite sides of the dock close up. It is not possible to see the quayside windows from close to, square on. The windows are always either black holes two hundred yards away, or obliquely seen reflective solids. The only elevations of the buildings which can be inspected from mid-distance on the quayside are the end elevations of blocks C, D, E and A. The roof is hardly visible across the dock on overcast days because it is 'sky coloured', and is not seen at all on oblique views. The modern lift tower heads are seen projecting arbitrarily above the parapet. They are noticeable but not intrusive, as the power of the arcade integrates almost any incident at the roofline.

The interiors

Though the interiors of the buildings are listed Grade 1, no one it seems has officially been inside the building other than the dock company and visitors with their permission. The interior is thus as unknown and is as private as a royal palace still in use. It is this interior that will be the future environment of thousands of people studying and relaxing. It is at least as important to conserve the character of the interior as that of the exterior, and it is a somewhat greater technical problem to do so.

Each floor has a distinct character. The structure is heaviest at the bottom, and the columns and openings show this difference in weight on each floor. Heights and windowsill slopes vary. Room proportions also vary from block to block with the layout variations discussed earlier.

The basement is windowless and perpetually cool, with natural ventilation via ducts in the wall thickness up to cornice level (*Figure 12.3*). Supporting the quayside, its vaults are ponderous, and spring from thick columns hardly 2 m (6 ft) tall. The brick vault rises and falls without ribs, as if formed on huge loaves of bread. In one compartment of D block, the iron columns and beams have been massively covered in brick and stone to insulate them for cold store use (1900). The effect is to heighten the character, with definite turn-of-the-century overtones.

It is on the ground floor, or quayside level, that the elegance of the interior structure is, or was, most obvious to the users, as the ground floor was open to the quayside (*Figure 12.4*). Apart from the vertical planes of the walls there are no straight lines. The columns taper on an entasis, then flare into simple capitals. A capital partway up the column allows for a mezzanine to be added. The beams camber, with a deepening cleft in their

soffits to the centre of each span. The vaults curve in both directions, billowing gently along the beam line. Their complex curvature is revealed in the iron frames let into the vaults where hoisting openings were required. Openings into the brickwork between compartments are golden-section rectangles, with elliptical arch heads, all the bricks being bullnosed.

On the upper floors the interiors are lower, generally white-washed, and beautifully lit. The large, if infrequent, windows deliver strong horizontal and upward light, reflected from the dock, to give a Vermeer-like washing of brick and tile surfaces. By the third floor the columns are so slim that the structure seems quite insubstantial, yet it can still carry loads far in excess of those for which modern office or educational buildings are designed (*Figure 12.5*).

The top floor is virtually column free, each compartment being roofed in wide span curved sheet iron on light wrought iron trusses. These are the major design failure of the building. Whilst of great interest historically, the roofs have never been structurally or thermally adequate. The trusses are untriangulated and useless, whilst the sheet iron acts as a stressed skin and lifts the entire roof off its supports when warm. The outer walls have been badly pushed out of plumb by the roof thrust.

Whilst movement for goods is easy, movement for people is restricted; one stair in each block of the warehouse is all that is provided. The stairs are purely functional, but exhibit rustication on the soffits of the cantilevered granite treads to give a Piranesian effect.

Materials and detail

The detailed character of the buildings arises from the choice and handling of the small palette of materials (*Figure 12.6*).

Figure 12.3 Basement of D block, overlaid with stone insulation in 1900

Figure 12.4 Ground floor — later wall on right obscures view of dock

Figure 12.5 Circulation route, upper floor

Figure 12.6 E block quayside

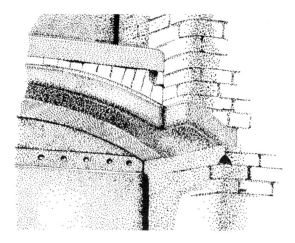

Figure 12.7 Loophole ironwork

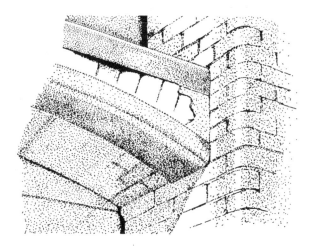

Figure 12.8 Quayside stonework

Figure 12.9 Quayside stonework

Brick, of course, predominates; this is of great colour and textural variety, giving a salmon orange colour when clean. A dense monolithic effect is produced by the rounding of corners, the flow of vaults, and the lack of perpend discipline. The brick rests on a base of grey granite. Granite also forms the 12 m (40 ft) high quayside structure, with superbly crafted cyclopean walling. The iron quayside columns, which are 25 mm (1 in) thick shells, are set in machine-accurate grooves in giant granite blocks, which are then sloped away from the column base to shed water. The resultant inflection of the quayside surface expresses the transfer of load most subtly. The quayside blocks are rounded at the arises to resist spalling, and keyed together with diamond shaped granite plugs. Granite quoins and cyclopean 'elbow patches' are used inside and out at the lowest level where heavy impacts from carts and goods were to be expected.

Softer Liverpool brown sandstone is used for 'architectural' stonework. This trim, consisting of sills, quoins and cornice, is essentially a concession to architectural taste. It has weathered far less well than the other materials and is soot blackened.

The cast iron structure is fluently formed. Individual patterns seem to have been made for the many variations in beam design. The empirical stress-following shape of these beams is extremely satisfying. Columns, where protected from surface corrosion, are smooth and polished. The many instances of iron reinforcing for openings and edges show great design skill in following and blending into the brick curves to form a robust, invulnerable surface (*Figures 12.7, 12.8 and 12.9*).

Sheet iron is used, ingeniously but disastrously, for the roof; it is also used for the doors. Doors are placed on pinties (hinge lugs) flush with the walls, to allow doors to fold flat like shutters against the wall when open. There are no door frames to be damaged. Pairs of doors on each side of a compartment wall provide a good fire break. Doors to the hoist loop holes, being aligned with the inside face of the wall, show off its diminishing thickness to advantage in views of the exterior. The brick bullnose on each side of the wall can be seen.

The iron windows have the fine astragals of the period, but with pane sizes smaller than usual to give security. Weathering has buckled the majority of them however, especially where salt spray has got at them. There are fifteen different frame types in all.

The floorscape in and around the buildings is important to the whole character. Large scale granite sets in drainage patterns are mixed with smaller sets, sheet granite and iron cover plates (many now lost). York stone was introduced to cover hydraulic mains runs added later along the quaysides.

The design proposals

Conservation of the character of the buildings can be achieved, by adherence to certain priority aims, as far as possible within functional and financial constraints. These aims are as follows:

1. The original form of the block should be restored, with incompatible additions removed and damage repaired;

2. The external character of the building should be retained as faithfully as possible, with the impact of the technical demands of the new use being controlled rather than suppressed;

3. Internally, the vault forms and the shapes of the iron columns and beams should be preserved, whilst providing adequate fire protection and the necessary servicing and sub-division; the existing structure generally should remain as undisturbed as possible;

4. New work and the additional elements required should be articulated from the existing building, and the finished environment should be fully up to present day standards.

The character of the buildings as historic docks depends on the retention of the dock water and quayside setting. The water must in any event be retained for structural reasons and not allowed to fall below a minimum level. Parts of the blocks are on timber piles which must be kept permanently below water level to avoid decay. Erosion by rapid water movement under tidal action is also damaging. It is therefore proposed to restore the limited tidal range of water movement which characterised the dock for all of its history until early 1975.

The quaysides and the roads behind the buildings need only to be cleared of weeds and refuse, with some settlement remedied, and missing paving replaced. Safety railing is needed to make the quaysides acceptable as public spaces. It is proposed to use a ball-jointed railing system, with cast aluminium posts, painted to match the cast iron. This type of railing is commonly used in marine environments. Wherever possible, area lighting will be provided from fittings mounted on the building and new lighting standards will be avoided.

Restoration and repair

No permission is needed in respect of works of repair or restoration to a listed building. In those instances where it is not proposed to repair or restore the building to its original form a full proposal is submitted, as consent is required. The following description lists in general terms the work of repairs and restoration to Block D, though their relevance to the other blocks is also shown from time to time.

The roof is structurally unsound and cannot be economically restored. The original design of unbraced trusses supporting a rivetted iron sheet has in practice become a stressed skin roof, with stiffening hanging from it. The skin spans longitudinally with the corrugation of the roof providing the stiffness. It lifts off the central column line in the eastern end of the block, and thrusts outwards on the north and south walls. These walls now lean outwards excessively and must be partly taken down and re-erected. The entire parapet level brickwork and stonework is affected and, in the eastern compartment of the block, the walls must be re-erected from fourth floor level.

External brick walls show cracks, sometimes due to settlement, sometimes due to expansion of embedded iron parts in the walls. Larger cracks will involve replacing bricks. Smaller ones will be grouted and pointed up.

Bricked-up windows will be opened up and replacement of all window frames is considered necessary with the exception of the four windows on the first floor inside each eliptical arch. These are protected from spray and are restorable, to retain the original character on the quayside arcade where it can be most closely seen.

Because of the repairs to parts of the external walls, it is proposed to clean all the exterior, so that replaced or cleaned bricks will not stand out in a 'piebald' effect. The existing pointing will be preserved as far as possible and this will influence the method of cleaning chosen.

Since the abandonment of the buildings in 1970, the lead flashings have been stolen from all the parapet gutters. Rainwater entering freely has led to deterioration of the entire structure to some degree, but particularly the washing out of ash fill in floors, and mortar in vaults and walls. Some corrosion of iron members is evident and some items may have to be replaced.

Parts of the fourth floor have been overloaded, leading to failures of beams in some areas, and shear failure of column/beam junctions in others. Repair beams and corsetted columns were installed at the time of the failures. These restrict headroom and use of affected parts of the third floor. Permanent repairs are proposed. The uneven basement floor, of rammed earth only, must be replaced with a new floor.

Removal of additions since original construction

The raised section of the roof on the south-west compartment will need to be removed and the cornice repaired. This is required to restore the original elevational balance and to achieve a homogeneous new solution for the top of the building. The courtyard which was infilled with an iron and timber goods handling complex will be restored and damage to walls from the fixings made good. The original courtyard paving, covered by the railway platform, will be relaid. The lift shaft, placed in the original hoistway in 1947, will be taken out. This will recover useful space on all floors and restore the form of the south-west compartment. Mezzanine floors added within the ground floor over a long period must be removed, at least in part. Headroom is generally restricted by the mezzanine and only small 'gallery type' sections could be usefully retained. The proportions of the ground floor space will be generally as the original. The raised ground floor, brought up to railway loading height from the track run in through the tunnel, will be removed to restore the original surface on the quayside.

On the quayside the security wall, built on the first column line back from the quay in 1898, will be removed as will all internal partitions. A new glazed wall on this line will enclose useful space, but without losing the continuity of quayside space which characterised the original. Infilling structures in the eliptical arches, used for cooling installations when the building was a cold store, will be removed. One addition, however, will be retained and restored: the brick and stone insulation added to the columns and beams in the east compartment of D block basement adds to the character and will be repaired.

The impact of new needs — circulation

Making the buildings habitable as educational buildings begins with the provision of access and toilet facilities, the limitations of the warehouses in these respects having already been described. A circulation pattern for Block D is proposed, establishing a principle which continues around the entire dock. The archways in the compartment walls define the route along the third bay back from the quayside. This would sometimes be in a corridor and sometimes through open space. Fire doors are needed in the archways and staircases are required at adequate intervals for fire escape. To supplement the existing stairs retained, new stairs at the ends of the block are placed in new wells made through the structure. An external location for these was studied, but considered too disruptive visually. Useful floorspace was not significantly sacrificed by an internal location.

The central stair and two twelve-person lifts are placed in a service tower standing in the re-opened courtyard. Off the corridor in the non-daylit corners of the east and west compartments, various combinations of male, female and staff toilets can be planned into the bays allocated.

Not included in first-phase proposals but needed in due course is the link bridge between Block D and the Dock Traffic Office. Linking the blocks would give the buildings greater flexibility for educational purposes. Sheltered circulation on this site is also very desirable. A simple glazed bridge is proposed, similarly detailed to the service tower link glazing. The flow of the wall will be interrupted as little as possible.

Servicing

The great depth of the floor plan, about 30 m (100 ft) from dock to roadside, coupled with the extreme exposure of the site, make the use of windows for natural ventilation impracticable. Many potential user departments have technical requirements involving piped services, and the ability to deliver and remove air and liquids over the entire floor area is important to the successful utilisation of the buildings. Heavily serviced departments cannot, however, be adequately catered for within the existing floors, and virtually new space is proposed on fourth and fifth floors for this purpose.

Hanging the piped and ducted services from the vaults in the conventional manner would have hidden the interior character of the building and, in some instances, headroom would have been reduced intolerably by service crossovers below the beams. The alternative adopted is in the form of an elevated floor. A new floor level, about 400 mm (16 in)

above the existing floor, is proposed on first, second and third floor levels, with a deeper floor on the 'new' fourth floor. Air supply to each level will be ducted in the floor cavity above, entering the space through inlets set flush with the brick vault. Return air will be drawn up through the light fittings back into the cavity above the vault. Piped services and most electrical services will be handled in the floor cavity below, or in the screed finish. The result is minimal interference with the visible flow of structure and space overhead.

No elevated floor is needed on the ground floor to serve the basement, as the latter can be ventilated from its own new floor. Some exposed ducts are introduced on the ground floor to combat downdraught and heat loss from the glazed wall to the quayside, and to service spaces below mezzanines.

Ventilation plant rooms are dispersed throughout the buildings. This cuts down the size of ducts needed, and enables each space to be converted and serviced specifically for the intended user, or phased to accommodate partial conversion of any block or floor. Heating and cooling plant is centrally located in the basement, as is bulk water storage. Small header tanks, and cooling towers if required, are placed on top of the service towers.

The pattern of air handling plant rooms is of four on each floor, each taking up one structural bay. Perimeter zones, the outer bays of the plan, are served by rooms beside the new stairs on the east and west ends of the plan. The core zones, all areas more than one way from the outer wall, are served by rooms adjacent to the toilets in the re-entrant angles of the courtyard, one being the old stairshaft. Air is drawn through the window openings in each case. The resultant use of interior space is of four islands of fixed space: stairs, toilets and plant rooms, set along the spine wall to leave the maximum amount of useful space.

Subdivision

Subdivision of the existing spaces will be essential to some degree. To retain the continuity of space inside, and to avoid the loss of a clear perception of the structure, a discipline has been evolved for positioning partitions.

Partitions will not run on beam lines or envelop columns. In the direction of the main beams there is a space between beam and tie bars where the vault can be cleanly met by a partition. These lines, centred 350 mm (14 in) each side of the column line parallel to the beams, are the only acceptable positions for partitions. In the case of a corridor, which would be too wide by this definition, walls may move closer, but above doorhead height would be glazed and tilted to meet the vault on the preferred line. Where the corridor arrives at the archway in a compartment wall it will be opened to full width to show the arch clearly.

At right angles to the beam direction the determining factor is the tie bars. The preferred centreline position for partitions will still lie on each side of the column line at a distance of 350 mm (1 ft 2 in) approx. from the column centreline, but additional positions are possible between tie bars at intervals of 1250 mm (4 ft 2 in approx).

Combining the preferred partition lines parallel and perpendicular to the beam direction line produces a 'tartan grid'. To get balanced spaces using the tartan grid the designer would, wherever possible, position rooms either enclosing columns on both sides or on neither.

Interior design

The decisions on circulation, services and sub-division described above provide the basis for the internal character of the buildings after conversion. The remaining elements of the interior design are the fire protection of the iron frame, the finish to walls and vault soffits and lighting.

The iron elements of the frame are not fireproof and must be raised to one-hour fire resistance (one-and-a-half hours in the basement) to comply with the Building Regulations. A 12 mm (½ in) thick cover on the iron is required and would be achieved by spray coating, trowelled to bring out the underlying shape of columns and beams. The tie rods will probably not need protection. A paint finish on the fire protection will restore the metallic surface quality. No protection will be needed to the quayside columns as they are outside the envelope.

Most internal surfaces of walls and vaults are limewashed at present and it is proposed to clean these. Walls will be left as clean brickwork but vaults will be re-whitened to give the necessary reflectivity for good working light on the first, second and third floors.

Lighting will be of different types for different areas but will always attempt to reveal the vault form rather than obscure it. On the first, second and third floors a bay sized 'racetrack' of fluorescent tubes will hang from the vault. It will be kept as light as possible, with its gear separated and recessed in the air extraction points in the vaults. The race track will not compete too strongly with the tie bars and the light spill will emphasise the bays. An alternative form of lighting for all areas, which will be used in the taller ground floor, is a discharge lamp. Two per bay would be needed, recessed into the vault and acting additionally as return air channels. Corridors and exhibition spaces will be lit more flexibly for effect as much as utility.

The ground floor which will be the entrance level, and that most seen either from within or outside by the public, will be most closely restored to its original condition. The stone flag floors will be retained and cleaned, and all brick surfaces cleaned, with the vaults left unwhitened.

The basement is to be used for social and communal purposes, making use of its massive vault and column forms to create a 'Cavern' or 'Bierkellar' atmosphere. Separate access stairs to the outside will be necessary for escape, and will enable it to be used outside working hours.

New roof and extra floor

Restoration of the existing roof would not be a worthwhile use of resources, though it is hoped that a section on another block might be preserved for museum purposes. The proposal is to remove the entire roof of Block D, including the raised section added in 1898.

The reconstruction of the top of the building gives the opportunity to accommodate activities of a more specialised technical nature. There is a substantial percentage of such space in educational buildings and it is a cornerstone in the feasibility of using Albert Dock warehouses that sufficient specialised space can be created to meet the needs of such users. It is necessary, economical and visually acceptable to add an extra floor to the building to provide such space. The resulting fourth and fifth floors also allow the potential for double height space if required. The fifth floor appears above the cornice in the form of a mansard roof.

This alteration in the basic proportions of the block is capable of being visually successful because of the inadequate weight of the original cornice and roofline, the roofs at present making little contribution to the composition. In most warehouses of the period, either a substantial parapet stands above the cornice, or else the roof is boldly visible. The 'string course' provided on Block C at fourth floor level by the upper rail of the travelling crane shows the effect of such a device in improving the balance of the wall.

Extensive model studies have been undertaken to explore the shape of the visible roof edge (*Figure 12.10*). The selected form is that of an ellipse, of similar size and curvature to the elliptical quayside archways, springing from behind the parapet and receding in the manner of the existing roof so that it is only partially visible from within the site. A cleaning and maintenance cradle will run in the space between parapet and roof edge. The roof reflects the form and discipline of the building. The mansard is of facetted panel construction, with bay sized elements of standard width and recessed tolerance zones in the column lines to take up the significant variations in bay width. Windows are contained within the lowest facet and aligned with existing windows below. The material for the roof edge will be a metallic or synthetic sheet of neutral mid-grey colour.

The central portion of the roof will usually be flat, asphalt surfaced, with white chipping finish. Where high ventilation rates are needed to spaces below, extra height will be required in the centre of the plan to accommodate plant, and the flat area will be raised. These 'mounds' will emphasize the pavilion plan when seen from a distance, but will be invisible from nearer to the buildings.

Service terminals will project through the roof, though their exact nature and position will depend on user needs, and may of course alter from year to year after occupation. The principles proposed are that any flue or exhaust having to break through the mansard will do so in a simple round stack, not

173

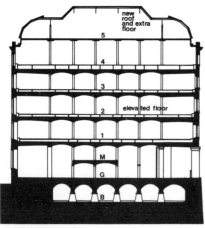

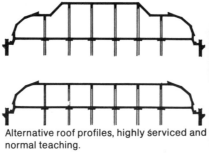

Alternative roof profiles, highly serviced and normal teaching.

Cross section.
Section of roof edge profile and new floor.

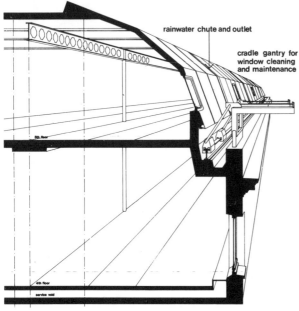

Figure 12.10 Cross section and alternative roof profiles: 'highly serviced' and 'normal teaching'

Figure 12.11 Service tower in courtyard – Design model

interrupting the flow of the mansard as a controlling element. Other ventilation terminals will be located in disciplined rows on the mound or flat surface and whilst of low profile can follow their functional requirements.

The total roofline produced will thus be a simple statement, reinforcing and balancing the existing form and proportions of the block, but with a degree of liveliness in response to the technical requirements within.

The service tower

Main circulation for the block needs to be at its centre. Two twelve-person passenger/goods lifts and the main staircase must be placed together at the centre of demand. To take these vertical elements through the existing frame would be costly and disruptive. Dimensional irregularity and structural difficulty, especially at the base, would create unnecessary expense. Useful floorspace and the clarity of horizontal space and circulation would be lost. It is proposed, therefore, to place

the lifts and stairs in a tower, freestanding structurally to avoid existing foundations, in the courtyard on the north side of the block. The form of the tower has been the subject of much study and discussion (*Figure 12.11*). After the public exhibition at which there was criticism of the intrusiveness of the tower, a complete redesign was undertaken. The tower is now axially symmetrical and articulated in form to moderate its impact on the courtyard space. Scale is given by the visible staircase landings at the centre, from which views of the pierhead should be splendid. A well at the base protects the tower from damage. At the top it steps out into twin rectangular lift motor rooms. Water storage is also accommodated in the cantilevered head (*Figure 12.12*). The staircase and landings connecting the tower to the existing building are glazed. The route from building into tower passes through the existing hoist loophole doorways, and the arched doorways at ground floor. No alteration of the existing building is involved. Thus it will be possible to walk outside the volume of the building and experience its surface

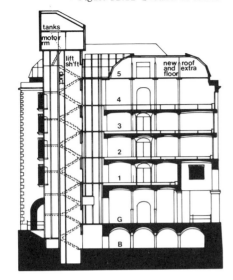

Figure 12.12 Section of tower

Figures 12.13 and 12.14 West elevation existing and proposed

Figures 12.15 and 12.16 North elevation existing and proposed

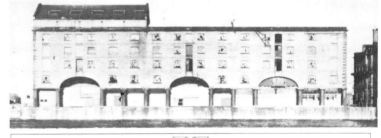

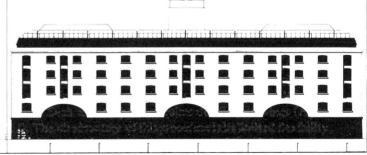

Figures 12.17 and 12;18 South elevation existing and proposed

175

detail and the courtyard space from elevated vantage points in the glazed link. At the new fifth floor level, approximately at parapet height, the link landing must pass through the parapet which is therefore removed over the link width. The glazing at this level then rolls overhead in the same profile as the roof edge, and meets the roof edge in a groin vaulted junction.

The material for the tower will be a brick skin over a concrete structure. This will resist the rugged environment and enable the tower to fit into context, even though its form is an uncompromising expression of the modern facilities added to the building. The brick wraps around all external and internal surfaces of the tower, only the stairs and landings being exposed concrete.

Windows and other openings

The simple, yet subtly varying, pattern of openings in the brick walls is one of the strongest elements of the building's character. It is not proposed to add any new openings, but those which are blocked-in are to be reinstated (*Figure 12.13 to 12.18*). Windows and hoist doorways are corroded and replacement is essential. Only on the first floor, in the archway recess, is it proposed to restore the original iron windows, where they can be closely seen from the quayside walkway.

The new windows must take account of the extreme climatic exposure of the site and the needs of the new use of the building. Robust, sealed windows, with additional summer ventilation by controlled slots only, and with simplicity of cleaning and maintenance, are the functional requirements. Modest cost is, of course, necessary in the context of the budgets for educational buildings.

Only two visually acceptable alternatives exist in our opinion: replica replacement with cast metal frames or undivided sheet glass. Any intermediate pattern of subdivision introduces disturbing scale changes and unresolved variations between the fourteen window types. The existing windows are all based on multiples of a very small pane, the small

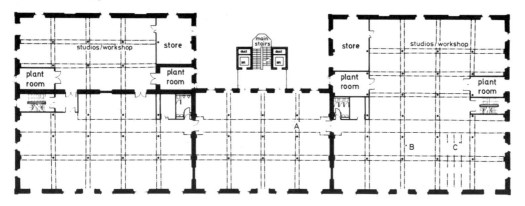

Figure 12.19 (*left*) Typical floor plan. A indicates offset corridor partitions; B shows preferred partition lines and C, secondary partition lines

Figure 12.20 (*below, left*) Interior design concept showing elevated service floor

Figure 12.21 (*below, right*) A typical bay showing the integration of elements

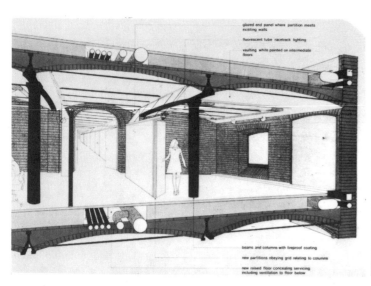

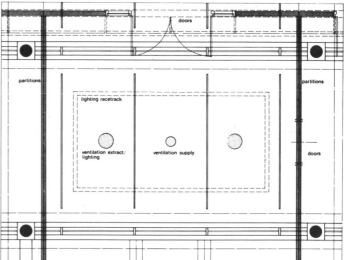

size being a security requirement. Cost exercises place the cast metal replica out of reach, and various difficulties make it an unwise choice for an educational building.

The building is now to be inhabited, rather than just full of inanimate objects and some character change in the windows is inevitable, as light will now shine out from them as well as into them. Taking out the glazing bar pattern removes the prison-like security image, the least attractive aspect of the building as a potential educational environment, and opens up fine vistas of the dock, river and city to the inhabitants. Consequently, the large sheet glass approach is recommended. The impact of this on the overall character will be muted by the limited way in which the buildings can be seen. The pattern of openings is far more significant than the texture within them, as can be seen from a typical floor plan (*Figure 12.19*). It is proposed that the windows be glazed in large single sheets of bronze tinted glass. This will retain some of the solidity presently provided by the iron grillage and clouded glass, as well as controlling solar gain and sky glare through contrast with the walls when viewed from inside.

The hoist loophole doors will be replaced, usually by solid insulating panels, though occasionally by glass where solar heat gain is not a problem. Some openings on the east, west and courtyard walls will have to accommodate ventilation

176

intakes and exhausts for the plant rooms. These will be handled as industrial ventilators in the way of so many mill and warehouse buildings of the period. A dark metal or fibreglass panel will incorporate an intake grille and exhaust cowling. The profile of the latter can only be fixed when site air-pressure conditions are fully understood. A large area of new window is introduced in the proposed screen to the ground floor quayside. This will extend from floor to ceiling behind the second line of columns and divide the usable space at ground floor level from the public walkway around the dock.

Fusion without confusion

The proposals which have been described and illustrated in the chapter represent a division of very limited resources between the elements of the building to produce what is expected to be a satisfactory total result: a fusion of old and new without confusion. Some idea of the result of this integration can be seen in *Figures 12.20 and 12.21*.

Balancing the needs of the future users with the safeguarding of an important part of our national heritage is an act of fine judgement, and it is for others to determine whether the balance struck in these proposals would in fact conserve the character of the building successfully.

Index